# BIOCHEMISTRY OF MENTAL DISEASE

# BIOCHEMISTRY

# OF MENTAL DISEASE

Theodore L. Sourkes, Ph.D.

*Senior Research Biochemist, Allan Memorial Institute of Psychiatry;*
*Associate Professor, Department of Psychiatry,*
*and Honorary Lecturer, Department of Biochemistry, McGill University,*
*Montreal, Quebec, Canada*

Foreword by R. A. CLEGHORN, M.D., D.SC.

HOEBER MEDICAL DIVISION
HARPER & ROW, PUBLISHERS

BIOCHEMISTRY OF MENTAL DISEASE

Copyright © 1962 by Hoeber Medical Division,
Harper & Row, Publishers, Incorporated
Printed in the United States of America

All rights reserved. For information address
Hoeber Medical Division, Harper & Row, Publishers
49 East 33rd Street, New York 16,
New York

Library of Congress catalog card number: 62-16855

*For my wife*

# CONTENTS

# FOREWORD

A troubled world can no longer successfully hide its mentally ill behind brick walls nor thoroughly conceal men's conflicts by the wrappings of rigid custom. Science has sprung the doors to the one and torn the cloak off the other by virtue of new insights and techniques. Though alienists were late in winning a place in the hierarchy of those benefited by developments in the basic sciences, they are now beginning to profit. Such progress was first of all preceded by the psychological conceptualizations of the late nineteenth and early twentieth centuries which supplied fresh ways of looking at tangled lives and rational grounds for psychotherapy. Then, less than thirty years ago, empirical therapies began to revolutionize the atmosphere of mental hospitals. While hope ran ahead, recoveries increased apace. Meanwhile anthropological, psychological and sociological studies shed fresh light on the nature of man in his relations to himself, his culture and his environment. But it is only within the last fifteen years that biochemists, profiting by refinements of technique and the elaboration of new and exquisitely sensitive apparatus, have been able to make measurements relevant to the study of processes formerly outside the realm of assessment. A short ten years ago the phrenotropic drugs appeared and began to elicit the interest which their efficacy has abundantly sustained. In this decade psychiatry has at long last been able to employ the fruits of basic science for immediate investigative and therapeutic ends and for the instilling of a new spirit of optimism and criticism. By way of a dividend a splendidly improved social milieu has also developed. Both clinicians and biochemists were ready for this serendipitous development.

In the advancement of the science of man no one discipline can claim an exclusive prerogative. Depending on available techniques and a variety of other circumstances, first one and then another will surge ahead. The present seems to be one of the periods when biochemistry can and is contributing with great pertinence. Few psychiatrists can keep abreast of the vast clinical literature, let alone the rapid advances in the esoteric realm of the chemistry of man. So it is fortunate that a colleague such as the author of this book has the courage, the skill, and the scholarly capacity to summarize those aspects of the biochemical field which are of relevance and interest for those who wish to know and to understand something of the complexities of biochemistry as applied to psychiatry. Working as he has for some nine years in the milieu of a psychiatric institute, Dr. Sourkes has imbibed some of the less baneful attitudes, and even the language of his clinical brethren. This, combined with a natural felicity of expression and a capacity for clear exposition, has resulted in a volume which is a literary delight as well as a mine of carefully documented data. Bronowski has defined science as "the organization of our knowledge in such a way that it commands more of the hidden potential in nature." This is a scientific work by that criterion.

The author's Preface outlines in succinct fashion the justification for the biochemical approach to psychiatry, if such were necessary. There is no special pleading and no claim that it supplies a key to all the answers. It is merely placed in its biological perspective. Like Shaw's Prefaces it should be read, though unlike his, it is brief. The first chapter on the structure of biochemistry is a more explicit and detailed elaboration of the development of biochemistry as it relates to topics of interest to the psychiatrist. It is comprehensive but non-technical, gently orientating, informative. Thereafter the unwary are led directly into a cataract of proteins and amino acids. This is followed in due course by explicit accounts of the chemistry of carbohydrates and fats. The place of trace minerals, of enzymes, of excesses and deficits of vitamins and hormones receives well proportioned treatment. In fact, all relevant biochemical functions which participate in the complex of metabolic processes pertinent to those behavior disorders associated with demonstrable biochemical deviation in some tissue fluid come under purview. Dr. Sourkes does not shirk the obligation to present the chemistry of the body in its complexities, but his account will daunt only the most frail of nonbiochemical readers, for recognizable islands of clinical familiarity appear with sufficient frequency to provide exciting rescue and perspective. It is like being led through a maze of often unfamiliar clues which suddenly converge to clarify in detective fashion the villain whose name is familiar, like phenylketonuria. The approach is that of a biochemist, but one who is properly familiar with the syndromes he tries to fathom further. This province of the psychiatrist he treats with neither undue familiarity nor condescension. He is a fellow worker in the field of behavior and does not claim for his techniques ultimate solutions or transcendental illumination.

This book is comprehensive and comprehensible. It should attract aspiring tyros and all other ages up to declining sages whose early education and subsequent busy life made acquisition of this order of learning impossible. Depending on taste and interest, various chapters will find their own devotees, but perhaps the last on biochemical pharmacology will exert a special and topical appeal. Here in a few short pages is concentrated the essence of the information which currently appears in scattered journals and huge monographs. Many will wish to thank the author for this as well as other clarifying chapters.

This reader has watched the diligent but unhurried growth of this book while the author carried out his laboratory investigations, attended conferences, advised students, taught and talked. While the clinician finds his satisfactions in his patients, as well as his disappointments, there is in his individual successes compensation for lack of continuity. For the laboratory investigator, on the other hand, it is the growth of a science of which he is a part which is his major reward. If he also has the opportunity to gain some acquaintance with the clinical side of the subjects on whom his studies throw light, as Dr. Sourkes has, he becomes doubly enlightened if not twice rewarded. So I hope other readers will be able to share with me a debt of gratitude for this able and lucid description of biochemistry in psychiatry. They will have to be content to envy me the opportunity of daily association with the author.

R. A. CLEGHORN, M.D., D.SC.

# PREFACE

The years following the Second World War have witnessed a rapid development in the amount of fundamental research being devoted to the investigation of mental disease, including its biochemical aspects. This phenomenon can be traced to at least three sources. One of these is overt and is recognized by medical science and government alike: it is the gradual acquisition of the knowledge and therapeutic armamentarium necessary to conquer nutritional and infectious diseases, victory over which was in sight by mid-century. The consequent shift in emphasis by public health leaders has been directed toward psychiatric illnesses and the degenerative diseases that accompany aging. Against a background highlighted by vitamins, sulfonamides, and antibiotics there was every reason to expect that the research methods of laboratory and clinic which have proved successful in the past would stand in good stead in these fields also. The manner in which the problem was approached is illustrated by the establishment of special research bodies and advisory councils recommending the disbursement of governmental funds in aid of basic and clinical research in psychiatry. In England this was signalized by the inauguration of the Mental Health Research Fund in 1949. In the United States two National Institutes, designated for research in mental diseases (1949) and in neurological diseases and blindness (1951), were set up within the Federal Security Agency. In Canada since 1948 there has been Federal-Provincial agreement on the financing of research in mental health and on the administration of the fund. In addition many private and semiprivate agencies, particularly in the United States, have entered this field, enhancing appreciably the amount of money available.

The second stimulus to basic research came from developments within psychiatry itself. Therapeutic successes with physical and chemical shock treatments—electroconvulsive therapy, metrazol shock, insulin coma therapy—naturally strengthened the conviction that physical and biochemical processes were being set right and that the nature of the disturbance was susceptible of analysis by the preclinical disciplines. The psychic changes in some endocrine disorders did not go unnoticed either, and a vogue in replacement therapy found its adherents in psychiatry too, particularly recommending the use of thyroid. The psychological effects of drugs such as mescaline, cocaine, hashish, and other members of the *phantastica* had been known for years but their significance for psychiatric research lay dormant until the serendipitous discovery of the remarkable actions of LSD-25 by Albert Hofmann in 1943. The ability of this compound in minute amounts to bring about an acute psychological disturbance raised anew the question: if an exogenous chemical of this kind can evoke dramatic changes in subjective experience, then is it possible that an endogenous chemical substance, resulting from some metabolic disturbance, is responsible for the development of psychoses?

The third stimulus to basic research into mental illness arose through the dynamics of growth of the fundamental scientific disciplines themselves. The evolution of new techniques along with the growth of a sizable body of knowledge made possible new and broader approaches to the obvious complexities inherent in the subject. The process can be exemplified by biochemistry. By the present date biochemistry has identified the main chemical structural constituents of the body and has described their formation and metabolic conversions. It has clarified the role of vitamins and the mineral elements in these processes. Methods are now available for measuring a host of substances or for estimating the rate of various biochemical changes in tissue samples ranging in size from the fragments removed at biopsy up to the point at which the physiologist must assume charge with his more sophisticated procedures. Analysis of blood and urine is no longer limited to the still highly important constellation of sugar and gross nitrogenous constituents, but has now embraced the techniques of paper chromatography, electrophoresis, spectrophotometry, and fluorescence analysis. Substances present in body fluids in very high dilution, such as specific amino acids, intermediary metabolites, and hormones, to name but a few, can be determined with a facility not even imagined fifteen or twenty years ago. All these techniques are, of course, available for use in the biochemical laboratory at the mental hospital. That they are, in general, being employed is evidenced by the growing number of publications on biochemical subjects in the psychiatric literature.

Behind this expanding program is the conviction that the basic sciences, including biochemistry, have something special to offer the psychiatrist and research worker that will aid them appropriately in their work. This thesis has had a long philosophical history, but it entered the modern period about one hundred and fifty years ago when the French physiologists made the mind, which had ruled an independent realm in the Cartesian system, a mere epiphenomenon of the body. This viewpoint was carried forward many years later in the materialism of the German physiologists. Although biochemists today do not seek evidence in the sense of the crude formulations of the nineteenth century they welcome the assurance that ideational processes have some physical basis that will not prove refractory to investigation by the techniques that have been successful in other branches of human physiology. In fact, the work of the basic scientist in psychiatry is implicitly founded upon the fact that mental phenomena have their counterpart in neurophysiological activity and cerebral metabolism, considered broadly.

No one would question today the statement that an alteration in the chemistry of the brain may result in an alteration in thought, perception, or behavior. The effects of dozens of drugs, including the narcotics, barbiturates, phenothiazines, Rauwolfia alkaloids, hydrazides, amphetamines, mescaline, and lysergic acid diethylamide, among many others, illustrate the principle. The finding of genetic and constitutional factors in the psychoses, and the availability of some measure of therapeutic control over them, encourage the belief that eventually organic etiology will be discovered here also. Indeed the traditional division of psychiatric disorders into organic and functional is (fortunately) undermined by the growth of the former group at the expense of the latter, as knowledge of etiological factors—neurological, chemical, hormonal, bacteriological—expands. This has been the case with epilepsy, general paralysis of the insane, the lipidoses, cretinism, phenylketonuria, the industrial toxicities, and others. Stanley Cobb, in his *Foundations of Neuropsychiatry* (Baltimore, Williams & Wilkins, 1948) emphasizes that "all function is organic, so the slang use of the terms 'organic' or 'functional' is meaningless. The same argument can be repeated substituting the terms 'physical' and 'mental.'"

There is clearly enough reason to be found in the history of medicine, in general, and of psychiatry itself to warrant the concerted search for significant physiological and chemical factors and processes in mental diseases. Certainly, if they are not actively sought, they are not likely to be detected. This is an admonition that hardly seems necessary nowadays, with the spate of conferences called to deal with a growing list of tranquilizing agents and psychotomimetic drugs. The work on these new drugs has caught the imagination of many workers in the basic sciences: the very persons who are equipped by their specialized training to study the physiological foundations of neurological and mental functions. Many, indeed, have now oriented their research toward these problems which, by this time, have lost some of their impregnable character. We have reached a point in scientific development where one begins to sense the acceleration in the field. If we are to control the direction of this development, then it is necessary to assess what has been achieved thus far in the biochemical study of mental diseases.

The idea for this book came from my experience as a member of an Institute devoted to research, treatment, and teaching in psychiatry. I have attempted to present a systematic appraisal of the literature of biochemistry as it applies to psychiatric problems, and have done so from the standpoint of intermediary metabolism. This approach has been tested in my lectures to postgraduate students in psychiatry with the intention of clarifying the relation of biochemistry to mental disease. Many of my colleagues in psychiatry and biochemistry have kindly read particular chapters and have given me their comments and corrections, for which I thank them. Errors and misstatements that remain are not their responsibility, but mine. I am indebted to various authors and publishers for permission to quote extensive sets of data or text from their papers. My manuscript was ushered to the book stage by Miss Inge Klement, who skillfully prepared the typescript, and by the publisher and his staff, for whose advice and cooperation I am very grateful.

I owe much to Professor D. Ewen Cameron, Chairman of the Department of Psychiatry, McGill University, and Director of the Allan Memorial Institute of Psychiatry, and to Dr. Robert A. Cleghorn, Professor of Psychiatry, for the support they have given me in this project. They were enthusiastic about it when I first discussed it with them, and have given me constant encouragement ever since. Dr. Cleghorn undertook to read through the manuscript and to write the Foreword, a task for which I thank him most sincerely.

T. L. S.

*Montreal, Quebec*

# Abbreviations

| | |
|---|---|
| ATP = ARPPP | Adenosine triphosphate |
| CSF | Cerebrospinal fluid |
| DNA = DRNA | Deoxyribonucleic acid |
| DPN = NAD | Diphosphopyridine nucleotide = nicotinamide adenine dinucleotide, Coenzyme I |
| DPT | Diphosphothiamine, cocarboxylase |
| $FH_4:NH$ | Folic acid coenzyme |
| GSH, GSSG | Glutathione, reduced and oxidized forms, respectively |
| GTP | Guanosine triphosphate |
| 5HIAA | 5-Hydroxyindoleacetic acid |
| 5HT | 5-Hydroxytryptamine, serotonin |
| 5HTP | 5-Hydroxytryptophan |
| RNA = PNA | Ribonucleic acid = Pentosenucleic acid |
| —SH | Sulfhydryl group |
| SRNA | Soluble ribonucleic acid |
| TPN = NADP | Triphosphopyridine nucleotide, NAD-phosphate, Coenzyme II |
| TPNH = NADPH | Reduced TPN |
| UDP, UTP | Uridine diphosphate, uridine triphosphate |
| UDPG | Uridine diphosphoglucose |

# BIOCHEMISTRY OF MENTAL DISEASE

# 1

# BIOCHEMISTRY AND PSYCHIATRY

## Structure of Biochemistry

Biochemistry is an experimental discipline which treats of the chemical changes undergone, as well as brought about by, living matter. It therefore shares part of its burden with chemistry in the investigation of the properties and reactions of chemical substances occurring within the organism. At times it also borders on physiology, and then the techniques of the two sciences are frequently exchanged by investigators. In fact, biochemistry had its origin in the last century in the application of chemistry to physiological, microbiological, and agricultural problems. Though still acknowledging these sources, biochemistry also concerns itself now with problems that belong to neither progenitor and are solved by the use of more or less independent techniques, such as the Warburg method for continuous analysis of respiratory metabolism and other changes in tissues and in extracts prepared from them; chromatography, invented in the course of biochemical investigation of plant pigments; paper chromatography, which has wrought a veritable revolution in biochemistry since it was first applied in 1942; and the variety of methods for the preparation of purified enzymes, the catalysts of change in living matter, as well as other proteins.

The position of biochemistry between chemistry and biology makes it a bridge between these two fields of scientific endeavor. Its Januslike role gives it an unusually deep perspective, with an appreciation of the problems and methods of several disciplines, as well as special concern with a fundamental theoretical problem of science and philosophy, namely the relationship between living and nonliving matter. Because this problem is the prototype of the theme of this book, namely, the relationship between thinking and nonthinking matter, it will be worthwhile to ponder some of its connotations. A not uncommon view is that the biological phenomenon will be understood when all the physicochemical elements making it up have been described. In other words, biological phenomena, according to this view, are nothing but physicochemical events packed together in multitude; nothing occurs in the biological world which cannot be resolved into components describable in the terminology of the physical sciences. The differences in the qualities of inanimate and living objects, the differences in the scientific laws descriptive of the movement of the one and the other: these remain without explanation. The mechanistic attitude, even in its naïve form as presented here, represents an effort to explain such differences without imposing a vital principle upon biological function. The exorcising of the spirits from biology occupied the attention of the natural philosophers for centuries, and it eventually met with success on various fronts and at various times. As far as biochemistry is concerned vitalism finally lost out when Fischer (1895) and Büchner (1896) prepared enzymes of fermentation from disintegrated yeast cells and demonstrated, as Liebig had maintained in the famous controversy with Pasteur, that intact organismic structure is not essential for exhibition of one of the prime features of many lower organisms: the ability to perform fermentations. It does not flow from this, of course, that biochemistry can thereby reduce biology to the terms of physics and chemistry. For in higher systems, such as the living organism, with its multiplicity of processes, each one simple in isolation, but all interacting *in vivo*, new qualities appear. These qualities are the result of the organization and arrangement of these processes into new patterns which are neither deducible from nor reducible to the underlying movement. The new level of organization is thus based upon the lower one and incorporates the physical and chemical mechanisms; however, it can be adequately described only by new laws appropriate to this level of integration. Thus, at some stage in the growth of material organization new qualities appear that we call life. It should not be concluded that biochemistry avoids the problem of intermediate stages, for with the newer knowledge of biochemical polymers, particularly the nucleoproteins, and their role in genetic, *i.e.*, duplication processes, there have been attempts to bridge the gap and to throw light upon the origin of life.

Biochemistry has many branches, reflecting the breadth of its scope and its contacts with other disciplines. One of these investigates chemical homology (same process, different functions in different organisms or *phyla*) and chemical analogy (different processes subserving the same function) in the animal and plant world; it goes under the name of comparative biochemistry. The challenge of evolutionary theory has thus penetrated biochemistry and delineated the basic bonds between animal, plant, and microorganism. One aspect of comparative biochemistry of which the fundamental investigator takes advantage daily is the similarity of biochemical processes and enzymatic reactions in related and even distant species. Species-specificity does, of course, exist and if it is kept in mind as a cautionary measure it is possible to extrapolate reasonably well from lower mammals to man. Differences in quantity of biochemical components and in rates of processes are found, but a variety of techniques makes it possible to check upon the information obtained by any one method and, insofar as cellular tissue metabolism is concerned, a direct check can occasionally be made for humans by use of biopsy, surgical, or post-mortem specimens. What will likely prove to be a profitable field of investigation in the future is the systematic biochemistry of the nervous system through the evolutionary scale. That this field has connotations for the experimental approach to psychiatry has already been borne out in the study of neurohumoral agents and transmitter substances.

Among the generalizations of biochemistry which merit discussion here is the antimetabolite hypothesis. In 1926 Quastel and Wooldridge found that malonic acid inhibits the bacterial oxidation of its next higher homologue, succinic acid, which is a normal metabolite. Their studies suggested to them that the malonic acid molecule was sufficiently like that of the substrate to be able to attach to the enzyme catalyzing the dehydrogenation but, because of the chemical difference, it could not undergo the actual chemical change. This inhibitor interferes with succinic acid breakdown, the argument ran, because it displaces the normal oxidizable substrate from the catalytic site. This example of inhibition by competition for the reactive sites of enzymes found a companion exemplar some fourteen years later in the action of the sulfonamides. These compounds are inactive in the presence of *p*-aminobenzoic acid (PABA), a tissue constituent and bacterial vitamin, which resembles sulfanilamide chemically. The sulfonamides interfere with bacterial metabolism through displacing PABA from its participation in essential intermediary reactions. Thus arose the concept described now as the antimetabolite hypothesis. This concept holds that it is possible to interfere with metabolism of specific substances by introducing into the cell a substance chemically identical with the metabolite in question except in some respect, this difference rendering the compound an inhibitor of reactions involving the metabolite, and usually guaranteeing that it will not be a participant in these metabolic pathways. Such a substance would be therapeutically ideal if it interfered with bacterial metabolism and not with that of the host, or if its toxicity for the bacteria were displayed well before harm is done to the host. By providing a rational approach to chemotherapy the antimetabolite hypothesis has stimulated a widespread search for compounds as useful in medicine as are the sulfonamides. Thousands of compounds have been synthesized as part of antimetabolite research programs. Many compounds with true antimetabolite activity have been prepared but have had to be discarded in the course of therapeutic testing because of toxicity to the host, lack of pharmacological specificity when tested *in vivo*, or some other reason. A number of useful compounds have resulted, but probably not as many as by more fortuitous methods. This is not to deprecate the value of theory, by any means, but simply to emphasize that the study of the relationships between chemical structure and biological activity, to which the antimetabolite concept is a contribution, is still incomplete, and the prediction of pharmacological effects of a newly synthesized compound on the basis of its chemical structure is still fraught with many uncertainties.

A second field in which biochemistry borders upon pharmacology is that which seeks to find the metabolic site of action of drugs, that is, to learn what effects the drugs have on the chemistry of the body, perhaps what chemical reactions they affect or what enzymes they inhibit, what part of their sequence of actions is correlated with the clinical result. This type of work is particularly important for alkaloidal drugs and others difficult to synthesize, for if the vulnerable site is known it may be possible to tailor synthetic compounds to specification as replacements. Such investigations are also being pursued with the psychopharmacological agents. Reserpine, for example, has been found to liberate certain amines from binding sites in the brain and other organs. The significance of this for the various clinical and pharmacological actions of reserpine is under continuing investigation.

Something has already been said about neurochemical studies. This branch was founded by Thudichum a century ago, and was revived in this century by a number of independent researchers. As the name indicates, neurochemistry is concerned with the chemistry of the nervous system, and accordingly has the highest significance for biological investigations into mental disease. True, the neurochemist's first concern is the relation of chemical processes to neurological function, and he therefore has the advantage of working with tangible structures, capable of being measured quantitatively as well as described qualitatively. However, neurological function also includes consciousness and here the neurochemist is acting at the same level as the biochemist who is psychiatrically oriented. It would obviously be unwise to dissociate to any degree these two branches of what must, from the nature of things, be a unitary study. If only for this reason it is important to resist the introduction of the neologism psychochemistry.

We may complete this catalogue of contacts of biochemistry with the various medical disciplines by referring to the use of chemical methods in research, diagnosis, assessment of organ function, and treatment by the internist. So many of these are now commonplace that it is easy to forget the skepticism with which they were first greeted. In psychiatry, as well, various biochemical tests contend for attention as biochemical indexes of disease. Although none of these tests has yet met the requirement of specificity, nevertheless they bind mental disease more closely with somatic illness by pointing up organic factors common to both groups. For the biochemist this is partial satisfaction of his aims.

## Development of Biochemistry

It is worthwhile tracing, even schematically, some of the history of biochemistry because in its development, especially in recent years, there can be seen some of the trends that have prepared it for the study of neurological and mental diseases. Biochemistry is a relatively new science. We are only a little more than 160 years away from Lavoisier, 90 from Bernard and Liebig. It is barely half a century since biochemical societies were formed in England and the United States. To be sure, such a step was feasible because of the increasing number of investigators specializing in this field and because of the accumulation of the corps of fundamental data prerequisite to it. Other measures, such as the founding of journals in England and the United States and even earlier in Germany for the publication of biochemical papers, had a salutary influence on the new science. In these early years biochemistry began to find numerous applications to clinical medicine, particularly in the study of the biochemistry of disease and in the elaboration of precise methods for the measurement of metabolites in blood and urine, and of gaseous exchange. This period culminated in the theory of metabolism proposed by Otto Folin.* According to this theory two types of process occur simultaneously in the animal body and these are exemplified in protein metabolism. One process goes on constantly, represents the wear and tear on the tissues, and results in the excretion of a relatively constant amount of creatinine in the urine. The rate of excretion of creatinine is a measure of this "endogenous" metabolism of the body. The second process reflects the fluctuating rate of utilization of protein in metabolism, which in turn is dependent upon the amount of protein consumed and the amount required for growth or production. This exogenous metabolism can be measured by the output of urea in the urine. The theory of a dichotomous metabolism brought to fruition the concept advanced by Claude Bernard earlier that cell constituents occupy two compartments described as the "éléments constant et variable," respectively. Like many major theories of science, it brought together many diverse facts and organized them into a single framework. Actually it summarized the knowledge of intermediary metabolism up to that time, knowledge gleaned not from direct observation on the intermediary processes but by comparison of what is consumed and what is excreted. This balance-sheet method suffered from the ignorance of what happens between the initial and final stages; it emphasized the easily recognizable end products of metabolism to the neglect of the transient intermediates.

In the next thirty years the accumulation of new facts about enzymology and intermediary metabolism expanded biochemical understanding beyond the confines of earlier concepts. This development was characterized toward its later stages by the introduction of heavy hydrogen in the study of water metabolism *in vivo* by Hevesy, and of the hydrogen and nitrogen isotopes in the study of organic metabolism by Schoenheimer and his colleagues. The use of the radioactive isotopes, now an entrenched technique in biology followed soon after. Schoenheimer expressed the new knowledge of intermediary metabolism in his theory of *the dynamic state of body constituents,* which he summarized in the following words:

* It is interesting that in 1899 Folin initiated biochemical research in a mental hospital (McLean Hospital, Waverly, Mass.). The difficulties in searching for biochemical characteristics of mental patients that would distinguish them from normal at a time when knowledge of the composition of the bodily fluids was so meager led Folin to investigate problems of metabolism.

The large and complex molecules and their component units, fatty acids, amino acids, and nucleic acids, are constantly involved in rapid chemical reaction. Ester, peptide, and other linkages open; the fragments thereby liberated merge with those derived from other large molecules, and those absorbed from the intestinal tract, to form a metabolic pool of components, indistinguishable as to origin. Those liberated molecules are again subject to numerous processes. Fatty acids are dehydrogenated, hydrogenated, degraded or elongated, and thereby continually interconverted. While some individual molecules of these acids are completely degraded, other individuals of the same chemical species are steadily formed from entirely different substances, notably from carbohydrate. Similar reactions occur among the split products and the nitrogen liberated is transferred to other previously deaminated molecules to form new amino acids. Part of the pool of newly formed small molecules constantly re-enters vacant places in the large molecules to restore the fats, proteins, and the nucleoproteins. Some of the small molecules involved in these regeneration reactions constitute intermediate steps in the formation of excretory products (1).

Schoenheimer's views, which were quickly and widely adopted, discarded the legacy of static concepts of metabolism based upon the single-entry metabolic ledger. They spurred biochemists to find further examples of the diverse and limitless reactions, the syntheses, the transformations, the interconversions, that were now recognized to be the commonplace of intermediary metabolism. Once again biochemistry found its horizon moving back with new experiments, new techniques, and new thinking required. This is the stage in which biochemical science now finds itself, and the current expansion of its activities in the direction of neurology and psychiatry may be recognized as a product of this stage.

## Biochemistry and Clinical Problems of Psychiatry

*Besides we see the mind to be born with the body, to grow with the body, and to decay with it . . . . The senses of no living thing can exist before the substance of the living thing itself is got together.—Lucretius, "Concerning the Nature of Things"* (2).

In the past fifty years biochemistry has assumed a strategic position in the various branches of medicine and as a consequence of this the aid of the biochemist has been solicited in solving clinical problems. That the invitation has occasionally resulted in embarrassment to biochemistry is not surprising, for it has not always been able to match its accumulated factual resources *pari passu* with the theoretical elegance required in undertaking new problems. In this sense the offer of cooperation with clinical science is perhaps most challenging when it comes from psychiatry. Just as in the somatic diseases, where illness is referable to an organ or to an organ system, so in mental disease the physical frame of reference is the brain. However, there is one major difference: in the former group the description of the disease is entirely in terms of organ function and, in fact, would be meaningless otherwise, whereas in the latter the pathological processes can be detailed without primary reference (in most cases) to any organ. By a twist of logic the disease is thereby "disembodied": it is divested of its character as a process emanating from highly organized, intricately structured matter, the brain, and becomes a rootless entity—a psychiatric thing-in-itself. This is the source of the dualistic approach to the mind-body relationship that specifically hampers biochemistry in exploring fully the influence of physiological-chemical processes in mental diseases, in other words, from enacting precisely the same role it has played in its contacts with other medical disciplines. To the biochemist, accustomed to deal with material processes, the abstractions of psychopathology offer no encouragement to his work, certainly no hope of experimental approach by the means he knows, *unless* he adopts the view that in mental disease there is something wrong in the function of the substratum of mentation, and that this substratum can be dealt with by the techniques of his science.

For the investigator carrying out scientific investigations in psychiatry it is necessary to have a clear appreciation of the extent of the hiatus between the basic disciplines and the psychological ones. It is too early in the development of the relations between biochemistry and psychiatry to question the precise mechanism whereby the action of a chemical or drug on the brain is ultimately translated into behavioral, psychological, and emotional changes. Through fundamental biochemical studies one may observe the inhibition of an enzyme, an alteration in the permeability of neural membranes, or a change in some other physicochemical process. As these new facts are found a base is established for the next attempts to penetrate the great intermediate *terra incognita* between the chemical event and the psychological one. It can be expected that the way across is a highly tortuous and indirect one, so that the attempts to simplify the route may introduce even more difficulties. For example, by undue emphasis upon the special character of mental processes, their complexity, and their distinctness from physical phenomena these processes are made to transcend their material roots, leading back to a vitalism or panpsychism from which biochemistry was freed in the nineteenth century. This by no means precludes recognition of the characteristic qualities of mental symptoms.

Taking one's standpoint on the indivisibility of mental and physical happenings, and on the indivisibility of mental disorder, whether for convenience it be called neurosis or psychosis, it is plain that the discovery of metabolic or other physiological disturbances of function does not prevent us from regarding an illness as predominantly a mental disorder, any more than a post-encephalitic, post-traumatic, or post-paretic behavior disorder ceases to be a mental illness because of its physical substrate (3).

On the other hand, elimination of the difference between physical and mental by postulating some simple direct relationship acts as a deterrent to teleology but contradicts too many facts to be acceptable as an alternative. The mechanistic standpoint, which holds that the description of the chemistry and metabolism of the brain is sufficient for the characterization of mental processes, is quite unable to explain the appearance of the new qualities of biological matter as described earlier or, on a higher plane, thinking matter. These new properties arise through the more complex organization of matter: through the magnification of the number of elements and processes participating and interacting until the point is reached where the individual processes and the scientific laws describing them are subsumed in the novel relationships that appear. This concept of interactive levels, acceptance of which is becoming more widespread, has been described succinctly by Gerard:

The class is, of course, a kind of individual and the more the members of the class interact—even to the extent of developing into differentiated subclasses—rather than coexist, the more does the superordinate group become a true individual rather than a collection of ordinate individuals . . . . The atom, an individual or unit, is built of subordinate differentiated and interacting units, the various nucleons and other ultimate (for the moment) particles, and is built into a superordinate molecule. The individual molecule, in turn with like or unlike fellows, becomes a crystal or some other material aggregate; the colloids form particulates; these, cells: cells, tissues, and organs; these, organisms; and organisms, species, and large taxonomic categories, or in another way, groups, communities, and larger ecosystems . . . . The important levels are those whose entities are relatively enduring and self-contained. Thus, a cell is more likely to continue as an individually maintained entity than is a given colloidal micelle or a cell particulate, and an organism will vary less in time than will its parts or organs (4).

The study of these levels has become formalized in the physical, biological, behavioral, and social sciences, for example, and it is only in the relatively recent history of science that investigation of the inclined bridges (such as biochemistry) that connect the various levels has been initiated.

The general aims of the biochemist in the study of mental disease are: the search for causative factors of a chemical nature; and the investigation of chemical parameters whereby the disease may be characterized, its severity quantified, or its course indicated. Richter points out that

> . . . biochemical research is especially urgent since the knowledge of biochemical defects can lead quite directly to the suggestion of remedies. Thus the discovery of specific biochemical deficiencies in rickets, diabetes, and pernicious anemia led rapidly to successful treatment by rational methods and replacement therapy. Faulty working of the brain due to an imbalance of enzyme systems or to a biochemical deficiency might also be rectified by similar methods (5).

Unfortunately, psychiatry, unlike the other divisions of medicine, lacks a large body of facts garnered for it by the fundamental sciences and therefore, at this inchoate stage, basic fact-finding is very much in order. Such knowledge can help to reveal the significant processes, including those amenable to pharmacological treatment, in the psychoses. Perhaps biochemical indicators of disease or guideposts to successful therapy can be found, advancing treatment beyond empiricism into the realm of therapy grounded in etiological understanding.

Hitherto biochemical investigation in psychiatry has been limited in scope and one may therefore be giving it too much credit if one implies that it has evolved any characteristic lines of research. In broaching mental disease biochemistry has attempted what has been found feasible in its investigation of other diseases. For example, a great deal of work has been done in the search for chemical differences between normal subjects and mental patients, but has met with only limited success thus far. The experimental approach has sought changes in liver function, inasmuch as the concept of disturbances in metabolism, with formation of a cerebrotoxic agent, has played a major role in several theories of the etiology of psychoses. Hence, much has been written about altered hepatic function and about variations in the pattern of urinary and blood constituents. Lately there has been emphasis upon some of the minor but not unimportant metabolites of the aromatic amino acids.

The early descriptions of endocrinological syndromes revealed the existence of a mental component in some of them. Such findings have spurred the search for more direct relationships between endocrine function and mental processes. At one time the adrenal medulla, together with the sympathetic nervous system, had been elevated by Cannon to a vanguard position in the body's responses to emergencies and in the maintenance of homeostasis. It was later overtaken by other endocrines. Investigators concentrated especially upon the thyroid and the adrenal cortex. With the discovery of norepinephrine as a second sympathin, the sympathoadrenal system has now swung back to a position in the forefront of psychosomatic research. A major problem for the endocrinologist is the unusual tolerance exhibited by many schizophrenic patients to exogenous hormones. Whether the tolerance is due to loss of sensitivity at the end organ or to antagonism of the exogenous hormone elsewhere in the body is not known. Normal variations in the degree of endocrine activity are sensitively adjusted in the case of certain glands by tropic hormones of the adenohypophysis. The dominant role of this gland has tended to endow the entire endocrine system with an aura of automatism, or independence from other bodily functions, and it is therefore encouraging to note the current trend toward investigation of the chemical and nervous control of hypophyseal function itself.

The emphasis in general biochemical research upon intermediary metabolism has profited medicine through the discovery of metabolic errors, frequently the result of deficiency of a specific enzyme. The study of these diseases was initiated by Sir Archibald Garrod, who labeled them "inborn errors of metabolism." The association of a metabolic block in the normal pathway of metabolism of phenylalanine with a certain type of mental deficiency indicated the possibilities for psychiatric investigation in this approach. Phenylketonuria is not the only cerebral disease associated with a specific biochemical lesion. Others are already well known, and new entities are being recognized all the time.

The metabolism of the amino acids is of great concern in mental diseases. The major role of glutamic acid in brain metabolism led to its trial several years ago in a number of disorders, particularly mental deficiency. Its decarboxylation product, γ-aminobutyric acid, is also a normal constituent of cerebral tissue and has now been found to function as an inhibitory substance in neural transmission. The significance of glutamic acid in neurophysiological function is therefore not a closed chapter. The study of the intermediary metabolism of the amino acids has also extended to the formation and breakdown of brain proteins. These substances are among the most complex of biochemical compounds, are endowed with a high degree of biochemical specificity, and possess structural, enzymatic, immunological, respiratory, and other functions. Much can therefore be expected from their exploration in the brain and the influence of various conditions upon their metabolism.

The carbohydrates and lipides have received a large share of attention. They are the major sources of energy in the diet and carbohydrate is the primary fuel of the brain, so that if general metabolic processes are affected in mental diseases these substances may well be involved. That they reflect hormonal and metabolic changes in emotional states has been shown now in many laboratories.

The minor constituents of the body—vitamins and minerals—have also featured to a small extent thus far in mental disease research. A number of the B-avitaminoses entail neurological symptoms and, in some cases, a frank psychosis. Alcoholic psychosis may be placed in this group also because of the role that nutritional deficiency plays in its etiology.

Contact with unduly large amounts of metals, industrially or otherwise, represents a hazard to health. In some cases neuropsychiatric symptoms appear. Through increased knowledge of the action of various metals upon the enzyme systems of the body there is now a biochemical basis upon which to investigate the clinical toxicity of these metals. Fortunately, these syndromes are not seen as frequently as in the past.

A modicum of work has been done on variations in enzyme content of the tissues in mental diseases. Obviously this has its limitations because the only easily accessible tissues are the blood and cerebrospinal fluid, and these have a restricted spectrum of enzymes. According to current views, enzymes bear specific relationships to genes; that is, the hereditary units exert their effects, as observed in the metabolic phenotype, through enzymes. One may well expect that in the future the enzymatic counterpart of the genetic factors in psychoses will yield to investigation.

# References

1. SCHOENHEIMER, R. *The Dynamic State of Body Constituents.* Cambridge, Harvard University Press, 1946.
2. LUCRETIUS, *in Lucretius on Life and Death,* trans. W. H. MALLOCK. London, Adam and Charles Black, 1910.
3. BAILEY, P. *Am. J. Psychiat. 113:*387, 1956.
4. GERARD, R. W. *Science 125:*429, 1957.
5. RICHTER, D. *in Prospects in Psychiatric Research, ed.* J. M. TANNER. Oxford, Blackwell, 1953.

# 2

# PROTEINS AND AMINO ACIDS

## Chemistry and Metabolism

Proteins are polymers made up of amino acids condensed together through peptide (carboxylamino) linkages:

$$\begin{array}{ccc} R_m & & R_n \\ | & & | \\ -NH-CH-CO-NH-CH-CO \end{array}$$

Two amino acid residues joined through the peptide bond are shown here. The specific structure, chemical and physical characteristics, and the biological properties of proteins are determined by the nature of the $R$ groups and their sequence in the molecule. Proteins are also known as polypeptides, and consist of hundreds of amino acid residues. Peptides with only a small number of constituent amino acids are termed oligopeptides. Anserine and carnosine, found in muscle, are dipeptides. Glutathione and ophthalmic acid are tripeptides. The neurohypophyseal hormones vasopressin and oxytocin are octapeptides. Glucagon contains 29 amino acid residues; $\beta$-corticotropin consists of 39; and synthetic adrenocorticotropin contains 23.

Besides the peptide bond several other types of linkage may occur in proteins. A free carboxyl group, such as the $\alpha$-carboxyl of glutamic acid or that of glycine when this amino acid is in a terminal position on the peptide chain, may form an amide linkage with ammonia. Two cysteinyl residues may become joined through oxidation of their —SH groups to

14

form a cystinyl residue. This reaction often serves to bind two parallel peptide chains together, as in the insulin molecule. In many proteins with enzymatic activity the catalytic function depends upon the presence of a free sulfhydryl group. The $\beta$-hydroxyl group of serine forms an ester linkage with phosphoric acid in the phosphoproteins.

Through detailed chemical analyses it is now possible to determine not only the amino acid composition but also the sequence of these structural units along the peptide chain. This type of analysis has succeeded in delineating the structure of insulin, ribonuclease, corticotropin, bradykinin, and other peptides.

Of the numerous amino acids found in nature only twenty-odd of their number occur in proteins. The number of polypeptides that can occur through various combinations of the amino acids is theoretically infinite, and the known proteins probably represent only a small proportion of the actual total number. These proteins perform various specific functions. In connective tissue, cartilage, bone, skin, and hair they serve protective, structural, and other mechanical functions.

Other proteins play a role in immunochemical processes. The remarkable specificity of action of the proteins, particularly those with immunochemical or enzymatic functions, is attributable not only to the particular arrangement of amino acid residues along the peptide chains, as already mentioned, but also to the topographical features of the molecule as a whole, that is, to its shape and the nature of the groups projecting from the surface. This surface, or parts of it (reactive sites), may be thought of as a template facilitating the juxtaposition of reacting molecules in space so that chemical reaction occurs. This concept corresponds to the older lock-and-key hypothesis of enzymatic action.

The body proteins are synthesized in the tissues from dietary constituents, primarily from ingested proteins after these have been broken down in digestion to the constituent amino acids. Only eight of the amino acids found in proteins are absolutely essential for maintenance of nitrogen equilibrium in the adult human (see "Nutritional Requirements," below). The remainder can be synthesized in the body from this essential group or from nonnitrogenous components together with ammonia or the amino group of another amino acid. In this way tyrosine is synthesized from phenylalanine (Reaction 2-1) by an oxidative pathway that is as

$$C_6H_5CH_2CH(NH_2)COOH + \tfrac{1}{2}O_2 \rightarrow$$
L-Phenylalanine

$$\text{para-}OH \cdot C_6H_4CH_2CH(NH_2)COOH \quad (2\text{-}1)$$
L-Tyrosine

$$HOOC \cdot CH_2CH_2COCOOH + NH_3 \leftrightarrows$$

α-Ketoglutaric acid

$$HOOC \cdot CH_2CH_2C(=NH)COOH + H_2O \quad (2\text{-}2)$$

[α-Iminoglutaric acid]

$$HOOC \cdot CH_2CH_2C(=NH)COOH + DPNH + H^+ \leftrightarrows$$

$$HOOC \cdot CH_2CH_2CH(NH_2)COOH + DPN^+ \quad (2\text{-}3)$$

L-Glutamic acid

$$\text{L-Glutamic acid} + \text{Oxaloacetic acid} \leftrightarrows$$

$$\text{α-Ketoglutaric acid} + \text{L-Aspartic acid} \quad (2\text{-}4)$$

yet incompletely understood. Glutamic acid is synthesized from α-keto-glutaric acid and ammonia (Reactions 2-2 and 2-3) in one of the chief paths of nitrogen assimilation. The formation of glutamic acid by this mechanism is further used in the transfer of the newly formed α-amino group of the glutamic acid to various α-keto acids, thereby giving rise to new amino acids. Reaction 2-4 exemplifies this transamination reaction in the biosynthesis of L-aspartic acid.

Little is known of the factors controlling the synthesis of proteins. The growth hormone of the anterior pituitary gland exercises some control, but other hormones also have protein-anabolic actions. Two types of specificity are involved in protein formation. One is concerned with providing a particular, specific amino acid sequence in the polypeptide. The other determines the macromolecular features such as the association of two or more polypeptide chains in one molecule, union with polysaccharide, lipide, or nucleic acid. There is considerable evidence favoring a role for ribonucleic acid (RNA) in the synthesis of proteins. However, none of the evidence is yet conclusive on the manner in which the nucleic acid exerts its influence. Hypotheses on this score are of two general types: those which postulate that RNA, or fragments of it, supply the energy for amino acid union through formation of peptide bonds, in the form of either phosphorylated nucleic acids or polynucleotide carriers of the individual amino acids which are to be incorporated into the poly-peptide. The other group of hypotheses assign to RNA the role of template, its projecting nitrogen bases (purines and pyrimidines) offering the necessary topographical specificity to control the order in which the amino acids ultimately line up in the newly synthesized protein molecule. In terms of information theory the RNA structure is a specific code for arrangement of the amino acid residues. The evidence for nucleic acid function in the synthesis of proteins is quite incomplete, and much remains to be explained. For example, protein synthesis can proceed even under conditions that inhibit the synthesis of deoxyribonucleic acid

(DNA) in the cell. Moreover, there is some evidence that protein itself is required under certain conditions for the formation of RNA.

The nature of the dynamic and structural association between nucleic acid and protein is at the present time one of the crucial problems of biochemistry, important for the advance of our knowledge of organismic growth, antibody formation, and enzyme synthesis. Because the nucleic acids—in the first place DNA, the chromosomal substance—are concerned with the replication of the genetic code (genotype), and because enzymes play a key role in the ultimate translation of this code into the specific features of the individual (phenotype), metabolic processes making up the link between nucleic acids and protein synthesis are of no little interest in the study of cell division as of reproductive processes. These relationships receive clear expression in hereditary diseases in which a single genetic factor is believed to operate: in many such cases the homozygous (recessive) individual lacks a particular enzyme, whose absence from the tissues gives rise to a specific metabolic disorder. Investigations on the etiology and mechanism of these diseases lend support to the dictum that each gene exercises control over the formation of a corresponding enzyme. This generalization is widely accepted as a working hypothesis and is in agreement with much genetic-biochemical experience. However, little is known about the action of multiple genetic factors upon single enzymes or clusters of enzymes. Scheinberg has dealt with this topic in terms of the significance of genetic defects in the synthesis of specific proteins in mental disorders (1).

## Protein and Amino Acid Composition of the Brain and Cerebrospinal Fluid

*It seems surprising that in spite of the obvious importance of a detailed knowledge of the structure and reactivity of the neuroproteins, both from the point of view of protein chemistry and from the standpoint of practical psychiatry, these substances have been so little studied.—R. J. Block (2).*

The modern phase of investigations on brain proteins was begun in the last century by Petrovsky and by Ewald and Kühne. In spite of this early start interest in the problem has lagged, with the result that most of our information on the proteins and amino acids of the brain and of nerve has come only in the last twenty years.

About 90 percent of the dry weight of the brain consists of protein. Relatively large amounts of it are insoluble in water, but are soluble in mixtures of chloroform, methanol, and water. These are the proteolipides, and they make up as much as 2.5 percent of the wet weight of white matter and somewhat less of the grey. Three different proteolipides are known; Folch and Lees (3) state that they may possess the same protein moiety which, in turn, may be identical with the insoluble and enzymatically indigestible protein described in the last century by Ewald, Kühne, and Chittenden as neurokeratin. In spite of its name neurokeratin contains less cystine and arginine, and more histidine and lysine than the true keratins. About 25 percent of the brain protein is phosphoprotein, a poorly characterized category, but nonetheless of importance in oxidative processes (4, 5, 6). The phosphate is present as peptide-bound phosphoserine. Small amounts of collagen and elastin occur among the brain proteins: these are derived from the blood vessels. The nucleic acids of the brain occur in combination with proteins, probably lipoproteins, in the nucleus and in the Nissl granules.

The proteins of peripheral nerve have received even less attention. Neurokeratin is found in the myelin sheath. The chief protein, or complex of proteins, of the axon has been named neuronin; it bears a resemblance to material extractable from the brain and spinal cord (7).

In recent years the classical methods of separating proteins by their differential solubility in aqueous solvents or in certain organic solvents have been supplemented by the newer techniques of electrophoresis and ion-exchange chromatography. Many investigators have begun to use horizontal paper-strip electrophoresis, in order to separate the proteins of the cerebrospinal fluid. The separation is made by electrophoresis at pH 8.6 (in sodium diethylbarbiturate buffer), for under these conditions the differing net charges on the proteins determine their mobility for a given voltage applied across the paper. The albumin and globulins of nervous tissue have been named according to the protein fractions of the plasma and serum having corresponding mobilities (Table 2-1). This concordance has not yet been achieved for cerebrospinal fluid so that the electrophoretic separation of the proteins of this fluid must, for the time being, merely be taken to represent the concentration of certain protein groups having various mobilities. The names used for the cerebrospinal fluid peaks are therefore simply adopted from those of serum having corresponding properties. Electrophoretic studies show wide variation in results (Table 2-1); the apparent discrepancies may be attributed to differences in technique as well as to real differences in the composition of cerebrospinal fluid drawn from different levels. Mumenthaler and Märki (9) have summarized some of the changes in the proteins of cerebrospinal fluid observed in clinical disorders. In dysproteinemic states such as liver cirrhosis there is an increase in the γ-fraction of both serum and CSF; in cardiac insufficiency the β-fractions tend to increase. The γ-protein of CSF is elevated in multiple sclerosis and in luetic disease of the central nervous system. Changes in serum proteins are not necessarily a prerequisite for an abnormal spinal fluid electrophoresogram; in many neurological diseases only the latter is abnormal.

TABLE 2-1. ELECTROPHORESIS OF PROTEINS OF BLOOD PLASMA, CEREBROSPINAL FLUID, AND BRAIN OF MAN*

| Fraction | Blood Plasma Mean† | Cerebrospinal Fluid Mean† | Gray Matter | White Matter |
|---|---|---|---|---|
| "Vorfraktion"‡ | — | 4 | 0.7† | 1.1† |
| Albumin | 55 | 57 | 1.9 | 3.0 |
| $\alpha_1$-Globulin | 5 | 6 | } 12.0 | 18.9 |
| $\alpha_2$-Globulin | 9 | 7 | | |
| $\beta_1$-Globulin and $\beta_2$-Globulin | 13 | 20 | 66.7 | 53.6 |
| Fibrinogen | 7 | — | — | — |
| γ-Globulin | 11 | 11 | 18.9 | 23.4 |
| References | 8 | 9 | 11 | 11 |

* For CSF and brain the nomenclature of the various fractions is based upon that of plasma or serum proteins with similar mobility.

† Percentage units (approximate values).

‡ Also referred to in the literature as the "X-fraction."

A similar type of investigation has been conducted on watery extracts of brain proteins. It has been shown that brain proteins (human, guinea pig) having a high mobility in the electrophoretic field (the albumin fraction) are present in low amounts, just as in other tissues (10, 11). One group of investigators, however, have reported a large albumin fraction in rat brain (12). An albumin has similarly been detected in peripheral nerve fibers and in the cerebral white matter (11, 13).

A small amount of material having a mobility even higher than that of albumins is found in brain and cerebrospinal fluid. This Vorfraktion is shown, along with other components, in Table 2-1.

The electrophoretic technique has thus helped to establish a pronounced parallelism between the heterogeneity in type and amount of cerebral proteins, and the histological and cytochemical complexity of the brain (*cf.* 14). That this heterogeneity extends into the metabolic sphere as well has been demonstrated by measuring the uptake of labeled amino acids into the brain proteins. Radioactive lysine has been used in this way in animal experiments. This amino acid passes readily from the blood into the brain where its limited repertoire of reactions guarantees that most of it entering that organ will be available for synthesis into peptide linkage in the cerebral protein. The lysine uptake studies have confirmed the variety of proteins in the brain, characterized by a spectrum of turnover rates (15). In growing animals this spectrum is truncated: only the rapidly metabolizing proteins are detected.

Cerebral histones have been implicated in the processes linking electrical stimulation with oxidative processes in separated brain slices: the histones inhibit the respiratory increase occasioned by application of electrical pulses (16).

In addition to its large protein content the brain contains small amounts of polypeptides and of uncombined amino acids, less than 0.5 gm. per 100 grams of fresh weight of tissue. The polypeptides predominate in the neurohypophysis, except in the case of glutathione, a tripeptide (γ-glutamylcysteinylglycine), which is more widely distributed. About half of the amino acid complement is represented by glutamic acid and its derivatives, including glutamine and γ-aminobutyric acid (Table 2-2). Relatively large amounts of aspartic acid also occur, some as the free acid, a little as the amide asparagine, but most of it as N-acetylaspartic acid. Many of the other amino acids occur in amounts less than 20 μmols per 100 grams (under 2 to 3 mg. per 100 grams). This is true for the basic amino acids, the prolines, the aromatic amino acids, and the β-amino acids which are derived from the pyrimidines. However, glycine, serine, and cystathionine are present in larger amounts. The high concentration of ethanolamine and its derivatives glycerophosphorylethanolamine and O-phosphorylethanolamine should be noted, and similarly for a decarboxylated derivative of cysteine, taurine, whose acidic character arises from the oxidized state of its sulfur atom. Taurine and the ethanolamines are not true amino acids, but they are separated and determined in the course of measuring the amino acids. Localization of these compounds in specific regions of the nervous system will undoubtedly prove important in determining their respective roles as members of the "amino acid pool" or as compounds performing particular functions.

Perry and Jones (16A) have compared the amino acid composition

TABLE 2-2. AMINO ACID COMPOSITION OF BRAIN AND PLASMA

| Constituent | Fasting Plasma mg./100 ml. | Whole Brain | |
|---|---|---|---|
| | | mg./100 gm. | μmols/100 gm. |
| Aspartic acid | — | 29.7 | 223 |
| N-Acetylaspartic acid | — | 100 | 572 |
| Asparagine | — | 1.4 | 11 |
| Glutamic acid | 0.4–1.2 | 133–180 | 905–1225 |
| Glutamine | — | 48–82 | 320–547 |
| γ-Aminobutyric acid | — | 23.4 | 230 |
| Glutathione | — | 27 | 88 |
| Arginine | 1.2–2.0 | 1.4 | 8 |
| Ornithine | 0.6–0.8 | 0.6 | 5 |
| Lysine | 2.5–3.0 | 2 | 13 |
| Histidine | 0.8–1.5 | 0.9 | 6 |
| Methylhistidine | — | 0.6 | 4 |
| Proline | 1.8–3.3 | 1.1–1.7 | 9–15 |
| Methionine | 0.3–0.4 | 1.5 | 10 |
| Cystine and cysteine | 1.0–1.3 | 1 | 8 |
| Taurine | 0.4–0.8 | 24 | 192 |
| Cystathionine * | — | 22–55 | 100–250 |
| Glycine † | 1.5–2.0 | 10 | 133 |
| Serine | 1.0–1.3 | 7.6 | 72 |
| Threonine | 1.2–1.7 | 2.6 | 22 |
| Ethanolamine ‡ | — | 40.9 | 482 |
| Phenylalanine | 0.7–1.0 | 1.2 | 7 |
| Tyrosine | 0.8–1.5 | 1.2 | 7 |
| Dihydroxyphenylalanine § | — | 0.02 | 0.1 |
| Tryptophan | — | 0.5 | 2 |
| Alanine | 3.0–3.7 | 8.4 | 93 |
| Valine | 2.3–3.7 | 2.1 | 18 |
| Leucine | 1.4–2.3 | 1.8 | 13 |
| Isoleucine | 0.7–1.3 | 1.2 | 9 |
| β-Alanine | — | 0.6 | 7 |
| β-Amino-isobutyric acid | 0.2–0.4 | 0.1 | 1 |
| Sources | 17 | 18, 19 | |

* Reference 21.
† Citrulline included with glycine.
‡ Includes ethanolamine, O-phosphorylethanolamine, and glycerophosphorylethanolamine.
§ Reference 20.

of the CSF in various mental deficiencies with that of normal fluid. Only in phenylketonuria was there a distinct abnormality, *viz.*, an increase in phenylalanine.

The brain peptides and polypeptides that have been characterized are few in number. The neurohypophysis contains vasopressin, oxytocin, and corticotropin-releasing factor (CRF) among others. The first two have been thoroughly studied chemically and their structure has been determined by analytical methods as well as by synthesis. They are octapeptides, with very similar arrangement of amino acids. Six of the constituent amino acids are the same for the two hormones: cystine, tyrosine, proline, glutamic and aspartic acids, and glycine. Beef vasopressin also contains arginine and phenylalanine; oxytocin has isoleucine and leucine. These hormones are essentially restricted to the neurohypophysis, but their presence in that organ may simply represent storage in view of evidence that they are secreted by cells of hypothalamic nuclei, the supraoptic, paraventricular, and others (22; *cf.* Chapter 23).

Substance P is a polypeptide containing 20 to 30 amino acid residues, and is found in intestine (muscularis mucosa and submucosa) and in the brain. It possesses a direct stimulating action on smooth muscle fibers, but this action has been overshadowed recently by studies attributing to it a neurohumoral function. Substance P is unevenly distributed in the nervous system: its concentration is high in the gray matter, but very low in the white. In human brain it has been noted that regions of high substance P content have a low choline acetylase activity (23). The largest amounts are found in the hypothalamus and in the basal ganglia (see Table 23-1). In the peripheral nervous system the dorsal roots (and sympathetic trunks) have the highest concentration, and this led Lembeck to suggest (24) a role for it in the activity of afferent fibers. Zetler (25) has, on the contrary, proposed that substance P is a centrally acting transmitter substance of inhibitory neurones, with anticonvulsant properties. Stern agrees with this view (26) and, indeed, recognizes this polypeptide to have a tranquilizing action.

## Synthesis and Metabolism of Proteins of the Nervous System (27)

Little is known of the mechanism of protein synthesis in the brain. Methodologically, two types of process must be distinguished: (*a*) net protein formation (balance of synthetic as against degradative reactions); and (*b*) incorporation of single amino acids, supplied in the isotopically labeled form. The latter process may involve simple exchange of the labeled compound for its unmarked counterpart. On the other hand, incorporation of an amino acid may represent an actual synthesis of protein *de novo* balanced by degradation of other protein molecules, so that there is no actual increase in the amount of protein. At present there is no way of distinguishing between these processes. The breakdown of proteins within cells is fostered by the tissue cathepsins, but these enzymes also catalyze reversible reactions. One type of peptide bond synthesis catalyzed by certain of these enzymes requires two peptides or peptidelike compounds as starting materials. The products are, respectively, higher and lower order peptides:

$$AB + CD \rightarrow ABC + D$$

Brain cathepsin is thought to have such a transpeptidase function in the gray matter (28). Proteinases also can participate in the formation of large peptides, as in the synthesis of plastein, starting with a concentrated solution of smaller peptides and amino acids. However, as in other phases of biochemistry the route of synthesis of biological polymers is not the same as the route of their degradation; protein synthesis is not simply the reverse of proteolytic digestion.

The initial step in protein formation requires the activation of the amino acids through the agency of adenosine triphosphate (ATP), symbolized in Reaction 2-5 as ARPPP (*i.e.*, adenine-ribose triphosphate). The activation consists of an energy-requiring formation of an anhydride between the amino acid and adenylic acid. The anhydride then reacts

$$RCH(NH_2)COOH + ARPPP \rightarrow RCH(NH_2)COPRA$$
L-Amino acid       ATP       Amino acyl adenylate
$$+ \quad PP \quad (2\text{-}5)$$
Pyrophosphate

Amino acyl adenylate + Amino acid → Dipeptide
$$+ \text{Adenylic acid} \quad (2\text{-}6)$$

with another amino acid to form a peptide (Reaction 2-6). It is presumed that each amino acid added to the peptide chain requires a mole of ATP. Other nucleotides, too, play a role in protein synthesis. The pyridine nucleotides stimulate protein formation in cell-free systems, probably through their obligatory role in the reductive amination of α-keto-glutaric acid, the only reaction through which a major net synthesis of amino acids appears possible (29). In the more immediate process of linking together the amino acid residues, guanosine triphosphate (GTP) also enhances the synthesis (30); its manner of accomplishing this is now being explored. Finally, a polynucleotide—soluble ribonucleic acid (SRNA)—is important in these synthesizing systems; it may serve to introduce the activated amino acids into the peptide or protein chain.

In what ways does the metabolism of the cerebral proteins reflect the physiological state of the brain? In the last century the answer to this question was given as "None at all." The proteins were thought to constitute an inert matrix, serving only to support the cerebral lipides; it was these lipides and related substances that underwent changes associated with cerebral function. It is now quite obvious that the proteins of the brain enter into the dynamic state of metabolism, and suffer change during brain activity although, admittedly, we are only at the beginning of our appreciation of the diversity and complexity of these changes. The work of Hyden's group (31) in Sweden established clearly the relationship between protein metabolism and the functional state of the brain, through the use of modern cytochemical techniques. For example, it was shown that fatiguing exercise brings about a decrease of RNA and protein in the anterior horn cells, with a slow return to normal levels during subsequent rest. This recalls the work of Gorodisskay (32) who showed that blindfolded cats develop a distribution of nitrogenous substances in the cerebral regions concerned with vision different from that found in the control animals which have been permitted use of their eyes. The measure that Gorodisskay used was the ratio of brain nitrogen soluble in phosphomolybdic acid to the total nitrogen (non-protein N/total N). The ratios for different regions of the brain of control and test cats, respectively, were: motor area, 0.103 and 0.113; lateral geniculate body, 0.117 and 0.080; caudate nucleus, 0.091 and 0.098; optic tracts, 0.089 and 0.071; striatum, 0.114 and 0.082. Unfortunately, the nature of the nitrogenous extractives and their relation to proteolysis of cerebral protein is not known. Brattgård measured the RNA and protein concentrations in retinal ganglion cells of rabbits maintained in darkness for long periods. Both components were very much lower than in animals permitted to use their eyes (33).

Hyden also found that the application of an adequate stimulus at the periphery causes the RNA or protein (or both) to increase in the cerebral cells. In this connection, it has been shown that peripheral stimulation increases the rate of incorporation of labeled methionine and glycine into the proteins of the brain (13) and causes a reversible increase in the free sulfhydryl groups of this organ (34).

Evidence for the participation of proteins in physiological brain processes has come from other directions also. Abood and Geiger (5, 35) have shown that glucose is not obligatory for the maintenance of the excitability of the isolated, perfused cat brain, at least for short periods. However, under conditions where the normal electrical activity persists with glucose omitted from the perfusate, there is a gross disappearance of protein and lipide from the microsomes and the supernatant portion of the brain cells. Many amino acids increase during the perfusion, particularly γ-aminobutyric acid and glutamic acid; glutathione also increases markedly, and creatinine and taurine less so.

A large variety of amines of physiological as well as exogenous origin are able to bind to liver proteins (36). This enzyme-catalyzed attachment may be the chemical basis of the biological action of these amines. It is therefore important to know whether a similar reaction occurs with specific cerebral proteins.

One of the important chemical results of nervous activity is the appearance of large amounts of ammonia in the tissue. The ammonia concentration decreases during abatement of activity (37). The source of this ammonia has been sought in many of the nitrogenous constituents of brain, but there is no agreement as to which one supplies it. Vrba considers part of the ammonia to come from the splitting of protein-bound glutamine (38). He has noted that along with the formation of ammonia there is a large increase in nitrogen extractives of the brain (39). During nervous activity not only does deamidation of the brain proteins occur, according to his work, but also some measure of proteolysis. These changes are reversible (40). In Weil-Malherbe's experiments (41) proteolysis, deamidation of protein, and breakdown of amino sugars were excluded as important sources of ammonia.

## Nutritional Requirements

Of the many amino acids that occur in the tissues, including those found in proteins, the great majority can be synthesized in the body. A few must be supplied in the diet because the enzymes needed for their formation are lacking or are insufficiently active to keep pace with requirements. Inasmuch as the requirements, both quantitative and qualitative, for the amino acids vary with the body's physiological state, the list of these "essential amino acids" can be expected to vary for states of growth, maintenance of body weight, pregnancy, and others. There is no evidence, however, for any change in the protein requirement, as a function of age, in healthy adults (42). The amino acids essential for the maintenance of body weight in adults are isoleucine, leucine, lysine, methionine, phenylalanine, threonine, tryptophan, and valine. The minimal requirements for maintenance of a just neutral or slightly positive nitrogen balance in young American adults have been estimated for men by W. C. Rose and his collaborators (43) and for women by R. M. Leverton and her colleagues (44). These requirements are listed in Table 2-3.

TABLE 2-3. REQUIREMENTS OF ESSENTIAL AMINO ACIDS FOR
MAINTENANCE OF NITROGEN EQUILIBRIUM

| | Range of Requirements Observed grams/day | |
| Amino Acid | Men* | Women† |
| --- | --- | --- |
| Isoleucine‡ | 0.65–0.70 | — |
| Leucine | 0.50–1.10 | 0.60 |
| Lysine | 0.40–0.80 | — |
| Methionine§ | 0.80–1.10 | — |
| Phenylalanine (no dietary tyrosine) | 0.80–1.10 | — |
| Phenylalanine (excess tyrosine supplied) | 0.3 | 0.22 |
| Threonine | 0.30–0.50 | 0.40 |
| Tryptophan | 0.15–0.25 | 0.16 |
| Valine | 0.40–0.80 | 0.65 |

\* Reference 43.

† Reference 44 (dash indicates requirement was not determined).

‡ All amino acids, except methionine and phenylalanine, must be supplied in the L-form. D-Methionine is equivalent to L-methionine. About half of the daily minimum requirement of phenylalanine may be supplied as D-phenylalanine.

§ Requirement shown for diets lacking cystine. Eighty to 89 percent of the methionine can be replaced by L-cystine.

If the protein requirement is not met by the diet the consequences are serious. The specific syndrome which ensues depends upon the relation of the protein deficiency to the concurrent supply of other nutrients and to the chronicity of the nutritional problem. The clinical deficiency may extend through a spectrum ranging from marked deficiency of all nutrients including protein (marasmus, wasting) to a deficiency of protein with a sufficient, or even excessive, supply of calories as in classical kwashiorkor. In infants and children kwashiorkor is characterized by diarrhea, edema, localized depigmentation of the skin and hair, anorexia, and apathy (45). The decrease in plasma protein and in the concentration of various enzymes indicates the intimate dependence of these constituents upon dietary protein. Even more sensitive changes have been detected by Horwitt and his colleagues in an extensive controlled study (the Elgin Project), in which they found that low levels of dietary protein lead to the development of hepatic dysfunction (46). The clinical changes stemming from protein-deficient diets have their counterparts in experimentally induced states in animals (47). The defects that have been described are corrected by instituting high protein feeding.

In addition to the hypoproteinemias there are deficiency states attributable to lack of a specific essential amino acid. The example of tryptophan and nicotinic acid deficiency in relation to pellagra is well documented (Chapter 6). Methionine deficiency or, rather dietary insufficiency of sulfur-containing amino acids, is apparently widespread (Chapter 8). An experimental deficiency of lysine results in nausea, vertigo, and hyperacusia, and is biochemically characterized by the excretion of large amounts of (nonketo) organic acids (48).

Keys and his colleagues have conducted important studies on the physical and psychological effects of starvation entailing, of course, a reduced intake of protein. In the experimental neurosis induced in their volunteers they noted increased complaints of fatigue, muscle soreness, apathy, increased irritability, hyperacusia, and depression. During the rehabilitation period no marked effect of protein supplementation was observed. The single most important nutritional factor in successful rehabilitation proved to be calorie intake (49). Rausch and Schwöbel (50) tested mental function in chronically underfed subjects. Dietary supplementation with small amounts of an amino acid mixture led to improvements in test results, which were not maintained when the supplement was omitted. The mechanism of action of the amino acid supplement is difficult to explain inasmuch as the amounts used could contribute only a small amount of extra calories. Moreover, several important amino acids were not included in the mixture, such as glutamic acid, histidine, phenylalanine, tryptophan, and cystine. The effects of glutamic acid on mental processes is discussed in Chapter 4.

## Disorders of Amino Acid Metabolism (51)

Small amounts of amino acids are normally excreted in the urine. In disease states such as hepatic necrosis or following the acute trauma of burns and surgery aminoaciduria occurs. By now, many additional conditions are known in which large amounts of one or more amino acids are lost in the urine. The reason for this can be traced in some cases to a defect in the kidney. For example, in cystinuria there is a relative inability of the tubules to reabsorb the dibasic amino acids: cystine, ornithine, arginine, and lysine. These four amino acids then occur in high concentrations in the urine, in a ratio approximating $1:1:2:4$. There is also increased excretion of isoleucine, but this is of a considerably lower order than in the case of the other compounds named (52). The Fanconi syndrome is also characterized by the failure of the kidney to reabsorb amino acids—all of them—but there is also a loss of glucose and phosphate. In other diseases the cause of the aminoaciduria resides in a specific disorder of metabolism, as in phenylketonuria, where the urine contains large amounts of phenylpyruvic and phenyllactic acids, as well as abnormally high levels of phenylalanine itself. Recently, new aminoacidurias have been described. In one of them, Hartnup disease, there is renal aminoaciduria and indoluria (*cf.* Chapter 6). Another involves loss of argininosuccinic acid in the urine (Chapter 9). Both conditions are characterized by mental deficiency, which is severe in the latter case. A form of mental deficiency, recently associated with a biochemical defect, is maple sugar urine disease; in this disorder the intermediary metabolism of the branched-chain aliphatic amino acids is affected (53).

A few studies have been undertaken to determine whether the concentrations of the amino acids in the plasma and CSF vary from normal in psychoses. According to Pond (54) there is no abnormality in the plasma acids. It has been reported that in periodic catatonia the catatonic phase is associated with changes in the amino acids of serum (55), which are particularly marked in the first part of this phase. Other investigators have found some differences from normal in the proportions of amino acids in the CSF of patients with organic psychoses and schizophrenia, but the changes are inconstant and are certainly not specific for the diseases (56).

# References

1. SCHEINBERG, I. H. *Dis. Nerv. System Monograph Suppl. 19:*25, 1958.
2. BLOCK, R. J. *Yale J. Biol. Med. 9:*445, 1936–37.
3. FOLCH, J., and M. LEES. *J. Biol. Chem. 191:*807, 1951.
4. LISOVSKAYA, N. P. *Doklady Akad. Nauk SSSR 96:*1033, 1954; *seen in Chem. Abstr. 48:*9509f, 1954.
5. ABOOD, L. G., and A. GEIGER. *Am. J. Physiol. 182:*557, 1955.
6. HEALD, P. J. *Biochem. J. 66:*659, 1957.

7. SCHMITT, F. O. *Advances Protein Chem. 1*:25, 1944.
8. EDSALL, J. T. *Advances Protein Chem. 3*:383, 1947.
9. MUMENTHALER, M., and H. MÄRKI. *Klin. Wochschr. 35*:1, 1957.
10. KAPS, G. *Arch. Psychiat. Nervenkrankh. 192*:115, 1954.
11. HOFMAN, G., and H. SCHINKO. *Klin. Wochschr. 34*:86, 1956.
12. DEMLING, L., H. KINZELMEIER, and N. HENNING. *Ges. Z. Exp. Med. 122:* 416, 1954.
13. PALLADIN, A. V. *In Metabolism of the Nervous System, ed.* RICHTER, D. London, Pergamon Press, 1957.
14. PORTUGALOV, V. V. *Zhur. Nevropatol. Psikh. 58*:641, 1958.
15. LAJTHA, A., S. FURST, and H. WAELSCH. *Experientia 13*:168, 1957; LAJTHA, A., S. FURST, A. GERSTEIN, and H. WAELSCH. *J. Neurochem. 1*:289, 1957.
16. MCILWAIN, H. *Biochem. J. 73*:514, 1959.
16A. PERRY, T. L., and R. T. JONES. *J. Clin. Invest. 40*:1363, 1961.
17. STEIN, W. H., and S. MOORE. *J. Biol. Chem. 211*:915, 1954.
18. TALLAN, H. H., S. MOORE, and W. H. STEIN. *J. Biol. Chem. 211*:927, 1954.
19. ANSELL, G. B., and D. RICHTER. *Biochem. J. 57*:70, 1954.
20. MONTAGU, K. *Nature 180*:244, 1957.
21. TALLAN, H. H., S. MOORE, and W. H. STEIN. *J. Biol. Chem. 230*:707, 1958.
22. SCHARRER, B., and E. SCHARRER. *Recent Progr. Hormone Res. 10*:182, 1954.
23. ZETLER, G., and L. SCHLOSSER. *Naturwiss. 41*:46, 1954.
24. LEMBECK, F. *Arch. exp. Path. u. Pharmakol. 219*:197, 1953.
25. ZETLER, G. *Naturwiss. 40*:559, 1953; *Arch. exp. Path. u. Pharmakol. 237:* 11, 1959.
26. STERN, P. *Izdanje Naucno Drustvo NR Bosne i Hercegovine* (Sarajevo), Part IX, *Section on Medical Sciences 5*:41, 1958; STERN, P., and R. MILIN, *Proc. Soc. Exp. Biol. Med. 101*:298, 1959.
27. RICHTER, D. *Brit. Med. J. i*:1255, 1959; WAELSCH, H., and A. LAJTHA. *Physiol. Rev. 41*:709, 1961.
28. ANSELL, G. B., and D. RICHTER. *Biochim. et Biophys. Acta 13*:87, 1954.
29. WILSON, J. D., and M. D. SIPERSTEIN. *J. Clin. Invest. 38*:317, 1959.
30. KELLER, E. B., and P. C. ZAMECNIK *J. Biol. Chem. 221*:45, 1956.
31. HYDEN, H. *In* Neurochemistry, *ed.* ELLIOTT, K. A. C., I. H. PAGE, and J. H. QUASTEL. Springfield, Ill., Charles C Thomas, 1955.
32. GORODISSKAY, H. *Biochem. Z. 176*:46, 1926.
33. BRATTGÅRD, S. O. *Acta radiol. Suppl. 96*, 1952.
34. UNGAR, G., and D. V. ROMANO. *Proc. Soc. Exp. Biol. Med. 97*:324, 1958.
35. GEIGER, A. *Physiol. Rev. 38*:1, 1958.
36. BLOCK, W. *Z. physiol. Chem. 296*:108, 1954; CLARKE, D. D., A. NEIDLE, N. K. SARKAR, and H. WAELSCH. *Arch. Biochem. Biophys. 71*:277, 1957.
37. WEIL-MALHERBE, H. *In Metabolism and Function in Nervous Tissue.* Biochemical Society Symposium No. 8, New York, Cambridge University Press, 1952.
38. VRBA, R. *Nature 176*:29, 117, 1955.
39. VRBA, R., J. FOLBERGR, and V. KANTUREK. *Nature 179*:470, 1957.
40. VRBA, R. *Uspekhi Sovremennoi Biol. 41*:321, 1956; *seen in Chem. Abstr. 50*:17092c, 1956.

41. WEIL-MALHERBE, H., and R. H. GREEN. *Biochem. J. 61:*210, 1955; WEIL-MALHERBE, H., and A. C. DRYSDALE. *J. Neurochem. 1:*250, 1957.
42. WATKIN, D. *Ann. N.Y. Acad. Sci. 69:*Art. 5, 902, 1958.
43. ANON. *Nutr. Rev. 14:*232, 1956.
44. ANON. *Nutr. Rev. 14:*269, 1956.
45. FLODIN, N. W., ed. *Protein Nutrition. Ann. N.Y. Acad. Sci. 69:* Art. 5, 855–1066, 1958; BEHAR, M., F. VITERI, and N. S. SCRIMSHAW. *Am. J. Clin. Nutr. 5:*506, 1957.
46. HORWITT, M. K. *Nutrition Symposium Series, No. 7,* New York, The National Vitamin Foundation, 1953.
47. KAPLANSKIY, S. Y. *Clin. Chem. 5:*186, 1959.
48. ALBANESE, A. A., L. E. HOLT, JR., J. E. FRANKSTON, C. N. KAJDI, J. E. BRUMBACH, JR., D. M. WANGERIN, and V. IRBY. *Proc. Soc. Exp. Biol. Med. 52:*206, 1943.
49. KEYS, A., J. BROZEK, A. HENSCHEL, O. MICKELSEN, and H. TAYLOR. *The Biology of Human Starvation.* Minneapolis, University of Minnesota Press, 1950.
50. RAUSCH, F., and G. SCHWÖBEL. *Klin. Wochschr. 27:*30, 1949.
51. HARRISON, H. E., and H. C. HARRISON. *J.A.M.A. 164:*1571, 1957.
52. STEIN, W. H. *Proc. Soc. Exp. Biol. Med. 78:*705, 1951.
53. MENKES, J. H., P. L. HURST, and J. M. CRAIG. *Pediatrics 14:*462, 1954; MACKENZIE, D. Y., and L. I. WOOLF, *Brit. Med. J. i:*90, 1959; DANCIS, J., M. LEVITZ, S. MILLER, and R. G. WESTALL. *Brit. Med. J. i:*91, 1959.
54. POND, M. H. *J. Ment. Sci. 96:*1048, 1950.
55. GJESSING, L., A. BERNHARDSON, and H. FRÖSHAUG. *J. Ment. Sci. 104:*188, 1958.
56. REITMAN, F., W. HULME, and B. THOMAS. *J. Ment. Sci. 100:*149, 1954; C. RIEBELING. *Confin. Neurol. 18:*205, 1958; KEMALI, D., E. J. PASTORE, and G. PORCELLATI. *Acta Neurol. 12:*419, 1957.

# 3

# GLYCINE, SERINE, AND THREONINE

## Metabolic Pathways

Glycine, serine, and threonine all occur in the body proteins, and in some important peptides; glycine is a constituent of glutathione, vasopressin, and oxytocin, among others. In the latter two it is present as glycinamide. It also enters into peptidelike (peptidic) linkages in the detoxication of many compounds such as benzoic acid, with which it forms hippuric acid (Reaction 3-1). Indoleacetic and 5-hydroxyindole-

$$C_6H_5COOH + H_2NCH_2COOH \rightarrow C_6H_5CO \cdot NHCH_2COOH + H_2O$$

Benzoic acid      Glycine      Hippuric acid
                                                  (Benzoylglycine)

$$(3\text{-}1)$$

acetic acids (Chapter 6) are excreted in part as glycine conjugates. Preliminary to these conjugation reactions the organic acid must be "activated" in a reaction with adenosine triphosphate (ATP), and then converted to its coenzyme A derivative. Indeed, it is the coenzyme A thioester of the acid that actually reacts with glycine.

Glycine and serine are interconvertible in metabolism through

31

the mediation of tetrahydrofolic acid ($FH_4:NH$), but the prevailing direction is from serine to glycine (Reaction 3-2). Threonine also

$$HOCH_2CH(NH_2)COOH + \quad FH_4:NH \leftrightarrows H_2NCH_2COOH$$

L-Serine        Tetrahydrofolic      Glycine
     acid

$$+ \quad FH_4{\cdot}NCH_2OH \qquad (3\text{-}2)$$

Hydroxymethyltetrahydro-
folic acid

$$CH_3CHOHCH(NH_2)COOH \rightarrow CH_3CHO + H_2NCH_2COOH \quad (3\text{-}3)$$

L-Threonine        Acetaldehyde      Glycine

gives rise to glycine (Reaction 3-3) but the reverse does not occur to an appreciable extent so that threonine must be classed among the essential amino acids. The glycine molecule is utilized as a unit in the formation of creatine, porphyrin, and the purines. The synthesis of creatine requires the metabolic participation of three amino acids, as shown in Reactions 3-4 and 3-5.

$$\text{L-Arginine} + \text{Glycine} \rightarrow \text{L-Ornithine} + \text{Guanidoacetic acid} \quad (3\text{-}4)$$

$$\text{Guanidoacetic acid} + \text{S-Adenosyl-L-methionine} \rightarrow \text{Creatine}$$
$$+ \text{S-Adenosyl-L-homocysteine} \quad (3\text{-}5)$$

In another type of process glycine and serine lose their amino group and yield residues akin to carbohydrate intermediaries. Thus, the transaminative product of glycine is glyoxylic acid, and of serine it is hydroxypyruvic acid. The latter can also arise from phosphoglyceric acid in the course of sugar catabolism (Chapter 11), and the reversal of the transamination (Reaction 3-6) accomplishes the biosynthesis of

$$\text{L-Serine} + \alpha\text{-Ketoglutaric acid} \leftrightarrows \beta\text{-Hydroxypyruvic acid}$$
$$+ \text{L-Glutamic acid} \quad (3\text{-}6)$$

serine. Serine has a further significance as a precursor of the important lipotropic agent choline. This comes about first through the decarboxylation of the amino acid to ethanolamine, followed by the transfer of methyl groups from a suitable donor to the nitrogen atom. Serine itself may contribute hydroxymethyl ($HOCH_2-$) groups, as in Reaction 3-2, and these can be subsequently reduced to methyl groups.

## Hippuric Acid Test of Liver Function

In the hippuric acid (Quick) test the sodium salt of benzoic acid is administered and the amount of hippuric acid excreted during a specified time interval is measured. The test has a multiple significance: presentation of the liver with a maximal load of benzoic acid calls into play the machinery of the parenchymal cells (*a*) to mobilize or synthesize glycine; (*b*) to provide coenzyme A; and (*c*) to conjugate glycine with the foreign acid. If there is liver insufficiency in any of these respects, then the rate of formation of hippuric acid decreases and this fact is reflected in the reduced rate of excretion of the compound in the urine.

The results of this test depend upon many factors. Body weight appears to affect the concentration of hippuric acid in the urine (1, 2) but the positive correlation is not so evident in the group of persons of average size well in from the extremes (3). Nevertheless, if body weight is not taken into account and if there is a systematic difference in the body weights of the groups being compared, the administration of a fixed dose of benzoic acid may make a relatively smaller demand on the group with the heavier weight, and the results with this heavier group will show bias toward higher values in the Quick test. Likewise, smaller liver weights as reported for schizophrenics (4) would favor the lower values. There is a tendency for lower excretion values in the less active subjects but this is not a consistent finding.

Delayed absorption of orally administered benzoate may contribute to low hippuric acid values in the urine (5). Similarly, renal dysfunction delays the excretion of this compound (3). To obviate the first difficulty the benzoate can be given intravenously.

If insufficient glycine is available the rate of conjugation of benzoic acid may be subnormal; to remove any limitation of this kind, some investigators have administered the amino acid along with the benzoate. The information obtained from the test is then somewhat narrower, for the conjugation process itself is more specifically measured under these conditions. On theoretical grounds the level of pantothenic acid in the tissues might affect the degree of conjugation, but clinical pantothenic acid deficiency in man has not been described. In any case, no one seems to have studied the hippuric acid test in subjects before and after their preparation with this important vitamin.

Two principal difficulties stand in the way of a simple interpretation of the results of the Quick test and its modifications. The first concerns the alternate pathways that benzoic acid pursues (6). Normally, these are represented by the free acid itself along with its glycine conjugate in the urine. However, in persons with impaired liver function some of the administered benzoic acid may be excreted as the glucuronide.

The other difficulty has been pointed out by Sherlock (3). She has questioned the validity of the hippuric acid excretion test on the grounds that low values occur not only in hepatic dysfunction but also in some anemias and in cases with nonhepatic malignant disease. She has found that the test correlates poorly with the histological picture of the liver as revealed by examination of biopsy specimens. It can, however, be debated whether it is necessary to expect all molecular dysfunctions to be detectable microscopically.

The Quick test was introduced into psychiatric research in 1938. Pugh and Quastel had not long before this demonstrated (7) that certain amines, including a number with toxic properties, depress oxidation processes in excised brain slices. This led Quastel to postulate that "if there was evidence for faulty detoxication in the liver in certain types of mental disorder there might be good reason for the belief that in such cases there would circulate in the blood greater than ordinary quantities of toxic amines and that these might lead ultimately, owing to their deleterious effects on the nervous system, to the manifestation of abnormal psychological reactions" (8). Hence, this test, as a measure of a detoxifying process, was favored over other liver function tests. In the initial study it was found that catatonic schizophrenics have abnormally low rates of hippuric acid excretion (all 18 patients tested), whereas only a small proportion of other schizophrenics (4 out of 27) do so. In a second study (9) Quastel and Wales confirmed the previous results, this time using intravenously administered sodium benzoate. They noted that some patients who had undergone remission or who had shown some improvement now achieved a higher rate of hippuric acid excretion than previously. Davies and Hughes (10), Berkenau (11), and Persky et al. (12) obtained similar results. Actually about a quarter of the noncatatonic schizophrenic patients investigated in these studies showed a low rate of hippuric acid excretion. Wong (13) reported the lowest values in simple deteriorated and catatonic schizophrenics. The hebephrenic and paranoid groups were a little higher (a few individuals giving normal values), but were still in the subnormal range. In manic states the excretion is normal. Some depressive patients have low values, others are normal. Persky et al. (12) claim that the higher the degree of free anxiety the higher the rate of hippuric acid excretion in the Quick test, as performed on patients in anxiety states.

In spite of these various reports, several groups of investigators have not been able to detect the altered rate of hippuric acid excretion in schizophrenia (1, 5, 14).

In the classical Quick test the glycine needed for the conjugation with benzoic acid is drawn from the body's pool of amino acids and proteins. Georgi and his colleagues reasoned (15) that any deficiency in the supply of glycine would result in low values in the hippuric acid test, although these would not necessarily reflect a defect in the enzyme system catalyzing the detoxication. For this reason they introduced the double test, in which the Quick test is repeated with the administration of glycine as well as benzoate 48 hours after the test with benzoate alone. Normal subjects showed a slight increase in hippuric acid excretion on the second test, but schizophrenic patients responded with a large increase in the rate. This normalization of the rate by glycine administration (16) indicates that the abnormal values in the Quick test may actually be a function of the glycine reserves of the body.

The Basle group has made extensive studies on the hippuric acid test. Two points are noteworthy in their results. In the first place, unlike the earlier studies mentioned, they observed low rates of hippuric acid excretion in schizophrenics generally. In the second place, they were able to confirm Quastel and Wales's findings that the rate increases in patients who have improved with treatment or who have undergone remission. Because of the reduced ability of their schizophrenic patients to mobilize glycine they undertook to correct this deficit by nutritional means. Georgi and his colleagues observed improvement in the mental state of patients treated by *Leberstütztherapie,* using a supplement of vitamins and lipotropic factors. This improvement was accompanied by an increase in the hippuric acid excretion (classical Quick test) toward normal levels (17); in these patients the second Quick test (including glycine) yielded no greater increase in hippuric acid excretion.

The findings on the mobilization of glycine in schizophrenia have been confirmed by Levi and Savich (18) and by Mall and Jünemann (19). Graetz, Reiss, and Weldon (20) used the duplicate Quick test, and reported that the results were essentially normal in eleven acute schizophrenic patients, but were abnormally low in 54 chronic cases. It has been established that the hippuric acid excretion tends to become normal in patients who improve, no matter what the treatment is—insulin, electroshock, or nutritional. Foster states that subnormal liver function as measured by the Quick test occurs consistently in toxic psychoses (21). He has used intravenous glucose combined with large doses of nicotinamide in these states. According to him, the rapid improvement in mental state that ensues is accompanied by an increase in the rate of excretion of hippuric acid on test. It is not clear how this treatment or the supplement used in "liver protection therapy" by Georgi et al. can bring about the changes claimed.

# Choline Esters

### ACETYLCHOLINE AND RELATED ESTERS

Acetylcholine was first studied pharmacologically over 50 years ago, and attracted attention through its pronounced actions on blood pressure, heart rate, and smooth muscle tone. Its mimicry of the effects of vagal stimulation led Dale to suggest that acetylcholine is a humoral agent released from the nerves, a hypothesis eventually confirmed experimentally. Because the amounts of transmitter substance released under physiological conditions are so minute, investigators have been confronted with great difficulties in the direct determination of acetylcholine. Nevertheless, the ester has been isolated from the spleen, brain, blood, and placenta, so that its natural occurrence is not the least in doubt. It appears to be the neurohumoral transmitter at motor nerve endings, transmitting the impulse across the myoneural junction; at autonomic ganglia; and at parasympathetic (and some sympathetic) postganglionic nerve endings (22, 23, 24). In addition to these sites the ester plays a role as humoral agent at some central synapses (22). A further function has been proposed for acetylcholine in relation to the nervous system: in the conduction of the impulse along the axon. The theory that intraneuronal acetylcholine plays a role in axonal conduction has been advanced primarily by Nachmansohn and his colleagues, who have been able to marshal many facts relating to it (25), but the evidence has been much disputed on physiological grounds (22, 24).

Recently additional choline esters have been found in animal tissues by application of the technique of paper chromatography to concentrated extracts. The acidic components are propionic acid (26), butyric acid (27), imidazoleacetic acid (28), and γ-aminobutyric acid (29) in mammalian tissue. Several choline esters have been identified in molluscan species, apart from acetylcholine itself. Two acids found in these invertebrate esters are urocanic (30, 31) and senecioic, or β,β-dimethylacrylic (31, 32). Inasmuch as enzymes capable of bringing about the synthesis of the constituents of these esters are present in mammalian tissues, it is not unreasonable to question whether the esters themselves occur in the mammalian organism also. Imidazoleacetic and urocanic acids are derived in metabolism from L-histidine (Chapter 7). Senecioic acid is formed in either of two ways: from the amino acid L-leucine through a series of transformations (Reaction 3-7) or by decarboxylation of $\beta$-hydroxy-$\beta$-methylglutaric acid. This compound is synthesized enzymatically from acetic acid (Reaction 3-8).

$$(CH_3)_2CHCH_2CH(NH_2)COOH \rightarrow (CH_3)_2CHCH_2COCOOH \xrightarrow{+H_2O}$$
$$(CH_3)_2C\!\!=\!\!CHCOOH + CO_2 + 4H \quad (3\text{-}7)$$
$$3CH_3COOH \xrightarrow{-H_2O} HOOC\!\cdot\!CH_2COH(CH_3)CH_2COOH \rightarrow$$
$$CH_3C(CH_3)\!\!=\!\!CHCOOH + CO_2 + H_2O \quad (3\text{-}8)$$

Choline has muscarinic and nicotinic activity, but its potency is far below that of its esters such as acetylcholine. Urocanylcholine lacks muscarinic action almost entirely, but displays blocking actions at ganglia and at the myoneural junction (30). Methacholine (acetyl-$\beta$-methylcholine), which is not naturally occurring, is hydrolyzed only very slowly by cholinesterases and therefore has a more persistent action than its lower homologue acetylcholine. Moreover, it also has a stimulating action on medullary vasomotor centers which, because of resistance of the drug to hydrolysis, can be elicited even when methacholine is injected at some distance from the site of action. The synthetic compound succinyldicholine, employed in anesthesiology as a skeletal muscle relaxant, interferes with one of the actions of acetylcholine. It is a powerful inhibitor of neuromuscular transmission, causing depolarization of the muscle end plate, which then does not respond to the natural choline ester. The action of succinyldicholine lasts for only a few minutes because the drug is rapidly hydrolyzed by the nonspecific cholinesterase of the plasma.

### CEREBRAL ACETYLCHOLINE

The acetylcholine content of the brain at any given time is determined by the balance between its synthesis, on the one hand, and its hydrolysis by cholinesterase and diffusion into the blood, on the other. The relative importance of these factors has not been adequately assessed; we know of their functioning through observing changes in the concentration of acetylcholine under various conditions. Most of the acetylcholine in the brain is present in some type of bound state that protects it from the action of esterases. Intracellularly, it is located in a cytoplasmic particle, which can be sedimented by differential centrifugation in the mitochondrial layer, but it is actually thought to be associated with a nonmitochondrial organelle (33). This may be the acetylcholine-containing vesicle described by Castillo and Katz (34). Nachmansohn regards acetylcholine as associated with a specific conjugated protein from which it is released in small amounts to the receptor substance (another protein) situated on the effector organ, in the course of performing its neurohumoral transmitter function (35).

The concentration of cerebral acetylcholine increases during anesthesia and sleep, and decreases during excitement and convulsions (36). When pentylenetetrazol or picrotoxin is administered to the unanesthetized animal, however, there is an increase in the cerebral acetylcholine (37). Fluctuations in the amount of acetylcholine can be studied in another way. Some of the free acetylcholine is diffusible and can be collected by appropriate techniques at the surface of the exposed brain. If the surface of the brain is irrigated with a physiological saline solution containing eserine (to inhibit the breakdown of acetylcholine by cholinesterase) small amounts of the ester leak into it from the cerebral cells. The amount of acetylcholine diffusing out in this way diminishes during anesthesia and, in fact, ceases completely when the electrical activity of the irrigated cortical area is silenced by undercutting (38). The injection of pentylenetetrazol or picrotoxin causes an increase in the amount of acetylcholine leaking out (37).

Acetylcholine is seldom found in normal cerebrospinal fluid, and it may be that any which leaks into it is readily hydrolyzed by the esterases present. On the other hand, relatively large amounts of acetylcholine appear in the CSF as a result of experimental or clinical craniocerebral injury (39, 40) and following electroshock convulsions (40). The level of acetylcholine in the CSF of cases of brain injury parallels somewhat the clinical state. With the highest concentrations of acetylcholine (over 1–2 $\mu$g. percent) there are disturbances of consciousness (up to coma) and decreased electroencephalographic activity. Towers and McEachern found that the level of acetylcholine decreases as clinical improvement gets under way.

## FORMATION OF ACETYLCHOLINE

The origin of choline has been briefly mentioned before: it is formed by the repeated methylation of the amino group of ethanolamine through N-methylethanolamine and N-dimethylethanolamine (deanol) to choline. These methyl groups are derived from methionine, by a transfer reaction from its metabolically active intermediate S-adenosylmethionine. Choline functions in esterified forms as a structural component of acetylcholine and the lecithins; but it may follow an oxidative pathway leading to the formation of betaine (N-trimethylglycine) which, like methionine, can serve as a methyl donor in metabolism. The rate of acetylation of choline appears to be governed by a fine regulatory mechanism so that even the administration of a surfeit of choline does not give rise to acetylcholine-like actions. However, the immediate precursor of choline, deanol, does have some specific pharmacological actions, including central ones; it potentiates audiogenic and pentylenetetrazol-induced seizures in the mouse and rat (41). In tests with mice receiving deanol chronically the amine eventually causes spontaneous epileptiform seizures (42). In acute tests in the rabbit it causes increased electrical activity of the brain (43). The observation that deanol increases somewhat the incidence of grand mal seizures in epileptic patients is in agreement with these experimental findings (41). It causes a mild stimulation of patients with depressive symptoms (44). There is as yet insufficient information about the biochemical role of deanol to be able to interpret all these actions. It has been postulated that it passes into the brain, there to be methylated and acetylated to acetylcholine. However, this has not actually been demonstrated. Moreover, its role as a central parasympathomimetic drug is quite uncertain, for parenterally administered choline is also taken up by the brain (45) but does not have the same pharmacological actions. Thus, deanol may exert its actions in another way than through the acetylcholine mechanism.

The esterification of choline, whether by acetic or some other acid, is preceded by "activation" of the acid, as described previously, and it is actually the acylcoenzyme A derivative which reacts with choline to form the ester (Reaction 3-9). The enzyme catalyzing the formation of acetylcholine (Reaction 3-9) is known as choline acetylase (46). It may

$$CH_3CO \cdot SCoA + HOCH_2CH_2N(CH_3)_3{}^+Cl^- \rightarrow$$
Acetylcoenzyme A          Choline chloride
$$CH_3COOCH_2CH_2N(CH_3)_3{}^+Cl^- + HSCoA \quad (3\text{-}9)$$
Acetylcholine chloride          Coenzyme A

be located in the same intracellular particle as the acetylcholine of the nerve cell (33). If this is so, then the view that acetylcholine is synthesized into the bound form will appear justified.

## BREAKDOWN OF ACETYLCHOLINE: CHOLINESTERASES

The action of acetylcholine is terminated physiologically by its enzymatic hydrolysis to its components. This is a two-step reaction, with the intermediate formation of acetylated enzyme (Reactions 3-10 and 3-11) and it represents a mechanism of hydrolysis which is general

$$\text{Acetylcholine} + \text{Enzyme} \rightarrow \text{Acetyl-enzyme} + \text{Choline} \quad (3\text{-}10)$$

$$\text{Acetyl-enzyme} + H_2O \rightarrow \text{Acetic acid} + \text{Enzyme} \quad (3\text{-}11)$$

for ester-splitting enzymes. Esterases acting upon acetylcholine have been studied for many years. It was early recognized that animal tissues contain two types distinguished one from the other by important physicochemical characteristics (47). The type found in nervous tissue and erythrocytes was first called true or specific cholinesterase because of its relatively greater activity toward acetylcholine than certain other model substrates. It is now more desirably labeled acetylcholinesterase. The other type of enzyme has a wider substrate specifically, recognized in the names pseudocholinesterase and nonspecific cholinesterase. Current usage terms it simply cholinesterase. It is found in plasma and in small amounts in other tissues. Its natural substrate is unknown. Acetylcholinesterase is located in nerve cells predominantly in the cytoplasm and dendritic processes, with somewhat lower amounts in the axon. The nucleus contains a little, but the nucleolus is devoid of the enzyme (48). The distribution of cholinesterases in dog brain has been mapped by Burgen and Chipman (49). The two enzymes are inhibited by numerous drugs and chemicals. Eserine (physostigmine), one of the best known of the anticholinesterases, is a competitive inhibitor. Excessively high substrate concentrations inhibit acetylcholinesterase, but not pseudocholinesterase. The latter is preferentially inhibited by dibucaine. Organophosphorus derivatives make up a large group of esterase inhibitors and are very important for their action on acetylcholinesterase. They inhibit irreversibly by a mechanism which is actually a replica of Reaction 3-10 and which is illustrated for di-isopropylfluorophosphate (DFP) in Reaction 3-12. The enzyme-inhibitor complex is stable in this

$$\underset{\text{DFP}}{(iso\text{-}C_3H_7O)_2FP{=}O} + \underset{\text{Enzyme}}{EH} \rightarrow \underset{\text{DFP-Enzyme complex}}{(iso\text{-}C_3H_7O)_2PO\text{—}E} + HF \quad (3\text{-}12)$$

case, and does not readily break down by hydrolysis as in Reaction 3-11. Other organophosphorus anticholinesterases form intermediates which are less stable and permit the regeneration of the enzyme, but at a rate too slow for it to function effectively in acetylcholine metabolism. The results of some experiments with anticholinesterases are discussed in Chapter 28.

Because of their pronounced effect on the nervous system, the organophosphorus inhibitors of cholinesterases are collectively known as nerve gases. Some of them have found a use in therapeutics (*e.g.,* glaucoma) and as economic poisons in agriculture. Their potential use as a weapon has directed considerable attention to the search for antidotes. Protection by atropine is of some value, but is limited because of the pharmacological actions of the antidote itself. In experimental work it has been found that 2-pyridine aldoxime methiodide (PAM) and trimethylene-*bis*-4-pyridine aldoxime diiodide (TMB-4) are useful protective agents against DFP and paraoxon (50). The central effects of the nerve gases are very serious and have been related to their inhibition of acetylcholinesterase. In man, overdosage with DFP leads to blurring of vision, dyspnea, tightness in the chest, headache, nausea, cramps, and tremor. Other symptoms include insomnia, restlessness, anxiety, frequent dreams and nightmares, emotional lability, vertigo, mental confusion, and visual hallucinations. There are also electroencephalographic changes (51, 52). Severe poisoning proceeds rapidly to convulsions and asphyxial death.

DFP has been tested for its possible therapeutic benefits in psychotic patients. In some schizophrenics the psychosis is activated with persistence of the florid symptoms for several months after withdrawal of the drug. An early effect in manic-depressive patients is a depressive action during the hypomanic state (52).

These results point to the obvious importance of cholinesterase activity for normal mental functioning and, furthermore, raise the question as to whether acetylcholinesterase undergoes any significant change in concentration in the genesis of mental disease. This has been studied by direct measurement of the enzymatic activity in surgical and post-mortem material, and it has been found that there is no significant abnormality in this enzyme in the cortex, basal ganglia, thalamus, and hypothalamus in psychotic subjects (53, 54). Attempts have also been made to correlate the concentration of cholinesterases in blood and CSF with mental activity. Tower and McEachern (55) could find no correlation of enzyme levels in the CSF with clinical diagnosis, except in craniocerebral trauma and in cases treated by electroshock therapy. In these the acetylcholinesterase was reduced and the nonspecific cholinesterase was increased (40). The normal pattern of enzymatic activity returned as the patient recovered from the brain injury. Birkhäuser found a markedly elevated esterase activity in the CSF of schizophrenic patients (53).

In experimental psychology it has been suggested that learning capacity in the rat is related to the balance of the acetylcholine system in the central nervous system (56).

The intracisternal injection of acetylcholine in experimental animals causes an abnormal behavior, as seen in brain injury (39). Similarly, the administration of acetylcholine, eserine, or DFP to the conscious cat causes the animal to enter into a catatonic stupor (57).

The use of succinylcholine as a skeletal muscle relaxant has led to the discovery of occasional patients who suffer a prolonged apnea after receiving the drug. In some cases this is due to decreased cholinesterase levels in the plasma as a result of faulty hepatic function. But in a very small percentage of the population—those with an unusually great sensitivity toward succinyldicholine—there appears to be present in the serum an abnormal type of nonspecific cholinesterase with low enzymatic activity and relatively resistant to inhibition by dibucaine (58).

## Glycinuria and Oxaluria

A hereditary, sex-linked glycinuria associated with the formation of oxalate calculi has been described by de Vries (59). Glycine is deaminated to glyoxylic acid ($O\!\!=\!\!CH \cdot COOH$) and at least some of the oxalic acid ($HOOC \cdot COOH$) is formed by the further oxidation of this compound. Normally, the decarboxylation of glyoxylic acid to formic acid is quantitatively more important than this oxidative pathway.

In primary hyperoxaluria the administration of sodium benzoate reduces the amount of oxalic acid in the urine (60). Presumably the benzoate, by conjugating glycine, diverts some of this amino acid from the deaminative-oxidative pathways.

## References

1. Michael, S. T., J. M. Looney, and E. J. Borkovic. *Arch. Neurol. Psychiat.* 52:57, 1944.
2. Scurry, M. M., and H. Field, Jr. *Am. J. Med. Sci.* 206:243, 1943.
3. Sherlock, S. *Lancet* i:159, 1946.
4. Buscaino, V. M. *Proc. First Intern. Cong. Neuropathol.* Rome, Turin, Rosenberg and Sellier, 1952. (Volume 1); Moore, M., and W. G. Lennox. *Am. J. Psychiat.* 92:1439, 1936.
5. Finkelman, I., J. Hora, I. C. Sherman, and M. K. Horwitt. *Am. J. Psychiat.* 96:951, 1940.
6. Snapper, I., and A. Saltzman. *Am. J. Med.* 2:327, 334, 1947.
7. Pugh, C., and J. H. Quastel. *Biochem. J.* 31:286, 2306, 1937.

8. QUASTEL, J. H., and W. T. WALES. *Lancet ii*:301, 1938.

9. QUASTEL, J. H., and W. T. WALES. *Lancet i*:402, 1940.

10. DAVIES, D. R., and T. P. E. HUGHES. *Lancet i*:403, 1940.

11. BERKENAU, P. *J. Ment. Sci. 86*:514, 1940.

12. PERSKY, H., S. R. GAMM, and R. R. GRINKER. *Psychosom. Med. 14*:34, 1952.

13. WONG, Y. T. *J. Nerv. Ment. Dis. 102*:183, 1945.

14. STRÖM-OLSEN, R., G. D. GREVILLE, and R. W. LENNON. *Lancet ii*:995, 1938.

15. GEORGI, F., R. FISCHER, R. WEBER, and P. WEISS. *Schweiz. Med. Wochschr. 78*:1194, 1948.

16. FABISCH, W., and C. FELLNER. *Psychosom. Med. 19*:320, 1957.

17. FISCHER, R., F. GEORGI, R. WEBER, and R. M. PIAGEL. *Schweiz. Med. Wochschr. 80*:129, 1950.

18. LEVI, R., and M. SAVICH. *Arch. Psychiat. u. Nervenkrankh. 188*:26, 1952.

19. MALL, G., and H. J. JÜNEMANN. *Arch. Psychiat. u. Nervenkrankh. 188*:289, 1952.

20. GRAETZ, B., M. REISS, and G. WALDON. *J. Ment. Sci. 100*:145, 1954.

21. FOSTER, T. L. *J. Nerv. Ment. Dis. 110*:1, 1949.

22. BURGEN, A. S. V., and F. C. MacINTOSH. *In Neurochemistry*, ed. ELLIOTT, K. A. C., I. H. PAGE, and J. H. QUASTEL. Springfield, Ill., Charles C Thomas, 1955.

23. HEBB, C. O. *Physiol. Rev. 37*:196, 1957.

24. FELDBERG, W. *In Metabolism of the Nervous System*, ed. RICHTER, D. London, Pergamon Press, 1957.

25. NACHMANSOHN, D. *In Neurochemistry*, ed. ELLIOTT, K. A. C., I. H. PAGE, and J. H. QUASTEL. Springfield, Ill., Charles C Thomas, 1955.

26. BANISTER, J., V. P. WHITTAKER, and S. WIJESUNDERA. *J. Physiol. 121*:55, 1953; HENSCHLER, D., *Naturwiss. 43*:522, 1956.

27. HOLTZ, P., and H. J. SCHÜMANN. *Naturwiss. 41*:306, 1954.

28. GRUNER, G., and H. KEWITZ. *Naturwiss. 42*:628, 1955.

29. KEWITZ, H. *Arch. Exp. Path. u. Pharmakol. 237*:308, 1959.

30. ERSPAMER, V., and A. GLÄSSER. *Brit. J. Pharmacol. 12*:176, 1957.

31. KEYL, M. J., I. A. MICHAELSON, and V. P. WHITTAKER. *J. Physiol. 139*:434, 1957.

32. WHITTAKER, V. P. *Biochem. J. 71*:32, 1959.

33. HEBB, C. O., and V. P. WHITTAKER. *J. Physiol. 142*:187, 1958; WHITTAKER, V. P. *Biochem. J. 72*:694, 1959.

34. DEL CASTILLO, J., and B. KATZ. *Progress Biophys. 6*:121, 1956.

35. NACHMANSOHN, D. *Proc. IVth Intern. Cong. Biochem.*, Vienna, 1958. London, Pergamon Press, 1959. Volume 3.

36. TOBIAS, J. M., M. A. LIPTON, and A. A. LEPINAT. *Proc. Soc. Exp. Biol. Med. 61*:51, 1946; RICHTER, D., and J. CROSSLAND. *Am. J. Physiol. 159*:247, 1949; CROSSLAND, J., and A. J. MERRICK. *J. Physiol. 125*:56, 1954; CROSSLAND, J. *J. Ment. Sci. 99*:247, 1953.

37. ELLIOTT, K. A. C., R. L. SWANK, and N. HENDERSON. *Am. J. Physiol. 162*:469, 1950.

38. MacIntosh, F. C., and P. E. Oborin. *Proc. 19th Intern. Physiol. Cong.,* Montreal, 1953.

39. Bornstein, M. *J. Neurophysiol. 9:*349, 1946.

40. Tower, D., and D. McEachern. *Can. J. Res., Section E, 27:*105, 120, 1949.

41. Pfeiffer, C. C., E. H. Jenney, W. Gallagher, R. P. Smith, and W. Bevan, Jr. *Science 126:*610, 1957.

42. Jenney, E. H. *J. Pharmacol. Exp. Ther. 122:*34A, 1958.

43. Goldstein, L. *Federation Proc. 18:*397, 1959.

44. Moriarty, J. D., and J. C. Mebane. *Am. J. Psychiat. 115:*941, 1959; Pennington, V. M. *Am. J. Psychiat. 116:*165, 1959; Schorer, C. E., and P. Lowinger. *Dis. Nerv. System 20:*267, 1959.

45. Groth, D. P., J. A. Bain, and C. C. Pfeiffer. *J. Pharmacol. Exp. Ther. 124:*290, 1958.

46. Quastel, J. H., M. Tennenbaum, and A. H. M. Wheatley. *Biochem. J. 30:*1668, 1936; Nachmansohn, D., and A. L. Machado. *J. Neurophysiol. 6:*397, 1943.

47. Augustinsson, K. B. *Acta Physiol. Scand. 15:*Suppl. 52, 1948; Dixon, M., and E. C. Webb. *Enzymes,* New York, Academic Press, 1958.

48. Giacobini, E. *Acta Physiol. Scand. 45:*Supplement 156, 1959.

49. Burgen, A. S. V., and L. M. Chipman. *J. Physiol. 114:*296, 1951.

50. Wilson, I. B. *Federation Proc. 18:*752, 1959.

51. Grob, D., J. L. Lilienthal, Jr., A. M. Harvey, and B. F. Jones. *Bull. Johns Hopkins Hosp. 81:*217, 1947; Grob, D., A. M. Harvey, O. R. Langworthy, and J. L. Lilienthal, Jr. *ibid. 81:*257, 1947; Koelle, G. B., and A. Gilman. *J. Pharmacol. Exp. Ther. 95:*Pt. II, 166, 1949; Holmstedt, B. *Pharmacol. Revs. 11:*567, 1959.

52. Rowntree, D. W., S. Nevin, and A. Wilson. *J. Neurol. Neurosurg. Psychiat. 13:*47, 1950.

53. Birkhäuser, H. *Schweiz. Med. Wochschr. 71:*750, 1941.

54. Pope, A., W. Caveness, and H. E. Livingston. *A. M. A. Arch. Neurol. Psychiat. 68:*425, 1952.

55. Tower, D. B., and D. McEachern. *Can. J. Res. Section E, 27:*132, 1949.

56. Rosenzweig, M. R., D. Krech, and E. L. Bennett. *In* Ciba Foundation Symposium, *The Neurological Basis of Behaviour,* ed. Wolstenholme, G. E. W., and C. M. O'Connor. London, J. and A. Churchill, 1958.

57. Feldberg, W., and S. Sherwood. *J. Physiol. 125:*488, 1954.

58. Lehmann, H., and E. Ryan. *Lancet ii:*124, 1956; Kalow, W., and N. Staron. *Can. J. Biochem. Physiol. 35:*1305, 1957; Kalow, W. *in* Ciba Foundation Symposium, *Biochemistry of Human Genetics,* ed. Wolstenholme, G. E. W., and C. M. O'Connor. London, J. and A. Churchill, 1959; Harris, H., M. Whittaker, H. Lehmann, and E. Silk. *Acta Genet. et Statist. Med. 10:*1, 1960.

59. de Vries, A. *Am. J. Med. 23:*408, 1957.

60. Archer, H. E., A. E. Dormer, E. F. Scowen, and R. E. Watts. *Brit. Med. J. i:*175, 1958; Crawhall, J. C., E. F. Scowen, and R. W. E. Watts. *Lancet ii:*806, 1959.

# 4

# GLUTAMIC AND ASPARTIC ACIDS

Glutamic and aspartic acids occupy key positions in many intermediary metabolic processes. These two monoamino dicarboxylic acids
are constituents of proteins and of certain physiologically active peptides
found in animal tissues, as well as of some peptides synthesized by plants
and microorganisms. In the amino acid form they constitute a measurable
and often significant fraction of the total nonprotein nitrogen of
various organs, readily available for participation in a large number
of metabolic reactions whose variety and scope are constantly being
extended by new research. Although some of the reactions they undergo
are general, occurring in many organs, others are specifically associated
with nervous tissue. It is necessary to assess the significance of both
groups of metabolic reactions for the normal functioning of the brain.

Recognition of the importance of these two amino acids in the
metabolism of the brain has led to their trial, or the trial of closely
related derivatives, in a variety of nervous, mental, and other illnesses.
The use of glutamic acid in epilepsy and mental deficiency has been
described in a large number of papers from North America and Europe
since 1943. The ability of this compound to provoke a blood sugar
rise in insulin hypoglycemia and to lift the coma has also been demonstrated, and possible utility in the treatment of hepatic coma has been

studied. The role of glutamic decarboxylase and the product of its action—γ-aminobutyric acid—in the convulsive process, including epileptic seizures, is also under study.

## Absorption

Glutamic and aspartic acids are nonessential amino acids, in that they are not required in the diet. Nevertheless, they are present in the dietary proteins, so that normally as much as 10 gm. of glutamic acid may be ingested daily. Because the peptide-linked amino acids are released slowly during digestion of the protein in the intestinal tract, only a low concentration of any particular amino acid is present at any time, and normal hepatic mechanisms are not taxed in metabolizing and distributing these protein digestion products. Therapeutically, glutamic acid has been employed in several forms, all varying in their solubility and absorbability from the intestine. L-Glutamic acid itself is only slightly soluble in water and is absorbed slowly by the oral route. In tolerance tests its administration may cause a large percentage increase in its level in the plasma, e.g., a doubling or tripling of the base-line values. Elevated values may persist for an hour and then fall to the normal range; the curve is in any case rather flat. The same is true of the hydrochloride of the amino acid. On the other hand, the monosodium salt, which is soluble to the extent of over 70 percent at room temperature, is readily absorbed and attains a high concentration in the plasma after a test load is given (1, 2). Differences have been noted in the tolerance curves between individual subjects and it has been suggested that a prolonged elevation of the glutamic acid level of the plasma during a tolerance test indicates deficient utilization of the glutamic acid by the tissues (2). Pond and Pond (3) also noted marked differences in the rate of absorption and excretion between sodium glutamate and the free acid, and found that these differences extend also to the respective effects of the two forms of the amino acid on the electroencephalogram.

## Intermediary Metabolism

Three main types of metabolic reaction are common to both glutamic and aspartic acids; these are protein formation, amidation, and transamination. The first two require an activating process in which ATP is utilized to convert the amino acid to a more reactive form. The over-all reactions of amidation are shown in Reactions 4-1 and 4-2.

$$\text{Glutamic acid} + NH_3 \xrightarrow{\text{ATP}} \text{Glutamine} \qquad (4\text{-}1)$$

$$\text{Aspartic acid} + NH_3 \xrightarrow{\text{ATP}} \text{Asparagine} \qquad (4\text{-}2)$$

In typical experiments the amino acid and ammonium chloride (as the source of ammonia) are incubated with tissue slices. After some time it is found that the reactants have decreased in amount and amide-nitrogen has increased proportionately. The amide linkage is formed on the carboxyl group distal to the α-amino group. This reaction functions as an intracellular mechanism for the binding (detoxication) of ammonia. It is a physiological process, as shown by comparison of the arterial and venous levels of glutamic acid and glutamine. The concentration of glutamic acid in the blood leaving the brain is lower than in the arterial supply, but the glutamine concentration is higher (4). Glutamine itself is involved in the detoxication of exogenous phenylacetic acid in man (5). The product, phenylacetylglutamine, is a normal constituent of human urine (6), the phenylacetic acid presumably coming from phenylalanine by one of its minor alternate metabolic pathways.

The amide linkage is to be distinguished from the analogous peptide bond, formed during the synthesis of proteins (Reaction 4-3), through

$$R\text{—}CH(NH_2)COOH + H_2N(COOH)CH\cdot CH_2CH_2COOH \rightarrow$$
Peptide with                                    Glutamic acid
free carboxyl group

$$\text{Glutamic acid-containing peptide} \quad (4\text{-}3)$$

the α-carboxyl and α-amino groups of the amino acids. Aspartic acid, asparagine, and glutamine also participate in protein formation in the same manner as illustrated for glutamic acid. In the case of asparagine and glutamine the carboxamido groups extend out from the peptide chain and do not participate in the linkage of amino acids to one another.

The third important reaction in which the two dicarboxylic amino acids play key roles is transamination (Reactions 4-4 and 4-5). Reaction

$$\text{Glutamic acid} + \text{Oxaloacetic acid} \rightleftarrows \alpha\text{-Ketoglutaric acid}$$
$$+ \text{Aspartic acid} \quad (4\text{-}4)$$

$$\text{Aspartic acid} + \text{Pyruvic acid} \rightleftarrows \text{Oxaloacetic acid}$$
$$+ \text{Alanine} \quad (4\text{-}5)$$

$$\text{Glutamic acid} + \alpha\text{-Keto acid} \rightleftarrows \alpha\text{-Ketoglutaric acid}$$
$$+ \alpha\text{-Amino acid} \quad (4\text{-}6)$$

4-6 generalizes the case, further examples of which are given in Table 4-1. In one direction the transamination reaction serves in the formation of many amino acids from the corresponding α-keto acids; this is of particular significance in the biosynthesis of the nonessential amino acids from dietary precursors. In the other direction transamination

TABLE 4-1. TRANSAMINATION REACTIONS

| Reacting Amino Acid* or Other Compound | Keto Acid Produced† | Occurrence of Keto Acid Under Physiological or Clinical Conditions |
|---|---|---|
| L-Aspartic acid | Oxaloacetic acid | Krebs cycle |
| L-Alanine | Pyruvic acid | Krebs cycle |
| L-Tyrosine | p-Hydroxyphenylpyruvic acid | Vitamin C deficiency |
| L-Phenylalanine | Phenylpyruvic acid | Phenylketonuria |
| L-Tryptophan | Indolepyruvic acid | Phenylketonuria, Hartnup disease |
| L-Ornithine | L-Glutamic semialdehyde | Precursor in formation of proline |
| γ-Aminobutyric acid | Succinic semialdehyde | Precursor of succinic acid |
| L-Glutamine | α-Ketoglutaramic acid | Hydrolyzes to α-ketoglutaric acid |
| L-Asparagine | α-Ketosuccinamic acid | Yields oxaloacetic acid on hydrolysis |
| Adenosine‡ | Inosine | In many tissues |

* The amino acids react with α-ketoglutaric acid in the examples shown.
† L-Glutamic acid is the other product.
‡ Adenosine is not an amino acid; inosine is not an α-keto carboxylic acid.

serves to remove nitrogen from the amino acids as the first step in their dissimilation along terminal metabolic pathways. Transamination requires an adequate supply of pyridoxine, for this vitamin serves as the coenzyme of the reaction in the form of pyridoxal phosphate. A small amount of the enzyme, transaminase, is normally present in the serum but it increases markedly in several clinical conditions when some cellular destruction occurs as in cardiac infarction or in damage to liver cells; this feature is used in clinical diagnosis.

In addition to transamination, a reaction not involving ammonia, the dehydrogenation of glutamic acid, mediated by a diphosphopyridine nucleotide-linked enzyme, also yields α-ketoglutaric acid, along with an equimolar amount of ammonia. The equilibrium of this reaction favors the formation of glutamic acid, so that the deamination occurs only when the product, α-ketoglutaric acid, is removed through operation of the tricarboxylic acid cycle. On the other hand an excess of ammonia traps α-ketoglutaric acid through amination forming glutamic acid. These reactions were described in Chapter 2 (Reactions 2-2 and 2-3). The amination of α-ketoglutaric acid represents one of the major ammonia-removing mechanisms in the tissues. An analogous enzyme catalyzing the deamination of aspartic acid in the above fashion has not been detected in mammalian tissues. Hence, transamination to the keto acid precedes the entrance of this dicarboxylic amino acid into oxidative pathways.

The last pathway of glutamic acid metabolism that will be mentioned here is its decarboxylation (Reaction 4-7). This reaction is

$$\text{Glutamic acid} \rightarrow H_2NCH_2CH_2CH_2COOH + CO_2 \qquad (4\text{-}7)$$
$$\text{γ-Aminobutyric acid}$$

essentially restricted to the brain, the only organ containing a significant concentration of glutamic decarboxylase. The product, γ-aminobutyric acid, acts in the brain as an inhibitory transmitter substance. It is converted to succinic semialdehyde by transamination and the semialdehyde is then oxidized to succinic acid. Both glutamic decarboxylase and the transaminase require pyridoxal phosphate as coenzyme, but they differ in their affinities for it. Roberts (7) has pointed out how these two enzymes—one catalyzing the formation of γ-aminobutyric acid, the other its metabolic degradation—together can control the actual concentration of the inhibitory amino acid in the brain.

## Occurrence in Tissues and Body Fluids (Table 4-2)

Glutamic and aspartic acids occur free as well as in combination in many organs. Glutamic acid is present in the brain in quantities which surpass, by far, those of the other amino acids. Together with its close relatives, glutamine and γ-aminobutyric acid, it constitutes about 70 percent of the nonprotein nitrogen of the brain (14). Weil-Malherbe points out that this bespeaks some stoichiometric rather than catalytic function for it (14). Because of these high concentrations some

TABLE 4-2. OCCURRENCE OF THE DICARBOXYLIC AMINO
ACIDS AND SOME OF THEIR DERIVATIVES IN ORGANS
AND BODY FLUIDS OF MAMMALS[a]

| Organ or Fluid | Compound | Concentration mg. %[b] |
|---|---|---|
| Brain | Glutamic acid[c] | 155 |
| | Glutamine[c] | 60 |
| | Glutathione, reduced[d] | 100 |
| | Glutathione, oxidized[d,e] | 3 |
| | γ-Aminobutyric acid[c] | 23 |
| | γ-Guanidobutyric acid[b] | 0.5–1 |
| | Aspartic acid[g] | 29 |
| | N-Acetylaspartic acid[d,g] | 100 |
| | Asparagine[d,g] | 1.4 |
| Liver | Glutamic acid | 19–85 |
| | Glutamine | 24–55 |
| | γ-Guanidobutyric acid[h] | 0.1–0.5 |
| Kidney | Glutamic acid | 78–138 |
| | Glutamine | 10–22 |
| | γ-Guanidobutyric acid[h] | 0.5–1 |
| | N-Acetylaspartic acid[g] | 3 |
| Blood[f] | Glutathione | 30–40 |
| Plasma[f] | Glutamic acid | 1.1 |
| | Glutamine | 8.3 |
| Urine[f] | Glutamic acid | 1–6 |
| | Glutamine | 66–112 |
| | Phenylacetylglutamine | 250–500 |
| | N-Acetylaspartic acid | not present |
| | γ-Guanidobutyric acid | up to 20 |

[a] Sources of the data are (references in parentheses): glutamic acid
and glutamine (8); glutathione in brain (9), in blood (10); γ-aminobutyric acid (11); γ-guanidobutyric acid (12); aspartic acid, asparagine, and N-acetylaspartic acid (11, 13).

[b] Mg./100 gm. of tissue or /100 ml. of fluid.

[c] Rat, mouse, cat, rabbit.

[d] Rat.

[e] Guinea pig.

[f] Man.

[g] Cat.

[h] Dog.

investigators have sought a disturbance of glutamic acid metabolism in mental illnesses, but have been able to find little evidence for this. The excretion of glutamic acid and of glutamine in schizophrenic patients is essentially normal (15), but the plasma glutamic acid concentration may be diminished, along with an elevation of the glutamine level (16). Since the work of Looney and Childs on glutathione in schizophrenia (17) the question of the concentration of this peptide in the blood has been discussed repeatedly in the research literature. Looney and Childs showed that a group of 37 schizophrenic patients had a blood level of 35.0 mg. percent of reduced glutathione as against 38.2 mg. percent for the 18 control subjects. The total glutathione values (*i.e.,* including the oxidized form) were 39.1 and 41.9 mg. percent respectively. Soon afterward Ljunberg reported data on a much larger series, showing that the glutathione content of the blood is the same in schizophrenics as in mentally normal persons (slightly over 36 mg. percent). However, his cases of schizophrenia of recent occurrence gave somewhat higher values (mean of 40.1 mg. percent), whereas the chronic patients fell in a lower range (mean, 32.7 mg. percent) (18). Similar results have been reported by others (19, 20, 21). Persky has noted a reduction in the reduced glutathione of the blood after severe psychological stress, and has suggested that chronicity of this type of stress eventually results in a persistent depression of the blood glutathione (22). Altschule and his colleagues have stated that electroshock treatment tends to raise the glutathione level in the blood in patients whose levels were well below the normal range before treatment was instituted (19). This group has also claimed that the repeated administration of certain pineal gland extracts raises the blood glutathione concentration in manic-depressive and schizophrenic patients (23). Martens et al. also found a low glutathione in chronic schizophrenics in two studies, but the difference from normal was much less in their second study than in their first (21).

The claim for an abnormality of glutathione metabolism in schizophrenia has not gone unchallenged. In two laboratories the supposed differences between normals and schizophrenic subjects have been critically examined, and new data have been contributed. This new work has led to the conclusion that the differences are minimal, if they exist at all (10, 24).

Glutathione is oxidized by the brain under physiological conditions. This has been demonstrated by the method of arteriovenous differences, using the rabbit (25).

# Special Metabolism of Glutamic and Aspartic Acids in Nervous Tissue

Specific enzymes present in cerebral tissues bring about the metabolic conversion of glutamic acid. These enzymes are: glutamic dehydrogenase, glutamic decarboxylase, the transaminases, and the glutamine-forming system. Whereas other amino acids are oxidized with difficulty, if at all, by separated slices of cerebral tissue, glutamic acid is readily metabolized (26). The conversion of glutamic acid to α-ketoglutaric acid, an intermediate in the tricarboxylic acid cycle, indicates the close relationship of this amino acid to the dominant metabolic processes of the brain, *i.e.*, those of carbohydrate metabolism. Measurements of cerebral glutamic acid before and after a period of hypoglycemia serve to illustrate this relationship (27). When insulin is injected into rats to induce hypoglycemia there is a decrease in the glutamic acid content of the brain. This fall can be forestalled by allowing the animals access to glucose. Hence, with a drop in the supply of glucose to the brain the oxidation of glutamic acid provides the necessary energy for maintenance of cerebral functions.

Shortly after the discovery of glutamic decarboxylase and γ-amino-butyric acid in brain (28), Florey found that certain extracts of mammalian brain and spinal cord inhibit the stretch receptor neurone of the crayfish; these extracts also blocked synaptic transmission in autonomic ganglia and monosynaptic spinal reflexes of mammals. The active material has been called Factor I because of the inhibitory effects, but these preparations also stimulate the hypoglossal nucleus and sometimes polysynaptic spinal reflexes (29). Purification of the crude extracts and comparison with known compounds have shown that most if not all of the Factor I activity of nervous tissue is attributable to its γ-aminobutyric acid content (30). Studies of the electrical activity of the brain in response to application of γ-aminobutyric acid indicate that this compound may be a synaptic transmitter for inhibitory neurones. This is supported by some of the results of pharmacological experiments, as in the antagonism of picrotoxin and pentylenetetrazol in the crayfish and of strychnine in mice to the inhibitory action of Factor I.

Many compounds have been tested for Factor I activity, but only a few behave like γ-aminobutyric acid. β-Hydroxy-γ-aminobutyric acid has about half the activity. This compound has been reported as occurring in brain to the extent of about 0.05% (31). Carnitine, a minor nitrogenous constituent of muscle probably derived from γ-aminobutyric acid, is inactive in the crayfish bioassay. It is the betaine of β-hydroxy-γ-aminobutyric acid, and possesses vitamin action for certain insects, but its function in mammals is unknown. γ-Guanidobutyric acid has been found in many animal tissues, including brain, and in plants. Upon hydrolysis it yields γ-aminobutyric acid (12). Its function is unknown. γ-Butyrobetaine has been identified in the brains of animals which have been made to convulse by administration of central nervous system stimulants. It has an acetylcholine-like action that is not affected by Factor I (32).

Berl and Waelsch have described methods for studying the distribution of glutamic acid, γ-aminobutyric acid, and some related derivatives in the brain (33). Elliott has summarized the basic data available on the biochemistry and function of γ-aminobutyric acid (34).

As is evident from the data collected in Table 4-2, aspartic acid and asparagine are not present in brain to the same extent as are glutamic acid and glutamine. However, N-acetyl-L-aspartic acid occurs in the cerebral gray matter in amounts up to 124 mg. percent, and in the spinal cord in lower concentrations. The largest amounts are seen in mammalian and avian brains; the lower species which have been examined have very little or no cerebral acetylaspartic acid (35). Its function in the brain is not known.

## Therapeutic Uses of Glutamic and Aspartic Acids

In 1943 Price, Waelsch, and Putnam reported on the successful use of glutamic acid in the treatment of patients suffering from the petit mal type of seizure. DL-Glutamic acid hydrochloride had been first tested by these investigators as a means of providing large amounts of acid which, judging from experience with the ketogenic diet in petit mal, might be expected to provide some therapeutic benefit. Price et al. reported that "improvement was noted in those cases in which seizures are related to slow wave activity in the electroencephalogram, namely petit mal and psychomotor seizures. Seizures are decreased in frequency on medication which previously had proven either ineffective or partially satisfactory" (36). Glutamic acid had no effect in grand mal. Later, the fixed acid (hydrochloric) was found to be unnecessary in achieving the reduction in seizure frequency, inasmuch as L-glutamic acid was also efficacious. This drew attention away from the acidifying function of the first preparation used to the possible specificity of glutamic acid itself.

Laboratory studies designed to determine whether glutamic acid actually possesses any anticonvulsant properties have not provided a conclusive answer (37). Sapirstein showed that this amino acid, given intravenously as the monosodium salt, protects rabbits against toxic intravenous doses of ammonium chloride (38), but the permissible time lapse between injection of the protecting and convulsing agents is rather short. In an extensive study of experimental convulsions in several laboratory species monosodium glutamate had no effect (39). In fact, this compound may cause increased motor activity and central excitability in rats given it by mouth (40). This type of response has been noted clinically in patients given large doses of glutamic acid, and it may well be this action of the compound which is responsible for some of the therapeutic benefits claimed in schizophrenia and other psychiatric as well as neurological disorders.

The report on the effect of glutamic acid in petit mal naturally aroused interest not only because of the therapeutic result but also because of the implication that the amino acid, occupying as it does a distinctive place in the metabolism of the nervous system, represented a form of replacement therapy. Actually the penetration of administered glutamic acid into the brain cell is rather limited (41) so that other mechanisms of action of glutamic acid must be considered.

In their first report on the use of glutamic acid, Price and his colleagues also noted that "universally, mental and physical alertness have been increased. The degree of improvement in mental efficiency cannot be correlated with the incidence of seizures . . . . Usually the patient is noted to be more energetic and happier, mood swings are less pronounced, behavior mannerisms are ameliorated and he is more congenial with associates" (36). These results suggested that glutamic acid might prove beneficial in mental deficiency. Many such patients have now been treated with glutamic acid for varying periods of time. The first tests were carried out by two groups at Columbia University in 1946 (42, 43), both of which later extended their investigations (44, 45). Their results indicated that glutamic acid, administered orally in amounts of 12 gm. per day or more, has a small but significant effect in raising the intelligence quotient of mentally defective persons. The beneficial effect of glutamic acid on intelligence of mental defectives at the higher I.Q. planes has been confirmed by others, but negative reports have also appeared, as shown in Table 4-3. Some of these reports are based upon work done, not with glutamic acid, but with its monosodium salt and therefore need not be considered the same type of trial because of the difference in properties (*e.g.*, rate of absorption, effect on plasma pH) of these two substances. Glutamic acid does not affect performance of normal persons in psychological tests (46, 47) nor the intelligence of subjects with very low I.Q., as in mongolism (50). Where it has been effective in

TABLE 4-3. USE OF GLUTAMIC ACID IN NERVOUS AND MENTAL DISEASES

| Diagnostic Group | Function Measured | Clinical Effect | Reference |
|---|---|---|---|
| Normal boys | Learning | − * | 46 |
| Normal children and adults | Psychological tests | − | 47 |
| Mental deficiency | Battery of psychological tests | { + <br> − | 43, 44, 48, 49 <br> 50, 51 <br> 39, 46, 52 |
| Mongolian idiocy | Intelligence quotient | { − <br> + | 50 <br> 53 |
| Mental deficiency in children with severe behavior problems | Intelligence quotient | − | 45 |
| Petit mal epilepsy | Seizure frequency | { + <br> − | 36, 54 <br> 3 |
| Grand mal epilepsy | Seizure frequency | − | 36 |
| Cerebral damage | Intelligence quotient | { − <br> + | 45 <br> 55 |
| Tertiary syphilis, meningo-encephalitis manifested by psychotic reaction, general paresis | Intelligence quotient | − | 56 |
| Chronic schizophrenia | Behavior, activity | + | 57, 58 |
| Various neurological and psychiatric categories | Behavior, motivation, psychological test | + | 2 *, 47, 59 |
| Mentally deficient children | Verbal intelligence | + | 60 |

\* Monosodium glutamate was used.

raising the I.Q., the increase has not been more than a few points and the benefits of attaining such a small increase have been questioned. It may be, however, that the subject is thereby brought to a new level of intelligence at which his improvement in performance makes a significant difference to himself and to the people around him.

Glutamic acid and monosodium glutamate have been tested in many other conditions, sometimes under carefully controlled conditions, but frequently with limited or inadequate controls. Some examples of these clinical trials and their results are provided in Table 4-3.

More recently asparagine and glutamine have also been studied in petit mal epilepsy (61, 62). These tests have been based upon their ability to antagonize the convulsant effects of methionine sulfoximine, the toxic factor in wheat flour treated with agene (nitrogen trichloride). A preliminary report in 1955 of clinical results (61) indicated that glutamine and asparagine are well tolerated; up to 25 gm. of the former and 40 gm. of the latter have been administered intravenously without untoward effects. In patients with an established history of seizures not satisfactorily controlled by other anticonvulsant medication, these amides were said to reduce the percentage of abnormal electroencephalographic activity, decrease the frequency of seizures, virtually eliminate the minor akinetic seizures, and lead to physical and psychic improvement. Tower states that the "metabolic loss" of glutamic acid occurring in separated epileptogenic cortical tissue is antagonized by the inclusion of asparagine in the incubation medium. γ-Aminobutyric acid and 2-pyrrolidinone are similarly active (63). He considers the derangement of glutamic acid metabolism, which is reversed by asparagine *in vitro,* to have a bearing upon the chemistry of the seizure process.

Glutamine has also been tested in other conditions. Rogers and Pelton have claimed some favorable responses to this substance in the treatment of alcoholism (64) and in improving the I.Q. of mentally deficient children (65), but their reports, like the above one, await confirmation from other clinics.

## Mechanism of Action of Glutamic Acid

The mechanism of action of glutamic acid in cases of petit mal and mental deficiency has been a matter for some discussion. Some of the pharmacological effects of glutamic acid and other amino acids point to autonomic stimulation. For example, infusion of amino acid mixtures for intravenous alimentation causes nausea, dizziness, and vomiting unless their glutamate content is reduced; these effects can be controlled, however, with atropine. Similar actions have been noted in some patients on oral feeding of glutamic acid and, especially, monosodium glutamate. More significant than these unwanted effects are the elevation of the blood pressure, increase in pulse rate, and rise in blood sugar, a triad indicating stimulation of the sympathetic nervous system. The hyperglycemia has been observed by several investigators after the infusion of monosodium glutamate (2, 66, 67), and has confirmed the earlier findings by Pollak (68) that some amino acids (aspartic, glycine, and alanine) have a sympathinlike action and by Nord a few years later (1926) that glutamic acid has this insulin-antagonizing action (69). The hyperglycemic action of glutamate may be sufficiently intense to effect the arousal of patients from hypo-glycemic coma (66, 67). Although brain glutamic acid can substitute as a cerebral fuel for glucose during insulin hypoglycemia (p. 52) the action of infused glutamate cannot be due to conversion of the amino acid to glucose for the glutamate is effective in amounts far too small to provide sufficient glucose for this purpose (67). As already pointed out, the low permeability of the blood-brain barrier to glutamic acid encourages consideration of an indirect mode of action such as through adrenergic activation, and not through utilization as a cerebral foodstuff.

The view that glutamic acid stimulates the sympathetic nervous system nonspecifically has been put forward particularly by Weil-Malherbe (14, 67, 69, 70). In addition to the adrenergic sequelae already mentioned he has demonstrated a close similarity of the action of glutamic acid to that of amphetamine in mental defectives (70). By direct measurement of the sympathoadrenal neurohumors he has found that glutamic acid causes an increase in the level of epinephrine (but not norepinephrine) in the plasma, presumably through reflex stimulation of the adrenal medulla. This may well explain the observation made by Maddock et al. that glucose, but not glutamate, can reverse the electroencephalographic changes caused by hepatectomy and abdominal evisceration including adrenalectomy in experimental animals (71). This finding also confirms the view that conversion of glutamate to glucose cannot explain the action of the amino acid.

## References

1. HIMWICH, W. A., and I. M. PETERSEN. *J. Appl. Physiol.* 7:196, 1954.
2. HIMWICH, H. E., K. WOLFF, A. L. HUNSICKER, and W. A. HIMWICH. *J. Nerv. Ment. Dis.* 121:40, 1955.
3. POND, D. A., and M. H. POND. *J. Ment. Sci.* 97:663, 1951.
4. ADAMS, J. E., H. A. HARPER, G S. GORDAN, M. HUTCHIN, and R. C. BENTINCK. *Neurology* 5:100, 1955.

5. SHERWIN, C. P., M. WOLF, and W. WOLF. *J. Biol. Chem. 37:*113, 1919.
6. STEIN, W. H., A. C. PALADINI, C. H. W. HIRS, and S. MOORE. *J. Am. Chem. Soc. 76:*2848, 1954.
7. ROBERTS, E., M. ROTHSTEIN, and C. F. BAXTER. *Proc. Soc. Exp. Biol. Med. 97:*796, 1958.
8. WAELSCH, H. *Adv. Protein Chem. 6:*299, 1951; FOSS, O. P. *Scand. J. Clin. Lab. Invest. 5:*334, 1953.
9. TRESIZE, M. A. *Biochem. J. 65:*P2, 1957.
10. BARAK, A. J., F. L. HUMOLLER, and J. D. STEVENS. *A. M. A. Arch. Neurol. Psychiat. 80:*237, 1958.
11. TALLAN, H. H., S. MOORE, and W. H. STEIN. *J. Biol. Chem. 211:*927, 1954.
12. IRREVERE, F., R. L. EVANS, A. R. HAYDEN, and R. SILBER. *Nature 180:*704, 1957.
13. TALLAN, H. H., S. MOORE, and W. H. STEIN. *J. Biol. Chem. 219:*257, 1956.
14. WEIL-MALHERBE, H. *In Metabolism and Function in Nervous Tissue,* Biochemical Society Symposium No. 8, Cambridge University Press, 1952.
15. FOSS, O. P. *Scand. J. Clin. Lab. Invest. 6:*107, 1954.
16. MUNKVAD, I. *Acta Psychiat. et Neurol. 25:*269, 1950.
17. LOONEY, J. M., and H. M. CHILDS. *J. Clin. Invest. 13:*963, 1934.
18. LJUNBERG, E. *Acta Psychiat. et Neurol. 11:*369, 1937.
19. ALTSCHULE, M. D., E. P. SIEGEL, and D. HENNEMANN. *A. M. A. Arch. Neurol. Psychiat. 67:*64, 1952.
20. EASTERDAY, O. D., R. M. FEATHERSTONE, J. S. GOTTLIEB, N. L. NUSSER, and R. V. HOGG. *A. M. A. Arch. Neurol. Psychiat. 68:*48, 1952.
21. MARTENS, S., B. E. LEACH, R. G. HEATH, and M. COHEN. *A. M. A. Arch. Neurol. Psychiat. 76:*630, 1956; ANGEL, C., B. E. LEACH, S. MARTENS, M. COHEN, and R. G. HEATH. *A. M. A. Arch. Neurol. Psychiat. 78:*500, 1957.
22. PERSKY, H. *Psychosom. Med. 16:*489, 1954.
23. ALTSCHULE, M. D., E. P. SIEGEL, R. M. GONCZ, and J. P. MURNANE. *A. M. A. Arch. Neurol. Psychiat. 71:*615, 1954.
24. McDONALD, R. K. *In Chemical Concepts of Psychosis,* ed. RINKEL, M., and H. C. B. DENBER, New York, McDowell, Obolensky, 1958.
25. McILWAIN, H., H. MARTIN, R. RODNIGHT, and M. A. TRESIZE. *J. Physiol. 136:*32P, 1957; *idem, Biochem. J. 65:*288, 1957.
26. WEIL-MALHERBE, H. *Biochem. J. 30:*665, 1936; VON EDLBACHER, S., and O. WISS. *Helv. Chim. Acta. 27:*1060, 1944.
27. DAWSON, R. M. C. *Biochem. J. 47:*386, 1950.
28. AWAPARA, J., A. J. LANDUA, R. FUERST, and B. SEALE *J. Biol. Chem. 187:* 35, 1950; ROBERTS, E., and S. FRANKEL, *ibid. 187:*55, 1950; UDENFRIEND, S. *ibid. 187:*65, 1950.
29. FLOREY, E. *Naturwiss. 40:*295, 1953; FLOREY, E., and H. McLENNAN, *J. Physiol. 130:*446, 1955.
30. BAZEMORE, A. W., K. A. C. ELLIOTT, and E. FLOREY. *J. Neurochem. 1:*334, 1957.
31. OHARA, K., I. SANO, H. KOIZUMI, and K. NISHINUMA. *Science 129:*1225, 1959.
32. HOSEIN, E. A., and H. McLENNAN. *Nature 183:*328, 1959.

33. BERL, S., and H. WAELSCH. *J. Neurochem. 3:*161, 1958.
34. ELLIOTT, K. A. C. *Rev. Canad. de Biol. 17:*367, 1958; and *Proceedings IVth Internat. Congress Biochem.*, Vienna, 1958. Vol. 3, *ed.* BRÜCKE, F. London, Pergamon, 1959.
35. TALLAN, H. H. *J. Biol. Chem. 224:*41, 1957.
36. PRICE, J. C., H. WAELSCH, and T. L. PUTNAM. *J.A.M.A. 122:*1153, 1943.
37. GOODMAN, L. S., E. A. SWINYARD, and J. E. P. TOMAN. *Arch. Neurol. Psychiat. 56:*20, 1946.
38. SAPIRSTEIN, M. R. *Proc. Soc. Exp. Biol. Med. 52:*334, 1943.
39. ELLSON, D. G., P. R. FULLER, and R. URMSTON. *Science 112:*248, 1950.
40. CZOK, G., and K. LANG. *Arch. Exp. Path. u. Pharmakol. 227:*214, 1955.
41. KLEIN, J. R., and N. S. OLSEN. *J. Biol. Chem. 167:*1, 1947; FRIEDBERG, F., and D. M. GREENBERG. *J. Biol. Chem. 168:*411, 1947; STERN, J. R., L. V. EGGLESTON, R. HEMS, and H. A. KREBS. *Biochem. J. 44:*410, 1949; SCHWERIN, P., S. P. BESSMAN, and H. WAELSCH. *J. Biol. Chem. 184:*37, 1950.
42. ALBERT, K., P. HOCH, and H. WAELSCH. *J. Nerv. Ment. Dis. 104:*13, 1946.
43. ZIMMERMAN, F. T., B. B. BURGEMEISTER, and T. J. PUTNAM. *Arch. Neurol. Psychiat. 56:*489, 1946.
44. ZIMMERMAN, F. T., B. B. BURGEMEISTER, and T. J. PUTNAM. *Psychosom. Med. 9:*175, 1947; ALBERT, K., P. HOCH, and H. WAELSCH. *J. Nerv. Ment. Dis. 114:*471, 1951; ZIMMERMAN, F. T., and B. B. BURGEMEISTER. *Arch. Neurol. Psychiat. 65:*291, 1951.
45. ZIMMERMAN, F. T., and B. B. BURGEMEISTER. *N.Y. State J. Med. 50:*693, 1950.
46. MILLIKEN, J. R., and J. L. STANDEN. *J. Neurol. Neurosurg. & Psychiat. 14:* 47, 1951.
47. KERGL, E. *Med. Monatsschr. 6:*790, 1952; *ibid. 7:*516, 1953; *idem, Arzneimittel Forsch. 4:*48, 1954.
48. BAKWIN, H. *J. Pediat. 31:*702, 1947.
49. FOALE, M. *J. Ment. Sci. 98:*483, 1952.
50. McCULLOCH, T. L. *Am. J. Ment. Defic. 55:*117, 1950.
51. ZABARENKO, R. N., and G. S. CHAMBERS. *Am. J. Psychiat. 108:*881, 1952.
52. LOEB, H. G., and R. D. TUDDENHAM. *Pediatrics 6:*72, 1950.
53. ZIMMERMAN, F. T., B. B. BURGEMEISTER, and T. J. PUTNAM. *Am. J. Psychiat. 105:*661, 1948–49.
54. WAELSCH, H., and J. C. PRICE. *Arch. Neurol. Psychiat. 51:*393, 1944.
55. KUNDRATITZ, K. *Wien. Klin. Wochschr. 69:*423, 1957.
56. KANTOR, R. E., and F. E. BOYES. *Science 113:*681, 1951.
57. EWALT, J. R., and E. I. BRUCE. *Texas Repts. Biol. Med. 6:*97, 1948.
58. FINCLE, L. P., and L. J. REYNA. *J. Clin. Exptl. Psychopathol. 19:*7, 1958.
59. SCHWÖBEL, G. *Nervenarzt 21:*385, 1950; ZINNITZ, F., and R. KUHR. *Med. Monatschr. 6:*181, 1952.
60. ZIMMERMAN, F. T., and B. B. BURGEMEISTER. *A. M. A. Arch. Neurol. Psychiat. 81:*639, 1959.
61. TOWER, D. B. *Neurology 5:*113, 1955.
62. TOWER, D. B. *Am. J. Clin. Nutr. 4:*330, 1956.

63. Tower, D. B. *Clin. Chim. Acta* 2:397, 1957.

64. Rogers, L., and R. B. Pelton. *Quart. J. Study Alcohol.* 18:581, 1957.

65. Rogers, L., and R. B. Pelton. *Texas Repts. Biol. Med.* 15:84, 1957.

66. Mayer-Gross, W., and J. W. Walker. *Biochem. J.* 44:92, 1949.

67. Weil-Malherbe, H. *J. Ment. Sci.* 95:930, 1949.

68. Pollak, L. *Biochem. Z.* 127:120, 1922.

69. Nord, F. *Acta Med. Scand.* 65:1, 1926–27.

70. Weil-Malherbe, H. *Physiol. Rev.* 30:549, 1950.

71. Maddock, S., J. E. Hawkins, and E. Holmes. *Am. J. Physiol.* 125:551, 1939.

# 5

# PHENYLALANINE AND TYROSINE

Phenylalanine is an essential component of the diet, needed for the formation of body protein and other functions. Tyrosine ($p$-hydroxyphenylalanine) is a normal metabolite of phenylalanine and, like that amino acid, is a constituent of dietary proteins. These two amino acids follow many paths of metabolism, some of which are of minor quantitative significance in normal individuals and, indeed, were not known until the application of the isotopic labeling and paper chromatographic techniques revealed the presence of previously unrecognized metabolic derivatives. Important metabolic functions of the two amino acids are found in their utilization for the synthesis of proteins and in the formation of thyroid hormone, the sympathoadrenal neurohumors, and melanin, among other substances. Several genetic defects in the metabolism of these amino acids have been recognized. One of them, phenylketonuria, occurs in individuals lacking the enzyme which catalyzes the oxidation of phenylalanine to tyrosine. Because of the blocking of this pathway, the excess phenylalanine accumulates in the tissues and body fluids, and some of it is diverted into minor routes of (normal) metabolism, which now assume major significance. In alcaptonuria homogentisic acid (2,5-dihydroxyphenylacetic acid) accumu-

61

lates because of a deficiency of the enzyme homogentisicase; and in albinism the melanogenetic system is absent. In addition to these genetic disorders an acquired biochemical lesion in tyrosine metabolism results from vitamin C deficiency, expressed in the excretion of inordinately large amounts of p-hydroxyphenylpyruvic acid. This condition resembles the tyrosinosis described by Medes in 1932.

# Phenylalanine Metabolism

## ALTERNATE PATHWAYS ( I )

The major route of metabolism of phenylalanine (and of tyrosine, which follows it in the biochemical sequence) leads to the formation of the terminal oxidation products carbon dioxide and water. The first step from tyrosine is its transformation to p-hydroxyphenylpyruvic acid. This acid undergoes oxidation and rearrangement, which result in its conversion to homogentisic acid. Three vitamins play roles in this transformation of phenylalanine: tetrahydrofolic acid is the coenzyme for phenylalanine hydroxylase, pyridoxine is required for the transamination of tyrosine, and ascorbic acid is needed to protect the enzyme p-hydroxyphenylpyruvic acid oxidase from inactivation (2). The ring structure of homogentisic acid is broken oxidatively by an iron ($Fe^{++}$)-containing enzyme to yield the straight-chain compound maleylacetoacetic acid. A glutathione-requiring enzyme isomerizes this, and the product is split to fumaric and acetoacetic acids; these substances are metabolized to $CO_2$ and water along well-known pathways.

The ring oxidation of tyrosine to 3,4-dihydroxyphenylalanine (dopa) opens up additional routes of metabolism (3), for dopa serves as the substrate of melanogenetic enzymes and of an amine-forming enzyme as well. The melanocytes are responsible for maintaining the production of the various melanin pigments by complex processes of oxidation and polymerization. In another direction dopa is decarboxylated very readily to 3,4-dihydroxyphenylethylamine (dopamine). This amine undergoes $\beta$-oxidation (on the side chain) to form norepinephrine; N-methylation of the latter results in epinephrine. Dopamine, norepinephrine, and epinephrine together comprise the naturally occurring catecholamines of the mammalian organism. They are found in the urine, partly free, partly conjugated with glucuronic acid. After the experimental ingestion of large amounts of epinephrine, the sulfuric acid conjugate appears in the urine. The metabolism of these catecholic compounds is considered at greater length in Chapter 25.

Although phenylalanine normally undergoes its first oxidation to tyrosine, a small amount of it is oxidized by way of the *ortho* (4, 5) route also. The origin of the benzoic acid moiety of urinary hippuric acid from phenylalanine is uncertain, and urinary metabolites such as *m*-hydroxyhippuric acid and *m*-hydroxyphenylpropionic acids are believed to be derived from dietary ingredients other than phenylalanine (6). Some phenylalanine is probably converted to phenylpyruvic acid or phenylethylamine (or both), because the oxidation product common to these compounds, phenylacetic acid, is excreted normally in the urine (as phenylacetylglutamine).

The formation of thyroid hormones is described in Chapter 24.

## LEVELS OF PHENYLALANINE AND ITS METABOLITES IN BODY FLUIDS

A partial list of phenylalanine derivatives found in the urine is given in Table 5-1, and the concentration of phenylalanine in the circulating fluids is shown in Table 5-2. Perusal of these tables will indicate the wide variety of compounds arising in mammalian metabolism, which possess the aromatic nucleus of phenylalanine and tyrosine. The compounds listed represent quantitatively only a small fraction of the turnover of these amino acids in the body, as most of the phenylalanine and tyrosine consumed in the diet is oxidized beyond the homogentisic acid stage. Nevertheless, some of the derivatives possess important pharmacological properties, which may actually influence bodily function and mental activity.

It has long been postulated that the body fluids of schizophrenic subjects contain some substance(s) not found in those of mentally normal persons, and the search for chemical distinguishing marks of this nature has frequently turned to the metabolism of the aromatic amino acids. Many of the current studies in this area were prompted by the report of Young et al. (17) that the urines of schizophrenics contain increased amounts of diazo coupling substances, making evident "the existence of a biochemical pattern strikingly different from that of normal controls." Other research groups have also reported this finding for urine as well as for other body fluids. Gorodkova has found an increase in the phenolic titer in the CSF of acute schizophrenic patients; the value returns to normal levels as the patient improves under treatment (18). A similar relationship has been claimed by Dotsenko for substances occurring in the urine (19) and by Poroshina

TABLE 5-1. PHENYLALANINE AND SOME RELATED
COMPOUNDS IN THE URINE

| Compound | Normal | Phenylketonuria | References |
|---|---|---|---|
| Phenylalanine | 10–30 mg./day | 20–70 mg./day | 7, 8 |
| Phenylpyruvic acid | | 112–170 mg./gm. of total nitrogen | 7 |
| Phenyllactic acid | | 40–91 mg./gm. of total nitrogen | 7 |
| Phenylacetylglutamine | 0.2–0.3 gm./day | 2–3 gm./day | 9, 10, 11 |
| Hippuric acid | 1–3 mg./kg./day | | 12 |
| Tyrosine | 15–50 mg./day | | 8 |
| o-Hydroxyphenylacetic acid | 0.3–0.5 mg./gm. of creatinine | 100–400 mg./gm. of creatinine | 4, 5 |
| m-Hydroxyphenyl-hydracrylic acid | 2–150 mg./day (mode = 10 mg.) | Same | 6 |
| m-Hydroxyhippuric acid | 2–150 mg./day | | 6 |

TABLE 5-2. CONCENTRATION OF PHENYLALANINE IN BODY FLUIDS

| Fluid | Condition | Concentration (mg. %) | References |
|---|---|---|---|
| Serum* | Normal | 0–1 | 11, 13 |
| | Phenylketonuric† | 17–60 | 11, 13–15 |
| | Phenylketonuric, on phenylalanine-low diet | 5 | 15 |
| CSF | Phenylketonuric | 3–12 | 11, 13, 14 |
| Sweat‡ | Phenylketonuric | 2–10 | 7, 11 |

* Plasma tyrosine is normally about 1.0 to 1.5 mg. % (16).

† No phenylpyruvic or phenyllactic acid was found in the blood of phenylketonurics (13).

‡ The amount of phenylpyruvic acid in the sweat of phenylketonurics is 6 to 56 mg. % (7).

for phenolic substances in the blood (20). McGeer and his colleagues (21, 22) have attempted to develop a chromatographic rating for urines, calculated from the number and intensity of spots on chromatograms of urine reacting with diazotized sulfanilic acid to yield a colored product. They estimate that the average rating for schizophrenics' urine is about twice as great as for that of patients with other mental disorders or of normal persons. This claimed excess in the production of phenolic substances by schizophrenics is postulated as being related to the production of an endogenous hallucinogen in schizophrenia (22). A hypothesis of this nature suggests that by withholding the aromatic amino acids—the sources of the hypothetical toxic agent—the titer of this agent in the circulating fluids would fall, and clinical amelioration might ensue. Two tests of this hypothesis have shown that giving patients diets deficient in the aromatic amino acids for as long as 3 to 6 weeks does not bring about significant clinical improvement (22, 23). The experimental results upon which the hypothesis rests have not gone unchallenged for, suggestive as they are, they are poorly quantified and give no indication of the substances which are involved. Fortunately, they have been followed up by more refined procedures leading to the characterization of some of the aromatic compounds found on the paper chromatograms. As these fractionation methods are applied the deviation of the schizophrenics' urinary aromatic constituents from normal tends to disappear (24). In one study, the abnormalities detected by paper chromatographic analyses were found to be due to metabolites of coffee, a beverage consumed by the patients but not by the controls (25).

## DIETARY REQUIREMENTS

Rose and his colleagues have established that tyrosine is not essential for the maintenance of nitrogen equilibrium in the human adult, although its inclusion in the diet can spare up to three quarters of the phenylalanine required (26). The fact that not all the phenylalanine is replaceable indicates that the oxidation of phenylalanine to tyrosine is an irreversible reaction. Rose's estimate of minimal requirements for L-phenylalanine is 1.1 gm./day (Table 2-3). Much of this can be replaced by D-phenylalanine, for maintaining nitrogen equilibrium (27). Paine et al. determined the optimal dietary level of phenylalanine for two phenylketonuric children (28). It was 25 mg./kg./day for one (age six months) and 5 to 15 mg./kg./day for the second (age fifteen years).

# Phenylketonuria (11, 29)

## THE BIOCHEMICAL DEFECT

In 1934 the Norwegian biochemist Fölling reported the existence of a metabolic abnormality in certain mental patients. He wrote:

> In investigations of mentally defective children, I have perceived an anomaly of metabolism which has not hitherto been described in man. The anomaly is expressed in the excretion of phenylpyruvic acid in the urine, and there appears to be a relation between this anomaly and the imbecility. I have so far found ten patients who excrete phenylpyruvic acid, and of these nine are undoubtedly mentally deficient, whereas the tenth is so young that nothing can yet be said about his psychic condition.

Fölling named the condition imbecillitas phenylpyrouvica (30). Since then it has received other names: phenylpyruvic oligophrenia (Jervis) and phenylketonuria (Penrose and Quastel). Although other inborn errors of metabolism were known at the time of Fölling's discovery, phenylketonuria quickly became the most celebrated if only for the fact that it was the first such error to be associated with a mental defect. The attention paid to it has yielded a large literature dealing with its genetic, psychiatric, demographic, and biochemical aspects. Most recently the research has extended to the prophylaxis and therapeutics of the abnormality.

In phenylketonuria the affected individual is unable to oxidize phenylalanine to tyrosine at a normal rate. Because of this, phenylalanine accumulates in the tissues and the blood, rises in concentration above the renal threshold, and "spills over" into the urine. At the same time a portion of it moves into metabolic routes that play little or no role in the healthy person and, as a consequence, many unusual compounds appear in the urine. The inability of the phenylketonuric to oxidize phenylalanine normally was long appreciated, but direct demonstration of this as a primary metabolic defect awaited the finding (31) that enzymic extracts prepared from the liver of phenylketonuric patients do not catalyze the oxidation of phenylalanine to tyrosine, as extracts of normal livers do. Studies with labeled phenylalanine reveal that phenylketonurics can convert this amino acid to tyrosine but only at a fraction of the normal rate (32). Because some phenylalanine does get through to tyrosine it appears either that another enzyme system is available, which can handle small amounts of the amino acid, or that the hydroxylation occurs on a small scale in other tissues. The most striking consequence of the deficient oxidation is the appearance of phenylpyruvic acid in the urine. This compound is readily detected by the characteristic greenish color it gives with ferric chloride. It occurs in the urine only after the serum phenylalanine level rises above 15 mg. percent (33). However, excretion of large amounts of phenylpyruvic acid is not the only metabolic abnormality, for phenylalanine itself is present in the urine in large amounts, and *m*-tyrosine, *o*-tyrosine, and *o*-hydroxyphenylacetic acid are also found there (4). The last compound is excreted in very much higher concentrations than normally. Phenylacetylglutamine excretion is increased in phenylketonuria, and phenylacetic acid can be detected. Abnormalities in the metabolism of tyrosine and tryptophan also exist, and the following organic acids are excreted in abnormally high concentrations: *p*-hydroxy-phenylpyruvic (quoted in reference 4); *p*-hydroxyphenyllactic and *p*-hydroxyphenylacetic (4); indolepyruvic and indolelactic (34) acids.

The serum of phenylketonurics contains about 20 to 60 mg. percent of phenylalanine, and the concentration of this amino acid in the CSF may rise above 10 mg. percent. The high values for some of these metabolites in the body fluids can be elevated even more by the oral administration of phenylalanine, phenylpyruvic acid, or phenyllactic acid, respectively (13, 35). The heterozygous parents of phenylketonurics have an elevated fasting level of phenylalanine in the serum, and loading tests show that they have a low tolerance for ingested phenylalanine (36, 37). In contrast to these examples of penetrance of the recessive factor, nonaffected controls excrete significant amounts of phenylpyruvic acid after a test load of this amino acid, but this occurs with little change in the blood level. If D-phenylalanine is used there is a much greater elevation in values than with the L-isomer (35). Contrariwise, the high values for phenylalanine metabolites in the body fluids can all be brought down to normal by sharply reducing the phenylalanine content of the diet. Administration of glutamine or asparagine causes some reduction in the concentration of phenyl-pyruvic and phenyllactic acids in the urine (38), a change which may be effected through inhibiting the transamination of phenylalanine; but this point is not established. The amino acid amides have no effect upon the excretion of phenylacetylglutamine, nor do they have a certain effect upon the blood level of phenylalanine, which would be expected to increase if it is regulated by the rate of transamination.

One of the noteworthy characteristics of most phenylketonurics is their decreased pigmentation, expressed in blue eyes and blond hair. It is of interest in this regard that in a case examined at post-mortem the substantia nigra and the locus ceruleus were both unpigmented (39). Perhaps melanization is inhibited by one or other of the excessive abnormal products of phenylalanine metabolism. For example, the natural isomer of phenylalanine, as well as phenylpyruvic, phenylacetic, and *p*-hydroxyphenylacetic acids inhibit mammalian tyrosinase (40). Such enzymatic inhibitions, if shown to be operative *in vivo* as well as *in vitro,* could provide the explanation for the reduced pigmentation in phenylketonuria. Various metabolites of phenylalanine and tyrosine inhibit dopa decarboxylase also (41), and if the former set act this way *in vivo* then the biosynthesis of the catecholamines could be expected to suffer some degree of inhibition. This may be the basis for the significantly lower levels of norepinephrine and epinephrine in the plasma of phenylketonurics (42). The inhibitory influence of phenylalanine upon metabolism of tyrosine extends into other metabolic areas as well, such as its catabolism and its incorporation into protein (43). Phenylalanine and some of the organic acids derived from it inhibit glutamic decarboxylase (44); a reduction of the γ-aminobutyric acid content of the brain resulting from this might be related to the seizure phenomena in phenylketonuria. Thus, the biochemical defect in this disorder has connotations for metabolism that are wider than those concerning phenylalanine alone.

Several suggestions have been made as to the precise nature of the toxic factor in phenylketonuria. The problem is complicated by the fact that no one has been able to correlate mental level and degree of biochemical abnormality. Moreover, some phenylketonuric children have now been identified who have an I.Q. in the normal range, but who exhibit the same chemical changes as their mentally deficient siblings (45). Woolf and Vulliamy (9) state that it is "most probable that phenylalanine or one of its breakdown products, circulating in the blood in concentrations much higher than normal, depresses the activity of the higher mental centres." Specific toxic symptoms have been described for *o*-tyramine and for phenylacetic acid, both minor constituents in normal persons, but significant ones in phenylketonuria. The amine causes excitement, among other effects (46). Phenylacetic acid, in doses of 5 gm., causes great thirst and hunger, nausea, headache, vertigo, drowsiness, irritability, tinnitus, eye pain, and lack of coordination of movements (47).

Another chemical change in the disease has been suggested as a possibility: an increase in the phenylalanine content of body proteins. Allen and Schroeder (48) state this hypothesis as follows: "One possible mechanism for phenylalanine toxicity in phenylketonuria is the abnormal accumulation of phenylalanine in body proteins and the displacement of other amino acids. A vital protein containing a single residue of phenylalanine might function abnormally and produce the clinical symptomatology." Block et al. (49) failed to detect an alteration in the phenylalanine content of the plasma proteins, and Allen and Schroeder (48) have since demonstrated by analysis of hemoglobin prepared from the erythrocytes of phenylketonuric subjects that the chances of this hemoglobin differing in structure from hemoglobin A (the normal adult type) are extremely slim.

The deficiency of hepatic phenylalanine oxidase has already been mentioned. It is not yet known if the actual enzymic protein is absent, or if it is present in a structurally defective and catalytically inactive form. This question can be decided when methods for the purification of phenylalanine oxidase have been worked out and are applied to phenylketonuric liver.

Waisman and his colleagues have produced experimental phenylketonuria in two laboratory species. Young rats fed a diet high in tyrosine suffer a sharp reduction in the phenylalanine oxidase activity of the liver; if they are then transferred to a diet containing much phenylalanine they begin to excrete phenylpyruvic acid (50). This happens also in monkeys given frequent large supplements of l-phenylalanine (51).

## THERAPEUTIC MEASURES

Penrose and Quastel (52) reduced the dietary protein by more than 50 percent in the attempt to relieve the flood of phenylalanine that constantly inundates the tissues of the phenylketonuric. There was an immediate biochemical response, in the virtual disappearance of phenylpyruvic acid from the urine on the first two days. However, this was not maintained, for by the eighth day the urine contained 75 mg. percent of the keto acid, and the patient was losing weight. The reduction in the intake of protein solved the problem of excess dietary phenylalanine, but created a new one because the intake of the other amino acids on a low-protein diet is insufficient for growth or for maintenance and repair of the tissues. In 1951 Woolf and Vulliamy solved this problem by the use of a diet specifically low in its phenyl-alanine content (9). This entailed planning the diet around protein hydrolyzates from which the aromatic amino acids had been removed by adsorption on charcoal and to which tyrosine and tryptophan (but not phenylalanine) have been added back. Phenylalanine-low diets have now been used in many centers with considerable though not exclusive success (11, 15, 28, 53). The biochemical findings reveal a fairly rapid drop in the urinary phenylpyruvic acid and a somewhat slower but steady drop in serum phenylalanine toward normal. The other abnormal metabolites in the urine also decrease to the levels seen in normals. Clinically, the phenylketonuric patients who are placed on this diet show a reduction in the frequency of petit mal type of seizures, decreased spasticity where it was previously evident, increased respon-siveness and motor development, along with intellectual growth at a faster rate than would otherwise have been expected. One of the most interesting findings has been a darkening of the hair. Patients who are returned to a natural diet for one reason or another or who received a supplement of phenylalanine while on the deficient diet eventually showed arrest of the physical and mental advances they had been making, with return of seizures, phenylpyruvicuria, and other biochemical abnormalities. The phenylalanine-low diet appears to be most successful when begun early, but Sutherland et al. consider that phenylketonurics who do not have the severe mental defect show a behavioral improvement even if given this regimen beyond the stage of infancy (45).

The favorable response of phenylketonurics on the phenylalanine-low diet and the deterioration observed when they receive excessive amounts of the amino acid represent strong evidence in favor of the intoxication hypothesis. Although the relation between the neurological changes and mental retardation on the one hand and the biochemical defect on the other has not been clarified yet, it appears evident that the latter is primary but not directly causative. Knowledge of the intervening processes await further research.

Woolf and Vulliamy also tested glutamic acid in some of their phenylketonuric patients (9). The total concentration of phenylalanine and its metabolic products in the urine increased in most cases, but the phenylalanine concentration in the blood remained steady. There was no increase in intelligence. The favorable influence of glutamine on the urinary excretion of phenylpyruvic and phenyllactic acids in acute experiments has brought the suggestion that this compound be tried therapeutically in phenylketonuria, in association with the phenyl-alanine-low diet (38).

## Tyrosinosis

In 1932 Medes reported the case of an individual who regularly excreted substantial amounts of $p$-hydroxyphenylpyruvic acid in the urine. To this metabolic abnormality she gave the name tyrosinosis (54). When the patient was given a diet containing increased protein or including a supplement of tyrosine the concentration of $p$-hydroxyphenylpyruvic acid in the urine increased, and in addition tyrosine and $p$-hydroxyphenyllactic acid were excreted. With the highest levels of ingested tyrosine some dopa appeared also. There was no abnormal pigmentation and no preformed melanin in the urine. That a metabolic block occurs at the $p$-hydroxyphenylpyruvic acid stage was demonstrated by the patient's ability to oxidize homogentisic acid. Many years later it was discovered that $p$-hydroxyphenylpyruvic acid is also excreted in experimental and clinical scurvy, and that supplements of vitamin C in these conditions cause the disappearance of this keto acid from the urine. When two more cases of spontaneous $p$-hydroxyphenylpy-ruvicuria were found, ascorbic acid was tested therapeutically, but without the anticipated response (55). In this way the clinical entity described by Medes was confirmed.

The unusual excretion of $p$-hydroxyphenylpyruvic acid as a result of ascorbic acid deficiency is a different type of metabolic abnormality from those described in phenylketonuria and alcaptonuria. Whereas the latter are genetically determined, the former is nutritionally con-ditioned in individuals of varying genotype. Vitamin C deficiency renders the enzyme oxidizing $p$-hydroxyphenylpyruvic acid more sus-ceptible to substrate inactivation (2). The scorbutic person excretes more tyrosine than does the normal (56). When tested with a tyrosine load (20 gm. orally) adults with scurvy excrete 7 to 15 times as much tyrosyl (*i.e.*, hydroxyphenyl) compounds as do normals, and the reducing ability of the urine toward phosphomolybdic acid is increased even more. This biochemical defect is corrected completely by a supple-ment of ascorbic acid (57). Aminoaciduria, probably of renal origin, is also present (56).

Recently it has been shown that the excretion of $p$-hydroxyphenyl-pyruvic acid is more common than previously thought. For example, it occurs frequently in liver diseases, and in many types of anemia, infection, and malignant tumors (58).

Felix' studies on the metabolism of tyrosine led him to use its keto analogue, p-hydroxyphenylpyruvic acid, in a test of liver function. The compound is normally metabolized rapidly and a healthy individual can handle as much as 5 gm. without excreting any phenolic material in the urine. In the test, 2 gm. of p-hydroxyphenylpyruvic acid are given. The excretion of more than 8 percent of the test load (as phenolic substances) in 24 hours signifies hepatic defect. Positive (abnormal) tests are found in cirrhosis, metastases to the liver, infectious hepatitis, hepatic jaundice (but not hemolytic jaundice), and in industrial chemical toxicity (59). Pathological results are found in all manic-depressive patients as well as in reactive depressions and in maniacal states (59, 60). As clinical improvement occurs a large proportion of the administered compound is metabolized (61). One inconvenience of the test is that control urines must be collected on the days preceding and succeeding the day on which p-hydroxyphenylpyruvic acid is actually administered.

## Alcaptonuria

This is a congenital defect of phenylalanine and tyrosine metabolism, which is specifically expressed in an inability to metabolize homogentisic acid. The disease has generally been considered to be inherited in a simple Mendelian recessive fashion, the recessive gene being contributed by both parents with a familial history of consanguinity, but several lineages have been described which are exceptions to this rule. The alcaptonuric individual excretes large amounts of homogentisic acid in the urine. On alkalinization of the urine this acid autoxidizes to form complex products, passing through the stages of yellow, brown, and eventually black pigment. Boedeker gave the name alcapton to this chromogen in 1859 and, incidentally, named the condition. Homogentisic acid reduces Benedict's and Fehling's reagents and so gives a false positive test for urinary sugar. However, it does not reduce alkaline bismuth solutions such as Nylander's, does not rotate polarized light, and is not fermented by yeast. The primary defect in alcaptonuria is the absence of homogentisicase from the liver (62). This enzyme catalyzes the conversion of homogentisic acid to maleylacetoacetic acid.

A second clinical characteristic of alcaptonuria is the deposition of pigment granules (homogentisate-melanin) in the cartilages, tendons, and ligaments, in the intima of the large blood vessels and the endocardium, in the kidneys, lungs, sclera, and other tissues. On gross inspection these tissues may appear dark but under the microscope the pigment is ocher in color. For this reason Virchow described the condition as *ochronosis*. Ochronosis also results from excessive absorption of phenols such as carbolic acid. Clinical symptoms may appear in the alcaptonuric adult; these have to do with arthritic changes.

## Albinism (63)

This is another striking congenital defect of tyrosine metabolism in which melanin is not formed at all. Albino skin contains the usual number of melanocytes but these cells lack tyrosinase, a copper-containing enzyme responsible for the oxidative reactions initiating the formation of melanin. The melanocytes are the only epidermal cells in which tyrosine and melanin formation are demonstrable histochemically in normal skin (64).

A related condition, vitiligo, is seen occasionally in adults. Patches of skin lose their pigmentation and develop a milky-white or ivory color. The cause and biochemical nature of vitiligo are unknown. A psychological component has occasionally been included in exploring the etiology.

There is some embryological evidence that tyrosinase-containing melanocytes originate in the central nervous system, and then migrate to the epidermis (64). This more than justifies mentioning two rare syndromes, in both of which there is an associated defect in melanin formation and in specific neural function. One of these is a syndrome described in part by Vogt in 1906 and later by Koyanagi, in which the prominent symptoms are iritis, followed by a short-lived encephalitis, and then nerve deafness and bilateral uveitis. Retinal detachment may occur. Within three months of the onset of these symptoms alopecia, poliosis and vitiligo (especially of the forehead) appear. In time the alopecia clears up, but the eye changes are not completely reversed. The syndrome has been recognized as following an attack of influenza, a transient encephalitis, or some severe emotional shock, but the cause is unknown. The primary lesion may be in the hypothalamus. Hague holds to the hypothesis of a viral origin of the syndrome (65).

The second of these syndromes in Waardenburg's. It includes the following features: broad nasal root and lateral displacement of the lacrimal puncta, medial hyperplasia of the eyebrows, heterochromia iridis, nerve deafness, and white forelock. The pigmentary defect and the deafness are related here just as they are in albinism among some of the lower mammals. Waardenburg's syndrome is an inherited disorder (66).

# References

1. KNOX, W. E. *In Amino Acid Metabolism*, ed. McELROY, W. D. and B. GLASS. Baltimore, The Johns Hopkins Press, 1955.
2. ZANNONI, V. G., and B. N. LaDu. *J. Biol. Chem. 235*:165, 1960.
3. PELLERIN, J., and A. D'IORIO. *Can. J. Biochem. Physiol. 33*:1055, 1955; SHAW, K. N. F., A. McMILLAN, and M. D. ARMSTRONG. *J. Biol. Chem. 226*:255, 1957.
4. BOSCOTT, R. J., and H. BICKEL. *Scand. J. Clin. Lab. Invest. 5*:380, 1953.
5. ARMSTRONG, M. D., K. N. F. SHAW, and K. S. ROBINSON. *J. Biol. Chem. 213*:797, 1955.
6. ARMSTRONG, M. D., K. N. F. SHAW, and P. E. WALL. *J. Biol. Chem. 218*:293, 1956.
7. JERVIS, G. A. *Proc. Soc. Exp. Biol. Med. 75*:83, 1950.
8. STEIN, W. H. *J. Biol. Chem. 201*:45, 1953.
9. WOOLF, L. I., and D. G. VULLIAMY. *Arch. Dis. Child. 26*:487, 1951.
10. STEIN, W. H., A. C. PALADINI, C. H. W. HIRS, and S. MOORE. *J. Am. Chem. Soc. 76*:2848, 1954.
11. WRIGHT, S. W., and G. TARJAN. *Am. J. Dis. Child. 93*:405, 1957.
12. ARMSTRONG, M. D., F. C. CHAO, V. J. PARKER, and P. E. WALL. *Proc. Soc. Exp. Biol. Med. 90*:675, 1955.
13. JERVIS, G. A., R. J. BLOCK, D. BOLLING, and E. KANZE. *J. Biol. Chem. 134*:105, 1940.
14. BOREK, E., A. BRECHER, G. A. JERVIS, and H. WAELSCH. *Proc. Soc. Exp. Biol. Med. 75*:86, 1950.
15. ARMSTRONG, M. D., and F. H. TYLER. *J. Clin. Invest. 34*:565, 1955.
16. HIER, S. W., and O. BERGEIM. *J. Biol. Chem. 163*:129, 1946.
17. YOUNG, M. K., JR., H. K. BERRY, E. BEERSTECHER, JR., and J. S. BERRY. *The Univ. Texas Publ. No. 5109*:189, 1951.
18. GORODKOVA, T. M. *Voprosy Fiziol. 211*, 1953; *seen in Chem. Abstr. 50*: 6652i, 1956.
19. DOTSENKO, N. P. *Voprosy Fiziol. 229*, 1953; *seen in Chem. Abstr. 50*:5895f, 1956.
20. POROSHINA, A. A. *Zhur. Nevropatol. i Psikh. 55*:266, 1955; *seen in Chem. Abstr. 51*:1435f, 1957.
21. McGEER, P. L., E. G. McGEER, and W. C. GIBSON. *Science 123*:1029, 1956.
22. McGEER, P. L., E. G. McGEER, and J. E. BOULDING. *Science 123*:1078, 1956.
23. BOGOCH, S. *A. M. A. Arch. Neurol. Psychiat. 78*:539, 1957; *idem, Am. J. Psychiat. 114*:261, 1957.
24. ACHESON, R. M., R. M. PAUL, and R. V. TOMLINSON. *Can. J. Biochem. Physiol. 36*:295, 1958; SMITH, D. M., R. M. PAUL, E. G. McGEER, and P. L. McGEER. *ibid. 37*:1493, 1959; ACHESON, R. M., and D. P. DEARNALEY. *ibid. 38*:503, 1960.

25. Mann, J. D., and E. H. LaBrosse. *A. M. A. Arch. Gen. Psychiat. 1*:547, 1959.
26. Rose, W. C., and R. L. Wixom. *J. Biol. Chem. 217*:95, 1955.
27. Rose, W. C., B. E. Leach, M. J. Coon, and G. F. Lambert. *J. Biol. Chem. 213*:913, 1955.
28. Paine, R. S., D. Y. Y. Hsia, H. H. Hsia, and K. Driscoll. *A. M. A. J. Dis. Child. 94*:224, 1957.
29. Schrappe, O. *Nervenartz 23*:175, 1952; Jervis, G. A. *Proc. Assoc. Res. Nerv. Ment. Dis. 33*:259, 1954.
30. Fölling, A. *Z. physiol. Chem. 227*:169, 1934.
31. Jervis, G. A. *Proc. Soc. Exp. Biol. Med. 82*:514, 1953; Wallace, H. W., K. Moldave, and A. Meister, *ibid. 94*:632, 1957.
32. Udenfriend, S., and S. P. Bessman. *J. Biol. Chem. 203*:961, 1953.
33. Armstrong, M. D., and N. L. Low. *Proc. Soc. Exp. Biol. Med. 94*:142, 1957.
34. Armstrong, M. D., and K. S. Robinson. *Arch. Biochem. Biophys. 52*:287, 1954.
35. Jervis, G. A. *Proc. Soc. Exp. Biol. Med. 81*:715, 1952.
36. Hsia, D. Y., K. W. Driscoll, W. Troll, and W. E. Knox. *Nature 178*: 1239, 1956.
37. Knox, W. E., and E. C. Messinger. *Am. J. Human Genet. 10*:53, 1958.
38. Meister, A., S. Udenfriend, and S. P. Bessman. *J. Clin. Invest. 35*:619, 1956.
39. Fellman, J. H. *J. Neurol. Neurosurg. Psychiat. 21*:58, 1958.
40. Miyamoto, M., and T. B. Fitzpatrick. *Nature 179*:199, 1957.
41. Sourkes, T. L., and A. D'Iorio. *In Metabolic Inhibitors, ed.* Hochster, R., and J. H. Quastel, New York, Academic Press. In press.
42. Weil-Malherbe, H. *J. Ment. Sci. 101*:733, 1955.
43. Bickis, I. J., J. P. Kennedy, and J. H. Quastel. *Nature 179*:1124, 1957.
44. Hanson, A. *Naturwiss. 45*:423, 1958; Tashian, R. E. *Metabolism Clin. & Exp. 10*:393, 1961.
45. Sutherland, B., H. K. Berry, and H. C. Shirkey. *J. Pediat. 57*:521, 1960.
46. Mitoma, C., H. S. Posner, D. F. Bogdanski, and S. Udenfriend. *J. Pharmacol. Exp. Therap. 120*:188, 1957.
47. Sherwin, C. P., and K. S. Kennard. *J. Biol. Chem. 40*:259, 1919.
48. Allen, D. W., and W. A. Schroeder. *J. Clin. Invest. 36*:1343, 1957.
49. Block, R. J., G. A. Jervis, D. Bolling, and M. Webb. *J. Biol. Chem. 134*: 567, 1940.
50. Auerbach, V. H., H. A. Waisman, and L. B. Wycoff. *Nature 182*:871, 1958.
51. Waisman, H. A., H. L. Wang, H. Harlow, and R. R. Sponholz. *Proc. Soc. Exp. Biol. Med. 101*:864, 1959.
52. Penrose, L., and J. H. Quastel. *Biochem. J. 31*:266, 1937.
53. Bickel, H., J. Gerrard, and E. M. Hickmans. *Lancet ii*:812, 1953; Woolf, L. I., R. Griffiths, and A. Moncrieff. *Brit. Med. J. i*:57, 1955; Horner, F. A., C. W. Streamer, D. E. Clader, L. I. Hassell, E. L. Binkley, Jr., and K. W. Dumars, Jr. *A. M. A. Dis. Child. 93*:615, 1957.

54. Medes, G. *Biochem. J. 26*:917, 1932.
55. Felix, K., G. Leonhardi, and I. von Glasenapp. *Z. physiol. Chem. 287:* 141, 1951.
56. Huismans, T. H. J., and J. H. P. Jonxis. *Arch. Dis. Child. 32*:77, 1957.
57. Rogers, W. F., Jr., and F. Gardner. *J. Clin. Invest. 28*:806, 1949.
58. Gros, H., and E. J. Kirnberger. *Klin. Wochschr. 32*:115, 1954.
59. Felix, K. *Schweiz. Med. Wochschr. 78*:1165, 1948.
60. Albert, E. *Nervenarzt 12*:542, 1949.
61. Chemnitz, H. J. *Nervenarzt 23*:31, 1952.
62. Seegmiller, J. E., B. N. LaDu, V. G. Zannoni, and L. Laster. *J. Clin. Invest. 36*:928, 1957.
63. Lerner, A. B., and T. B. Fitzpatrick. *Physiol. Rev. 30*:91, 1950; Lerner, A. B. *Adv. in Enzymol. 14*:73, 1953.
64. Fitzpatrick, T. B., S. W. Becker, A. B. Lerner, and H. Montgomery. *Science 112*:223, 1950; Becker, S. W., T. B. Fitzpatrick, and H. Montgomery. *A. M. A. Arch. Dermatol. Syph. 65*:511, 1952.
65. Hague, E. B. *Arch. Ophthalmol. 31*:520, 1944.
66. Partington, M. W. *Arch. Dis. Child. 34*:154, 1959; DiGeorge, A. M., R. W. Olmsted, and R. D. Harley. *J. Pediat. 57*:649, 1960.

# 6

## TRYPTOPHAN

A substance giving specific color reactions, now known to be those of tryptophan, was recognized in animal tissues as long ago as 1825, but the amino acid itself was not isolated until 1901. A few years later tryptophan was recognized to be an essential component of the diet of mammals, being required for the synthesis of proteins and other constituents. It follows many metabolic pathways in the organism, and this is reflected in the variety of metabolic products derived from it: kynurenine and 3-hydroxykynurenine; the quinaldic acids, kynurenic and xanthurenic; anthranilic and 3-hydroxyanthranilic acids; quinolinic, picolinic, and nicotinic acids; indoleacetic and 5-hydroxyindoleacetic acids; tryptamine and 5-hydroxytryptamine (5HT, serotonin). Unlike some of the other essential amino acids, tryptophan can be utilized for growth in some species in its D-form as well as in its naturally occurring L-modification, but D-tryptophan does not play a significant role in human metabolism.

Once the structure of tryptophan had been elucidated it was inevitable that the compound should be considered a precursor of the indole formed in bacterial fermentation, as occurs in the intestinal tract. The toxic actions of indole, skatole, and related compounds on the central nervous system led Herter to suggest that such compounds play a role in schizophrenia, but the hypothesis did not stand up to the evidence mustered by Folin. After 1920 Buscaino proposed a similar theory. Later, nicotinic acid was found to be a product of tryptophan metabolism in animals and man, and the etiological relationship of niacin deficiency to pellagra was recognized; this established one type of link between tryptophan metabolism and mental disease. Currently, the metabolic pathway that has focused attention on tryptophan and the indoles in psychiatry is the one which leads to 5HT. The existence of a compound with the vasoconstrictor properties of 5HT had been postulated over 50 years ago, but the substance responsible was isolated from animal sources, identified, and synthesized only in the period 1947–52. Its presence in the brain, where it is differentially distributed among the various functional regions, has aroused intense interest because of a role suggested for 5HT in the pathogenesis of mental diseases.

## Pathways of Tryptophan Metabolism

The most complex path is that which results in the ultimate oxidation of the carbon skeleton of tryptophan; it may represent a major route in the degradation of the amino acid (1). Initially the indolic ring of tryptophan is cleaved by a specific pyrrolase and this reaction is followed by hydrolysis, yielding formic acid and kynurenine as products. Oxidation of the kynurenine to its 3-hydroxylated derivative and the loss of most of the side chain then follow, with the formation of 3-hydroxyanthranilic acid. This compound undergoes a further cleavage, in which an aliphatic product, aminoacroleylfumaric acid, is formed and rapidly funneled into enzymic systems catalyzing its complete oxidation to carbon dioxide and water. A small portion pursues another course than that described: it recyclizes to yield three related compounds, quinolinic acid (whose formation in this way is reversible); picolinic acid (by $\beta$-decarboxylation and condensation to the ring structure); and nicotinic acid (by $\alpha$-decarboxylation). Of these three ring compounds nicotinic acid is formed in the largest quantity and is by far the most important in the body's economy. It enters metabolism by conversion to nicotinamide, which is a constituent of the pyridine nucleotides (Chapters 15 and 18). Prior to its excretion it is methylated on the pyridine nitrogen atom to form N'-methylnicotinamide, and some of this is oxidized to form N'-methyl-2-pyridone-5-carboxamide.

Normally the urine contains small amounts of indoleacetic acid (2). This substance is formed by the oxidation of tryptamine, the decarboxylation product of tryptophan. It is possible that some comes also from indolepyruvic acid, the product of transamination of tryptophan.

Some tryptophan undergoes oxidation on the ring, forming 5-hydroxy-tryptophan. This amino acid is readily decarboxylated in many tissues to 5HT. 5HT is oxidized by monoamine oxidase in the same way as tryptamine; its terminal oxidation product is 5-hydroxyindoleacetic acid (5HIAA), another normal urinary acid. An alternative route of metabolism takes 5HT to N-substituted derivatives, such as bufotenine (3) and melatonin (4). The latter substance is 5-methoxy-N-acetyl-tryptamine, very small amounts of which have been isolated from bovine pineal glands. Melatonin has an antagonistic action toward melanophore-stimulating hormone and causes a lightening of amphibian skin (contraction of the pigment cells). It has also been found in human peripheral nerves, but its function is not yet known in the mammalian body.

Tryptophan serves as a building-block for many biologically active substances synthesized by plants, and one can depict the elements of its derivative tryptamine in many nitrogenous bases, such as psilocybin, strychnine, reserpine, harmine, harmaline, and members of the ergot family, including lysergic acid diethylamide (LSD).

Through the action of intestinal bacteria tryptophan is degraded to indole and skatole (3-methylindole). Portions of these products are absorbed from the intestinal lumen, are oxidized in the liver, and eventually appear in the urine as indoxyl (3-hydroxyindole) and 6-hydroxyskatole (5). This 6-hydroxylative pathway also operates in the metabolism of the hallucinogen, N,N-dimethyltryptamine, and of melatonin.

Two indolic pigments have been isolated from urine. They are urorosein, which is formed from indoleacetic acid, and tryptochrome (6). N-($\beta$-Indolyl-3-acryloyl)-glycine, a urinary conjugate, forms a red pigment in strong acid (7).

In the adult only 10 to 20 percent of the dietary tryptophan has been accounted for as urinary compounds. Of this fraction tryptophan itself represents about 40 percent; N'-methylnicotinamide and its pyridone, another 20 percent; anthranilic acid and indoleacetic acid, each approximately 10 percent. Kynurenine, acetylkynurenine and 3-hydroxy-kynurenine together constitute a little over 5 percent of the total known products. Indican and the 5-hydroxy group of substances are each less than 5 percent. Tryptamine is a distinctly minor constituent. This estimate leaves a high proportion of the daily intake of tryptophan with an unknown fate, and unless some other pathway leading to aromatic compounds remains to be discovered it is likely that a large amount of the amino acid is metabolized to ammonia, carbon dioxide, and water.

## Tryptophan and Its Metabolites in Body Fluids and Brain
### (Table 6-1)

Tryptophan is present in human blood plasma to the extent of 0.7 to 1.7 mg. percent; in erythrocytes the levels are about one quarter of

TABLE 6-I. TRYPTOPHAN METABOLITES IN THE URINE *

| | μmols/24 hours | |
| --- | --- | --- |
| Compound | Normal | After Tryptophan Load |
| Kynurenine | 6–21 | 9–83 |
| $N_\alpha$-Acetylkynurenine | 6–22 | 8–32 |
| 3-Hydroxykynurenine | 11–61 | 7–76 |
| Kynurenic acid | 2–19 | 30–99 |
| Xanthurenic acid | 4–15 | 18–71 |
| Anthranilic acid conjugates | | |
|   Glucuronide | 2–9 | 2–19 |
|   o-Aminohippuric acid | 15–36 | 23–94 |
| N'-Methylnicotinamide | 15–88 | — |
| N'-Methyl-2-pyridone-5-carboxamide | 34–149 | 74–213 |
| Tryptamine | 0.3–0.8 | — |
| Serotonin | 0.2–1.0 | — |
| Indoleacetic acid | 30–80 | — |
| 5-Hydroxyindoleacetic acid | 8–50 | — |

* Most of the data of Table 6-1 have been taken from Reference 8. See also References 9 and 10.

these. Hence, whole blood contains about 0.5 to 1.0 mg. percent of free tryptophan (11). Free tryptophan in the urine amounts to about 12 to 30 mg./24 hr., with an additional 18 mg. in the combined form (12). Metabolites of this amino acid in urine have been measured by paper chromatographic separation, ion exchange chromatography, or specific chemical methods. Price and his colleagues (8) have shown that some schizophrenic patients have abnormally high concentrations of certain tryptophan metabolites in their urine, but this is by no means true of all such patients. Abnormalities in the excretion of one or more tryptophan metabolites occur also in other psychoses (8).

Estimates of serum concentration vary; normal levels are below 0.3 $\mu$g./ml., and the CSF contains much less than this.

Tryptophan-loading tests have been applied as a diagnostic tool. The aim of these tests is to saturate the enzymes of tryptophan metabolism with their substrates so that any deficiencies in the concentration of these enzymes or of their coenzymes can be detected by the appearance of excess, unreacted intermediary metabolites in the urine. For example, an unduly high excretion of xanthurenic acid occurs in the course of pyridoxine deficiency, when the tryptophan-loading test is applied (13). In a study made by Price et al. (8) schizophrenic patients could be divided into two groups. Some metabolized the orally administered amino acid abnormally; the other patients showed values in the normal range. The major deviations in the schizophrenics and other psychotics following tryptophan were low N′-methyl-2-pyridone-5-carboxamide and abnormally high kynurenine, acetylkynurenine, hydroxykynurenine, kynurenic acid, and o-aminohippuric acid. Brown et al. (14) noted that their patients excreted less nicotinamide metabolite than the controls did before the loading test, but not after it. This result may indicate a relative dietary deficiency of nicotinic acid, tryptophan, or both.

The excretion of 5HIAA following the administration of tryptophan has been studied by several groups, but the results have been contradictory. Lauer et al. observed an increased output of 5HIAA in normal subjects but not in schizophrenic ones (15). Banerjee and Agarwal found opposite results (16), and other groups of investigators have seen no difference in response between the two groups (17). It is, however, generally agreed that schizophrenics excrete normal quantities of *endogenous* 5HIAA in the urine (18).

The cerebral distribution of tryptophan, 5HT, and some enzymes concerned with their metabolism has been of great interest, for the association of these substances with specific functional regions may provide important clues as to their role in central processes. High concentrations of tryptophan are found in the hypothalamus, midbrain regions, cerebellum, and pons, but not in the cerebral hemispheres or spinal cord (19).

# Pharmacological Activities of Indoles (20)

Tryptophan is without pharmacological action, but if it is given to a person previously treated with a monoamine-oxidase inhibitor, then it elicits signs of central nervous system stimulation (21). The effects may well be due to tryptamine or other amines formed from tryptophan (*cf.* Table 6-2) which accumulate, attaining toxic levels through inhibition of monoamine oxidase. In animals tryptamine has notable pharmacological actions, both central and peripheral. Low doses cause peripheral vasoconstriction, followed by hyperemia of the extremities, hypotonia, bradypnea, and exophthalmia. Larger doses (10 mg./kg. intravenously, and higher) are followed by body tremors, and the highest doses studied

TABLE 6-2

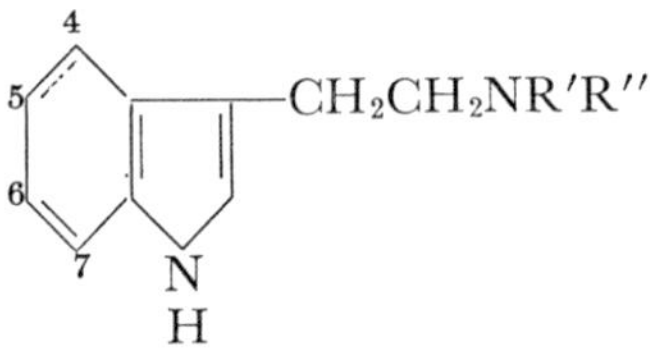

$-CH_2CH_2NR'R''$

|  | Position | | | | |
|---|---|---|---|---|---|
| Compound | 4 | 5 | 6 | R' | R'' |
| Tryptamine | H | H | H | H | H |
| Serotonin | H | OH | H | H | H |
| Melatonin | H | $CH_3O$ | H | $CH_3CO$ | H |
| Bufotenine | H | OH | H | $CH_3$ | $CH_3$ |
| Psilocybin | $O \cdot PH_2O_3$ | H | H | $CH_3$ | $CH_3$ |
| N-Diethyl-tryptamine | H | H | H | $C_2H_5$ | $C_2H_5$ |
| 6-Hydroxy-diethyltryptamine | H | H | OH | $C_2H_5$ | $C_2H_5$ |
| Bufothionine ($\alpha,\beta$-dehydro) | H | $HSO_4$ | H | $CH_3$ | $CH_3$ |

(40 mg./kg.) cause clonic convulsions which are not overcome with phenobarbital, diphenylhydantoin, or trimethadione (22).

The initial discovery of 5HT in blood drew attention to those functions of the amine which relate to clotting and hypertension. The high 5HT content in the platelets associated the amine with the first process, and its vasoconstrictive properties with the second. However, the concentration of 5HT in the blood and urine of patients with essential hypertension is not unduly high, and the amine has been absolved from etiological responsibility in that direction. Erspamer has stressed the prominent action of 5HT on the renal arterioles. This property renders the amine a powerful antidiuretic agent in experimental animals, but less so in man. Indeed, Erspamer has suggested that the function of 5HT lies in renal regulation.

The action of 5HT on blood vessels extends to other types of smooth muscle. Intestine, stomach, and uterus are all made to contract when treated with 5HT in pharmacological experiments. It has been shown that intestinal segments, depleted of their stores of 5HT, no longer exhibit peristaltic movement, but regain their rhythm when small amounts of 5HT are added to the medium in which they are bathed.

5HT has a number of actions on central nervous system structures. It depresses central ganglionic transmission, as tested in the transcallosal system of Marrazzi (23). Although it is not specific in this respect, it is many times more potent than the next most active substance tested, which was epinephrine. Iproniazid mimics the action of these amines. This has been interpreted as stemming from inhibition of the enzymatic oxidation of endogenous amines, thereby permitting their accumulation in the brain. It is believed that when sufficient endogenous 5HT has accumulated in the perisynaptic region the amine exerts inhibitory action (24).

5HT, together with adrenochrome, epinephrine and LSD, causes a reduction in the amplitude and frequency of spontaneous electrical activity of the brain. The similarity of action of the four drugs suggests that they are all active at the same site, possibly in the reticular formation (25). 5HT is one of the compounds which, upon intraventricular injection, causes cataleptic behavior (26).

The intravenous infusion of 5HT in man causes flushing of the skin of the head and neck. There are no specific subjective symptoms, and this agrees with the demonstrated impermeability of 5HT through the blood-brain barrier in experimental animals. Hence the question of central actions of this amine in the intact animal or in man cannot be answered by this type of infusion experiment. However, it has been shown that the administration of 5-hydroxytryptophan (5HTP), the precursor of 5HT, raises the level of the amine in the brain and other tissues (27). This occurs because of the penetration of the amino acid into the brain, where it is rapidly decarboxylated. Very large doses of 5HTP are required to produce pharmacologic effects, and the actions are potentiated by a monoamine-oxidase inhibitor such as iproniazid. The main effects of 5HTP in the rat are severe diarrhea and cutaneous vasoconstriction, the latter followed by hyperemia. Woolley et al. have shown how to circumvent these peripheral effects of 5HTP: they pretreat their animals with 1-benzyl-2-methyl-5-methoxytryptamine (BAS), a synthetic antiserotonin agent. Such animals appear lethargic, but ultimately they convulse, concomitant with the increase in cerebral 5HT

(28). 5HTP has been tested in humans also. Its infusion causes the same effects as in animals. Because of the serious diarrhea it is impossible to give enough to determine whether there are effects upon the central nervous system (10), but if the subjects receiving the amino acid are first prepared with BAS, then the peripheral effects are abolished and larger amounts of 5HPT can be given (see below).

BAS has been studied in its own right as a tranquilizing agent (30). In doses up to 200 mg./day, given to patients with chronic psychoses, it causes a feeling of weakness and fatigue. Some patients exhibit ataxia. Its sedative action is like that of reserpine.

N-Dimethylserotonin, or bufotenine, has been reported to have hallucinogenic activity when it is administered intravenously in doses up to 16 mg. (31). It causes a desynchronized, alerting pattern of the electroencephalogram (32). Bufotenine has been identified in the Caribbean phantasticum cohoba (*Piptadenia peregrina*), of which it may be an active ingredient. Other indoles with hallucinogenic actions are N-dimethyltryptamine (33, 34), which also occurs in *Piptadenia,* and N-diethyltryptamine (35). These bring about their effects in doses of about 0.6 to 1.0 mg./kg., beginning within a few minutes of intramuscular injection and lasting for about an hour. However, Turner and Merlis reported negative results with bufotenine (34).

Another remarkable drug of the indolethylamine series is 4-O-phosphoryl-N-dimethyltryptamine, or psilocybin. This is found in mushrooms of the genus *Psilocybe* and of others, and it is considered the active principle of the "holy" mushrooms used by the curanderos of the highland villages of southern Mexico in their ceremonies. Doses of psilocybin, in the range of 0.2 to 0.5 mg./kg., are said to induce a hallucinatory episode, just as during the ritual eating of the mushrooms (36). Despite its structural resemblance to 5HT and, therefore, the possibility of its exerting an antimetabolite action, psilocybin does not affect the metabolism of endogenous 5HT, as measured by the urinary excretion of 5HIAA (37). Delay and his colleagues have given an extensive description of the mental effects of this drug (38).

Indole itself has a toxic action upon the central nervous system. As much as 2 gm. by mouth are required to elicit effects in man. These are restlessness, insomnia, headache, and sometimes dizziness or a sense of fatigue (39). The dose required to produce these effects is very much higher than the amount of indole available from bacterial action in the intestines.

# Serotonin (40)

## BIOSYNTHESIS AND METABOLIC FATE

The origin of 5HT from tryptophan by way of 5HTP has already been mentioned. Following the injection of 5HTP into animals it is possible to detect 5HT in many tissues, even those that do not normally contain this amine (27, 29). The enzyme oxidizing tryptophan to 5HTP is probably much more restricted in its distribution than is the decarboxylase, but there are as yet few data available on this subject. The major site of formation of these 5-hydroxy compounds is in the enterochromaffin Kulschitzky cells, found principally in the mucosa of the small intestine (41).

The main product of 5HT metabolism is 5HIAA, which is present free as well as conjugated with glycine in urine. The mono- and di-methylated derivatives of 5HT probably yield the same end product as 5HT itself, but this is not so for the trimethyl quaternary ammonium base, bufotenidine (42). Actually, the immediate oxidation product of 5HT is 5-hydroxyindoleacetaldehyde, a highly reactive intermediate which can be trapped in enzymatic experiments with carbonyl reagents such as semicarbazide. The aldehyde derivatives of tryptamine and 5HT are the source of the brownish pigments formed when these amines are incubated with crude extracts of tissue containing monoamine oxidase. Under physiological conditions the aldehydes are readily oxidized a further stage, probably by aldehyde dehydrogenase, to indoleacetic acid and 5HIAA, respectively.

## CONTENT OF 5HT IN THE TISSUES

5HT occurs in many tissues but most prominently in the intestine, brain, and platelets. Its distribution in the brain is shown in Table 23-1. According to Erspamer (43) 5HT is released from the entero-chromaffin tissue in the intestine into the circulation and it is con-centrated by the platelets. These elements store it until it is released once more, as in the clotting process (43, 44). Small amounts of 5HT are regularly excreted in the urine but the main metabolite there is the corresponding acid, 5HIAA.

The normal concentrations of 5HT in the organs are such that were the amine present in the free state, *i.e.*, in solution in the cytoplasmic sap, and were it freely diffusible, profound pharmacologic effects could be anticipated. Actually the amount of 5HT in the free state is probably small, certainly much less than that found when the tissue is excised, ground, and extracted. In other words, a reservoir of 5HT exists which is drawn upon for whatever physiologic functions this agent performs. The action of reserpine is instructive in this respect: administration of this drug is followed by the loss of 5HT from the tissues (45), as well as by the excretion of increased amounts of 5HIAA, derived from the 5HT stores in the body. This lasts for a few hours after which the rate becomes normal once more (46). With chronic administration of reserpine, the blood 5HT is no longer measurable; on withdrawal of the drug the 5HT returns to normal very slowly (47). The results using reserpine have led to the concept of a bound form of 5HT which is released by application of the appropriate physiologic stimulus or by certain drugs, of which reserpine is the prime example. Binding of amines to subcellular fragments is already well known in the case of the catecholamines and the fact that reserpine also causes the release of norepinephrine from the brain suggests that there may be a common mechanism of binding for these compounds and for 5HT.

## ROLE OF HT IN NEURAL AND MENTAL PROCESSES

Many years ago Masson and Berger described a relationship between the nervous structures of the intestine and the 5HT-secreting Kulschitzky cells there (48). They found evidence for the migration, in certain abnormal conditions, of the argentaffin cells into the surrounding nervous plexus, with transfer of secretory granules of the former to the nerves. They described this as intraneuronal secretion, to distinguish it from endocrine secretion into the blood. The identification of 5HT in the brain (49, 50) and the establishment of its presence there in relatively high concentrations in specific locations (50) have raised anew the question of the relation of 5HT to the nervous system. When the action of 5HT on smooth muscle was found to be antagonized by the powerful hallucinogenic agent LSD it was suggested that this antagonism has a parallel within the nervous system, and that the subjective experience following the ingestion of LSD may be accountable as a biological antagonism of the (unknown) physiological action of 5HT in the brain (50). It has been pointed out that this antagonism does not offer a completely rounded argument because of the fact that many drugs having anti-5HT actions on smooth muscle preparations lack hallucinogenic effects. Among such drugs is the 2-bromo derivative of LSD (BOL). Furthermore the LSD-5HT antagonism is not consistent for a variety of biological preparations (51). Woolley and Shaw have nevertheless concluded from their studies on alkaloidal and synthetic antimetabolites of 5HT that the latter compound is probably present in low concentration in the brain of psychotic patients (52).

The next finding that implicated 5HT in mental processes was the action of reserpine previously mentioned: after adequate reserpine dosage in animals there is a depletion of the 5HT content of the tissues, including the brain. The specificity of this action is illustrated by the fact that the *Rauwolfia* alkaloids which induce sedation also affect the binding of 5HT, but those without biological activity lack this action (*cf.* Chapter 28). Some benzoquinolizines and other synthetic compounds have a similar action upon the metabolism of 5HT (53). Neurophysiological data on the relation of 5HT insufficiency to the sedative effects of these compounds are urgently required.

Brodie and Shore have brought together many of the experimental facts which tend to show that the pharmacological actions of reserpine are mediated through 5HT in a specific way. These authors state that the parasympathomimetic actions of reserpine are correlated with low levels of 5HT in the brain. The reverse situation can be produced experimentally by injecting reserpine into animals pretreated with iproniazid: now the animals have a high cerebral content of free 5HT and they show signs of excitement and sympathomimetic effects comparable to those caused by LSD or 5HTP. An obvious difficulty in this argument is the fact that norepinephrine and other amines are also lost from the brain as a result of treatment with reserpine. Brodie et al. assert, however, that the sedative action of reserpine is more closely associated with the fall in cerebral 5HT; this is based upon studies on the differential decrease in the brain 5HT and norepinephrine under the influence of a series of reserpinelike compounds (54). These investigators have, therefore, proposed the existence of serotonergic innervation in the central nervous system, passing to centers regulating homeostasis through the autonomic nervous system (55). 5HT would be the transmitter at synapses of these serotonergic fibers and its long-lasting action would be evident when the endogenously formed amine could not be bound (reserpinized animal) or detoxified by the action of monoamine oxidase (iproniazid-treated animal). Transmission would be blocked by excessively high and persisting concentrations of 5HT, as in animals given 5HTP: these show an excited behavior.

Electroshock in man does not influence the 5HT concentration in the blood (47) but it does cause a large and rapid increase in the 5HT content of the brain, along with a fall in intestinal 5HT, in experimental animals (56).

It can be seen that many facts point to a role of 5HT in cerebral processes, and some of them have fostered speculation as to the function of this amine in the pathogenesis of psychoses. Data conflicting with the serotonin hypothesis of schizophrenia have also been adduced, and it is clear that the evidence favoring the hypothesis is by no means decisive, but only suggestive for further experiments. Bleuler has recognized the outstanding opportunity offered by these recent discoveries in the field of 5HT biochemistry and pharmacology for studying the relationship of cerebral metabolism to psychic activity, but he is sharply critical of attempts to weave the facts presently at hand into a simple concept of the etiology of schizophrenia (57), an assessment in which others concur (58). Therapeutic trials based upon the hypothesis of Woolley and Shaw have been carried out in several clinics. In one of them chronic schizophrenic patients were given BAS, BAS together with 5HTP (to raise the concentration of cerebral 5HT without eliciting the peripheral actions of the amine), or BAS, 5HTP, and iproniazid together (the last to maintain the amine levels as high as possible) (59). No combination of drugs was useful. Woolley refers to the results of four different trials of combined BAS and 5HTP treatment (60). Three of 12 patients treated in this way showed favorable responses at the beginning, but failed to maintain the reported gain.

## MALIGNANT CARCINOID

In 1930 Cassidy (61) described a patient who had severe flushes, recurrent attacks of diarrhea, chest pain, and dyspnea. The next year Scholte (62) reported upon a metastasizing tumor of the small intestine, originating in the enterochromaffin cells of the mucosa; this patient exhibited cardiac insufficiency, pulmonary stenosis, and skin changes. These respective clinical and pathological pictures have been recognized within the last few years to be merely different aspects of a syndrome known variously as malignant carcinoid, argentaffinoma, or Kulschitzky cell carcinoma (63). The demonstration by Lembeck (64) of the presence of a large amount of 5HT in extracts of the tumor has lent biochemical interest to this condition.

Large amounts of 5HT are constantly released from the carcinoid tumor and its metastases. The blood 5HT level is usually high, especially during the flush, as is the concentration in the urine. Urinary histamine is also high, but this may be merely a reflection of the effectiveness of

5HT as a histamine releaser. As might be expected the released 5HT is oxidized by monoamine oxidase so that increased amounts of 5HIAA are found in the urine. Indeed, the 5HIAA excretion may rise many times above the normal output, and demonstration of excessive 5HIAA excretion is a valuable aid in the diagnosis of the argentaffinoma. 5HTP, the precursor amino acid giving rise to 5HT, has been identified in the urine of a patient having metastases of the carcinoid tumor in the kidney (65). 5HTP is usually not present in the urine. Symptoms of nicotinic acid deficiency occur in some carcinoid patients. This finding is not difficult to understand on the basis of the biochemical relationship in this disease. Thus, tryptophan is the dietary precursor not only of 5HT but of nicotinic acid also, and though the amount of the latter is not considerable it may assume some importance if the diet is already marginal in its nicotinic acid content; when tryptophan metabolism is diverted to an abnormally large extent into 5HT production, deficiency symptoms may appear. The diarrhea characteristic of the malignant carcinoid syndrome also contributes significantly to failure of absorption of essential dietary constituents.

No specific mental symptoms have been associated with this disease.

## Indole Metabolism in Phenylketonuria

Indolepyruvic and indolelactic acids have been identified in the urine of phenylketonuric patients. These substances are distinctly minor constituents of urine normally so that their excessive excretion in phenylketonuria must be considered pathological. Whether they have a primary toxic action on the brain or not is an open question at present. It has been suggested that the biochemical lesion in phenylpyruvic disease—the defect in the oxidation of phenylalanine to tyrosine—has a parallel in the deficient formation of 5HTP from tryptophan, with a diversion of more of the available tryptophan into the transaminative or deaminative pathway. This would give rise to a larger proportion of the keto analog of tryptophan and of its reduction product, indolelactic acid. The lower serum level of 5HT in phenylketonuria (66) fits into this picture, but the block in the 5-hydroxylative pathway is not complete. Pare et al. (67) have reported a decreased activity of 5HTP decarboxylase in phenylketonuria, a finding that agrees with the inhibition of this enzyme by some of the abnormal metabolites encountered in phenylketonuria, such as phenylpyruvic, phenyllactic, and phenylacetic acids (68). Baldridge et al. have shown that the phenylketonuric fed on a low-phenylalanine diet excretes much more 5HIAA than untreated phenylketonurics (69).

## Hartnup Disease

This is a rare condition, characterized as a clinical entity of hereditary nature. It is manifested in affected persons by a pellagralike skin rash, somewhat intensified by exposure to sunlight; cerebellar ataxia, mental retardation (70), or psychosis (71) ; renal aminoaciduria; excretion of large amounts of certain indoles in the urine; and increased protoporphyrin in the feces. The resemblance to pellagra is striking and cases of Hartnup disease may receive this diagnosis first (70, 71).

Baron et al. (70) have described the occurrence of a specific pattern of aminoaciduria in four siblings of a first-cousins' marriage. One of the four excreted 0.5 to 1.1 gm. of amino nitrogen daily. The amino acids excreted in excessive amounts were: alanine, glutamine, histidine, isoleucine, leucine, phenylalanine, serine, tryptophan, and tyrosine. The proportions of these were approximately the same in the four siblings (72). Plasma amino acid levels were within normal limits. The defect leading to the aminoaciduria is in renal tubular reabsorption.

Indolic compounds found in the urine in large amounts, other than tryptophan, were indoxylsulfate, indoleacetic acid, and N-(3-indoleacetyl)-glutamine (70, 73). Administration of tryptophan did not affect the amount of indican excreted, but following treatment with aureomycin the indicanuria disappeared. The excretion of nicotinic acid, nicotinamide, and N'-methylnicotinamide is somewhat low, but within normal limits.

Urinary porphyrins and porphobilinogen are normal in quantity, as far as this has been investigated, but the fecal porphyrin excretion is increased.

Because of the diagnosis of pellagra for his patient, Hersov administered nicotinamide and found it of benefit (71). Baron and his colleagues used nicotinamide also in the treatment of two patients during the course of exacerbations of the disease (70). This therapy paralleled improvement in the patients' condition, but it was not clear if the two were related, because of the tendency to spontaneous remission.

## References

1. Dalgliesh, C. E., and H. Tabechian. *Biochem. J.* *62*:625, 1956.
2. Dietrich, J., and R. Müller. *Naturwiss.* *38*:561, 1951; Wieland, O. P., R. S. De Ropp, and J. Avener. *Nature 173*:776, 1954.

3. Bumpus, F. M., and I. H. Page. *J. Biol. Chem.* *212*:111, 1955.

4. Lerner, A. B. *Federation Proc.* *19*:590, 1960.

5. Horning, E. C., C. C. Sweeley, C. E. Dalgliesh, and W. Kelly. *Biochim. et Biophys. Acta* *32*:566, 1959.

6. Fearon, W. R., and W. A. Boggust. *Biochem. J.* *46*:62, 1950.

7. Kimmig, J., W. Sticherling, R. Tschesche, and H. G. Urbach. *Z. Physiol. Chem.* *311*:234, 1958.

8. Price, J. M., R. R. Brown, and H. A. Peters. *Neurology* *9*:456, 1959.

9. Rodnight, R. *Biochem. J.* *64*:621, 1956.

10. Weissbach, H., W. King, A. Sjoerdsma, and S. Udenfriend. *J. Biol. Chem.* *234*:81, 1959.

11. Johnson, C. A., and O. Bergeim. *J. Biol. Chem.* *188*:833, 1951.

12. Woodson, H. W., S. W. Hier, J. D. Solomon, and O. Bergeim. *J. Biol. Chem.* *172*:613, 1948.

13. Knapp, A. *Klin. Wochschr.* *38*:74, 1960.

14. Brown, F. C., J. B. White, Jr., and J. J. Kennedy. *Am. J. Psychiat.* *117*:63, 1960.

15. Lauer, J. W., W. M. Inskip, J. Bernsohn, and E. A. Zeller. *A. M. A. Arch. Neurol. Psychiat.* *80*:122, 1958.

16. Banerjee, S., and P. S. Agarwal. *Proc. Soc. Exp. Biol. Med.* *97*:657, 1958.

17. Kopin, I. J. *Science* *129*:835, 1959; Shaw, C. R., J. Lucas, and R. D. Rabinovitch. *A. M. A. Arch. Gen. Psychiat.* *1*:366, 1959.

18. Rodnight, R., and H. McIlwain. *Brit. Med. J.* *i*:108, 1956; Buscaino, G. A., and L. Stefanachi. *A. M. A. Arch. Neurol. Psychiat.* *80*:78, 1958.

19. Price, S. A. P., and G. B. West. *Nature* *185*:470, 1960.

20. Erspamer, V. *Pharmacol. Rev.* *6*:425, 1954; Sprince, H. *Clinical Chem.* *7*:203, 1961.

21. Sjoerdsma, A., J. A. Oates, P. Zaltzman, and S. Udenfriend. *J. Pharmacol. Exp. Ther.* *126*:217, 1959; Pollin, W., P. V. Cardon, Jr., and S. S. Kety. *Science* *133*:104, 1961.

22. Tedeschi, D. H., R. E. Tedeschi, and E. J. Fellows. *J. Pharmacol. Exp. Ther.* *126*:223, 1959.

23. Marrazzi, A. C., and E. R. Hart. *Science* *121*:365, 1955.

24. Gluckman, M. I., E. R. Hart, and A. S. Marrazzi. *Science* *126*:448, 1957.

25. Slocombe, A. G., H. Hoagland, and L. S. Tozian. *Am. J. Physiol.* *185*:601, 1956.

26. Feldberg, W., and S. L. Sherwood. *J. Physiol.* *123*:148, 1954.

27. Udenfriend, S., H. Weissbach, and D. F. Bogdanski. *J. Biol. Chem.* *224*:803, 1957.

28. Woolley, D. W., E. Van Winkle, and E. N. Shaw. *Proc. Natl. Acad. Sci. U.S.* *43*:128, 1957.

29. Davidson, J., A. Sjoerdsma, L. N. Loomis, and S. Udenfriend. *J. Clin. Invest.* *36*:1594, 1957.

30. Rudy, L. H., E. Costa, F. Rinaldi, and H. E. Himwich. *J. Nerv. Ment. Dis.* *126*:284, 1958.

31. Fabing, H. D., and J. R. Hawkins. *Science* *123*:886, 1956.

32. Rinaldi, F. *J. Nerv. Ment. Dis.* *126*:272, 1958.

33. BOSZORMENYI, Z., and S. SZARA, *J. Ment. Sci. 104:*445, 1958.
34. TURNER, W. J., and S. MERLIS. *A. M. A. Arch. Neurol. Psychiat. 81:*121, 1959.
35. BOSZORMENYI, Z., P. DER, and T. NAGY. *J. Ment. Sci. 105:*171, 1959.
36. HOFMANN, A., R. HEIM, A. BRACK, and H. KOBEL. *Experientia 14:*107, 1958; CERLETTI, A. *Deutsch. Med. Wochschr. 84:*2317, 1959.
37. WISEMAN-DISTLER, M. H., and T. L. SOURKES. *Annals N.Y. Acad. Sci. 96:* 142, 1962.
38. DELAY, J., P. PICHOT, and T. LEMPERIENNE. *Presse Médicale 67:*1731, 1959.
39. HERTER, C. A. *N.Y. Med. J. 68:*89, 1898.
40. PAGE, I. H. *Physiol. Rev. 34:*563, 1954; *idem, 38:*277, 1958; LANGEMANN, H. *Schweitz. Med. Wochschr. 85:*957, 1955.
41. ERSPAMER, V. *Rendiconti Scient. Farmitalia 1:*5, 1954; BARTER, R., and A. G. E. PEARSE, *J. Path. Bacteriol. 69:*25, 1955; DALGLIESH, C. E., and R. W. DUTTON. *Brit. J. Cancer 11:*296, 1957.
42. ERSPAMER, V. *J. Physiol. 127:*118, 1955; *idem, 133:*1, 1956.
43. ERSPAMER, V., and A. TESTINI. *J. Pharmacy Pharmacol. 11:*618, 1959.
44. HUMPHREY, J. H., and C. C. TOH. *J. Physiol. 124:*300, 1954; HARDISTY, R. M., and R. S. STACEY. *J. Physiol. 130:*711, 1955.
45. PLETSCHER, A., P. A. SHORE, and B. B. BRODIE. *J. Pharmacol. Exp. Ther. 116:*84, 1956.
46. ERSPAMER, V., and C. CICERI. *Experientia 13:*87, 1957; TODRICK, A., M. DICK, and A. C. TAIT. *Brit. Med. J. i:*496, 1958.
47. GREEN, J. P., M. K. PAASONEN, and N. J. GIARMAN. *Proc. Soc. Exp. Biol. Med. 94:*428, 1957.
48. MASSON, P., and L. BERGER. *Compt. rend. Acad. Sci. (Paris) 176:*1748, 1923.
49. TWAROG, B. M., and I. H. PAGE. *Am. J. Physiol. 175:*157, 1953.
50. AMIN, A. H., T. B. B. CRAWFORD, and J. H. GADDUM. *J. Physiol. 126:*596, 1954.
51. GADDUM, J. H. *Annals N.Y. Acad. Sci. 66:*663, 1957.
52. WOOLLEY, D. W., and E. SHAW. *Brit. Med. J. ii:*122, 1954.
53. PLETSCHER, A., H. BESENDORF, and H. P. BÄCHTOLD. *Confin. Neurol. 18:* 137, 1958.
54. BRODIE, B. B., K. F. FINGER, F. B. ORLANS, G. P. QUINN, and F. SULSER. *J. Pharmacol. Exp. Ther. 129:*250, 1960.
55. BRODIE, B. B., and P. A. SHORE. *Annals N.Y. Acad. Sci. 66:*631, 1957.
56. GARATTINI, S., A. VALSECCHI, and L. VALZELLI. *Experientia 13:*330, 1957.
57. BLEULER, M. *Deutsch. Med. Wochschr. 81:*1084, 1956; *German Med. Monthly 1:*272, 1956.
58. SOURKES, T. L. *Canad. Psychiat. Assoc. J. 1:*73, 1956; KETY, S. S. *Science 129:*1528, 1590, 1959; SOURKES, T. L. *Canad. Med. Assoc. J. 85:*487, 1961.
59. FELDSTEIN, A., H. FREEMAN, J. M. HOPE, I. M. DIBNER, and H. HOAGLAND. *Am. J. Psychiat. 116:*219, 1959.
60. WOOLLEY, D. W. *In Chemical Concepts of Psychosis, ed.* RINKEL, M., and H. C. B. DENBER, New York, McDowell, Obolensky, 1958.

61. Cassidy, M. A. *Proc. Roy. Soc. Med. 24:*139, 1930.
62. Scholte, A. J. *Beiträge Path. Anat. 86:*440, 1931.
63. Thorson, A., G. Biörck, G. Björkman, and J. Waldenström. *Am. Heart J. 47:*795, 1954.
64. Lembeck, F. *Nature 172:*910, 1953; *idem, Arch. Exp. Path. Pharmakol. 221:*50, 1954.
65. Smith, A. N., L. M. Nyhus, C. E. Dalgliesh, R. W. Dutton, B. Lennox, and P. S. Macfarlane. *Scottish Med. J. 2:*24, 1957.
66. Pare, C. M. B., M. Sandler, and R. S. Stacey. *Lancet i:*551, 1957; *idem, Arch. Dis. Childh. 34:*422, 1959.
67. Pare, C. M. B., M. Sandler, and R. S. Stacey. *Lancet ii:*1099, 1958.
68. Davison, A. N., and M. Sandler. *Nature 181:*186, 1958.
69. Baldridge, R. C., L. Borofsky, H. Baird, F. Reichle, and D. Bullock. *Proc. Soc. Exp. Biol. Med. 100:*529, 1959.
70. Baron, D. N., C. E. Dent, H. Harris, E. W. Hart, and J. B. Jepson. *Lancet ii:*421, 1956.
71. Hersov, L. A. *J. Ment. Sci. 101:*878, 1955.
72. Evered, D. F. *Biochem. J. 62:*416, 1956.
73. Rodnight, R., and H. McIlwain. *J. Ment. Sci. 101:*884, 1955; Jepson, J. B. *Biochem. J. 64:*14P, 1956.

# 7

# HISTIDINE

## Biosynthesis and Metabolism

Histidine belongs to the group of basic amino acids by virtue of its imidazolyl group. All natural diets contain histidine as a constituent of protein. However, the amino acid can be synthesized in the body from pentose phosphate, formate, and ammonia, which condense together and undergo other changes to yield the final product.

Histidine is partitioned along several routes of metabolism. These include the formation of protein, carnosine, anserine, thiolhistidine, imidazolepyruvic acid, histamine, and glutamic acid. Carnosine is a dipeptide formed from $\beta$-alanine and histidine; anserine is an analogous compound, $\beta$-alanyl-N$^1$-methylhistidine. Both are found in skeletal muscle; their function in that tissue is unknown. Thiolhistidine and its betaine, ergothioneine, occur in erythrocytes. Their role in red blood cell metabolism has not been extensively studied, but it has been suggested that ergothioneine acts as the coenzyme for a diphosphopyridine nucleotide-splitting enzyme. Indeed, certain hydrolytic enzymes such as cholinesterase require for their action the imidazole group of the histidine linked in the peptide structure.

Transamination plays an important role in the disposal of histidine:

L-Histidine + $\alpha$-Ketoglutaric acid $\rightleftarrows$ Imidazolepyruvic acid

$+$ L-Glutamic acid   (7-1)

Not only can imidazolepyruvic acid be identified in the urine but its reduction product, imidazolelactic acid, and its oxidation product, imidazoleacetic acid, can also be found there. Another way in which imidazolepyruvic acid is formed is by the action of L-amino acid oxidase upon histidine.

Much of the body's histidine is ultimately degraded to glutamic acid, a transformation which is accomplished in a stepwise fashion. The first reaction is the loss of the α-amino group, as ammonia:

$$\text{L-Histidine} \rightarrow \quad \text{Urocanic acid} \quad + \text{Ammonia} \qquad (7\text{-}2)$$
$$\text{Im.CH}{=}\text{CHCOOH}$$

The urocanic acid is oxidized at the imidazolyl group (Im), $NH \cdot CH{=}N \cdot CH{=}C—$, following which the ring undergoes scission to formiminoglutamic acid or N-formylisoglutamine. Hydrolysis of the intermediate leads to L-glutamic acid. The over-all reaction shows the products:

$$\text{L-Histidine} + 4H_2O \rightarrow \text{L-Glutamic acid} + 2NH_3 + \text{Formic acid}$$
$$(7\text{-}3)$$

Folic acid is involved in this breakdown at the stage of transfer of the formyl group, the source of the formic acid. Thus, when folic acid is deficient in the tissues the conversion of histidine to glutamic acid is limited. Indeed, formiminoglutamic acid appears abnormally in the urine of folic acid-deficient individuals (1). Conversely, such individuals can be detected by the abnormally great excretion of formiminoglutamic acid following a metabolic loading test with histidine (2).

The choline ester of urocanic acid has been identified in certain invertebrates. It is a chemical analogue of acetylcholine. Two questions about it have not yet been answered: whether it is also a physiological analogue of acetylcholine, and whether it plays a role in mammalian metabolism.

# Histamine (3)

### FORMATION, BINDING, EXCRETION

Histamine is formed in the tissues through the decarboxylation of L-histidine:

$$\text{L-Histidine} \rightarrow \text{Histamine} + CO_2 \qquad (7\text{-}4)$$

The enzyme responsible for this conversion is found in many tissues. In the brain it is unevenly distributed, the highest concentration being found in the vermis of the cerebellum and in the hypothalamus (4). Small amounts of histamine are found in peripheral nerve (2 to 50 $\mu$g./ gm.) and brain (0.3 $\mu$g./gm.) (5). The hypothalamus and the median eminence are richer in the amine than are other parts of the brain.

Histamine is excreted in the urine at the rate of about 2 to 24 $\mu$g./day (6), but this represents only a small part of the total amount of histamine turned over (7). Another small portion is contributed by the pharmacologically inactive N-acetylhistamine. The major pathway of metabolism in man, as judged from the urinary excretion products of labeled histamine, is through methylation to 1-methyl-4-(2-aminoethyl)-imidazole. Most of this compound is oxidized by monoamine oxidase to the corresponding carboxylic acid. Another large portion of histamine is excreted as the sugar derivative ribosylimidazoleacetic acid. A substantial amount of imidazoleacetic acid itself is excreted and this, in contrast to its methylated cogener, is formed through the action of histaminase (diamine oxidase).

Very high concentrations of histamine (about 1 percent of the wet weight) have been found in the mast cells. These also store heparin, and it has been suggested that histamine is bound to this acidic compound in the cell through a salt linkage. Apparently mast cell histamine is the chief form in which this amine occurs in the adult tissues. A lower concentration of histamine is found in the platelets. Hence, most of the histamine in the body exists in "bound" form, but it can be liberated by various means. Among these are the administration of certain drugs, or chemical agents such as the polymer 48/40 (consisting of N-methyl-homoanisylamine and formaldehyde units). Tissue trauma or the occurrence of the antigen-antibody reaction also releases histamine. By way of contrast the glucocorticoids of the adrenal cortex are antagonistic to histamine: they inhibit its formation and promote its metabolic degradation. In stress the increased histamine is occasioned by an increase in the tissue content of histidine decarboxylase (8). Schayer has pointed out the possible physiological utility of this overproduction of histamine in combating ischemia resulting from release of epinephrine and non-epinephrine under conditions of stress (9). According to his hypothesis, imbalance of amine production and release may be a fundamental determinant in the shock process.

Great interest has attached to the problem of histamine for many years because of the profound pharmacological actions of this amine and its possible role in anaphylactic shock. Within the last few years there has been a rapid development of our knowledge of all aspects of this compound, but it is nevertheless still not possible to define precisely the role of histamine in physiological responses of the organism.

## METABOLISM OF HISTAMINE IN THE BRAIN

Incubation of histamine with cerebral tissue results in the formation of methylhistamine primarily. Methylimidazoleacetic acid is a lesser product, and imidazoleacetic acid formation is negligible. Histamine is oxidized at its amino group by histaminase, which belongs to the group of diamine oxidases by virtue of its substrate specificity, coenzyme requirements, and action (cf. Chapter 9). The immediate product is an aldehyde, which may possibly have pharmacological activity of its own, but which does not appear in detectable amounts among the metabolic products. It is susceptible to the action of aldehyde-oxidizing enzymes such as aldehyde dehydrogenase and xanthine oxidase. Imidazoleacetic acid is then the terminal product.

Transmethylation of histamine is a major route of its metabolism. The product has virtually no histaminelike activity. The oxidation of this compound, 1-methyl-4-(2-aminoethyl)-imidazole, is catalyzed by monoamine oxidase.

## HISTAMINE IN MENTAL DISEASE

At one time histamine underwent tests as a therapeutic agent in the psychoses (10, 11). Its release in the tissues during electroshock therapy has been presumed on the basis of observed vasodilatation (12) and an actual increase in the histamine content of the blood in insulin treatment has been reported (13). Although several studies have compared histamine therapy favorably with the other physical treatments, the use of histamine has not attained any continuous or widespread use in psychiatry.

The reported relative resistance of psychotic subjects to the actions of histamine has been attributed to an increased amount of histaminase in the serum (14). This finding is also proposed as the explanation for the infrequent manifestation of allergic disease in schizophrenic patients.

According to Leblanc and Lemieux the mast cell count of the abdominal skin is subnormal in mental patients, but is increased after a course of therapy with tranquilizers (15).

# References

1. LUHBY, A. L., J. M. COOPERMAN, D. N. TELLER, and A. M. DONNENFELD. *J. Clin. Invest. 37*:915, 1958; BROQUIST, H. P., and A. L. LUHBY. *Proc. Soc. Exp. Biol. Med. 100*:349, 1959.

2. LUHBY, A. L., J. M. COOPERMAN, and D. N. TELLER. *Proc. Soc. Exp. Biol. Med. 101*:350, 1959.

3. TABOR, H. *Pharmacol. Revs. 6*:299, 1954; WOLSTENHOLME, G. E. W., ed. Ciba Foundation *Symposium on Histamine*, London, J. and A. Churchill, 1956; SCHEIFFARTH, F., and M. GEMÄHLICH, *Deutsch. Med. Wochschr. 83*: 729, 1958; KAHLSON, G. *Lancet i*:67, 1960.

4. NAITO, T., and K. KURIAKI. *Arch. Exp. Pathol. Pharmakol. 232*:481, 1958; WHITE, T. *J. Physiol.* (London) *149*:34, 1959.

5. WERLE, E., and G. WEICKEN. *Biochem. Z. 319*:457, 1949.

6. DUNER, H., and B. PERNOW. *Scand. J. Clin. and Lab. Invest. 8*:296, 1956.

7. SCHAYER, R. W. *Physiol. Rev. 39*:116, 1959.

8. SCHAYER, R. W., and O. H. GANLEY. *Am. J. Physiol. 197*:721, 1959.

9. SCHAYER, R. W. *Science 131*:226, 1960.

10. HILL, H. *The Histamine and Insulin Treatment of Schizophrenia*. London, Baillière, Tindal and Cox, 1940.

11. HOCH, P. H. *Am. J. Psychiat. 109*:229, 1952.

12. SACKLER, A. M., M. D. SACKLER, R. R. SACKLER, and J. H. W. VAN OPHUISEN. *J. Nerv. Ment. Dis. 110*:149, 1949.

13. BILLIG, O., and F. HESSER. *Arch. Neurol. Psychiat. 52*:65, 1944.

14. BERNSTEIN, J., W. P. MAZUR, and E. J. WALASZEK. *Medicina Experimentalis 2*:239, 1960.

15. LEBLANC, J., and L. LEMIEUX. *Medicina Experimentalis 4*:214, 1961.

# 8

# THE SULFUR-CONTAINING
# AMINO ACIDS

## Nutritional Requirements

The sulfur-containing amino acids found in proteins are cysteine, cystine, and methionine. The last is an important constituent of the human diet and can serve as a precursor of the other two. The importance of this group of compounds in human nutrition can hardly be overemphasized, for methionine is an essential dietary requirement. Moreover, the nutritive value of the protein of human diets is correlated with their sulfur content (1) and the sulfur amino acids tend to be low in many human dietary regimes. A relative deficiency of this type may make quite useless for protein synthesis a complementary portion of the other amino acids of the diet, leading to their catabolism (with extra urea formation) along pathways that are, in effect, wasteful to the organism. In kwashiorkor, a disease resulting from gross, chronic protein deficiency, supplemental methionine causes a rapid reduction of the blood pyruvate to normal (2).

## Metabolism of the Sulfuramino Acids

Cysteine is readily oxidized to cystine (Reaction 8-1). It is formed from methionine with the intervention of serine. In the first step methionine is divested of its methyl group to form homocysteine, and the latter amino acid condenses with serine. Once formed, the intermediate, cystathionine (Reaction 8-2) undergoes scission at a different linkage than that through which it was formed. Cysteine is one of the products.

$$2HS{\cdot}CH_2CH(NH_2)COOH \rightarrow \begin{matrix} SCH_2CH(NH_2)COOH \\ | \\ SCH_2CH(NH_2)COOH \end{matrix} + 2H \quad (8\text{-}1)$$

$$\text{Homocysteine} + \text{Serine} \rightarrow \text{Cystathionine} + H_2O$$
(from methionine) $\qquad\qquad\qquad\qquad\qquad\qquad$ (8-2)

Cysteine is a constituent of the tripeptide glutathione ($\gamma$-glutamyl-cysteinylglycine), symbolized as GSH; its sulfhydryl (—SH) group renders it liable to oxidation in a manner analogous to that described in Reaction 8-1. Oxidized glutathione (GSSG) results. Cysteine also undergoes de-gradative reactions in which it is decarboxylated (Reaction 8-3) or in which its sulfur atom is progressively oxidized (Reaction 8-4). In the first case mercaptoethylamine, or cysteamine, is formed; this enters into the coenzyme A molecule along with pantothenic acid and other constituents. In the second, cysteic acid results; it may be decarboxylated to taurine, the oxidized analogue of cysteamine (Reaction 8-5), or transaminated to $\beta$-sulfonylpyruvic acid. Enzymatic hydrolysis of this last compound brings the sulfur atom of the amino acid to its metabolic terminus, the sulfate ion (Reaction 8-6). Isethionic acid, hydroxyethylsulfonic acid, may be derived by deamination of taurine. It is a constituent of inverte-brate nerve.

$$\underset{\text{Cysteine}}{HSCH_2CH(NH_2)COOH} \rightarrow \underset{\text{Cysteamine}}{HSCH_2CH_2NH_2} + CO_2 \quad (8\text{-}3)$$

$$\text{Cysteine} + 3O \rightarrow \underset{\text{Cysteic acid}}{HSO_3{\cdot}CH_2{\cdot}CH(NH_2)COOH} \quad (8\text{-}4)$$

$$\text{Cysteic acid} \rightarrow CO_2 + \underset{\text{Taurine}}{HSO_3{\cdot}CH_2CH_2NH_2} \quad (8\text{-}5)$$

(Pyridoxal phosphate is the coenzyme in Reactions 8-3 and 8-5.)

$$\underset{\text{Sulfonylpyruvic acid}}{HSO_3{\cdot}CH_2COCOOH} + H_2O \rightarrow \underset{\text{Sulfuric acid}}{H_2SO_4} + \underset{\text{Pyruvic acid}}{CH_3COCOOH} \quad (8\text{-}6)$$

Methionine plays a central role in transmethylating reactions, and does so through formation of a sulfonium compound with adenosine, known as adenosyl-L-methionine. It is this compound that donates the sulfur-linked methyl group to appropriate acceptor molecules such as guanidoacetic acid (the precursor of creatine), dimethylaminoethanol (the precursor of choline), and others. The remainder of the methionine molecule splits off as homocysteine. Adenosylmethionine can also undergo enzymatic decarboxylation to form adenosylthiomethylpropylamine. The propylamine portion of this molecule is utilized with putrescine (formed from ornithine) in the biosynthesis of the nitrogenous bases spermine and spermidine. It has been shown that the sulfur of methionine labeled with $S^{35}$ can be converted by the brain into other sulfur compounds, including cystine, taurine, and sulfate (3).

# Role in the Metabolism of Other Substances

## LIPOTROPIC ACTION

The transfer of the methyl group of methionine in intermediary metabolism is a process of primary importance in the physiological economy of the organism. A small proportion of the total number of methyl groups turned over in the body is derived from endogenous processes (for example, from serine) with the participation of folic acid, but the major supply of labile (*i.e.*, transferable) methyl groups is derived from the diet, in the form of L-methionine and choline. These two compounds are nutritionally interchangeable with respect to methyl group supply. In experimental deficiency states where the animal is deprived of dietary sources of methionine and choline the liver accumulates fat (triglycerides). Methionine and choline serve as specific lipotropic agents, reversing the deposition of fats. Both compounds have been used with some success to protect against the hepatotoxic action of certain drugs and chemicals known to cause fatty degeneration of the liver.

## CONVERSION OF NOREPINEPHRINE TO EPINEPHRINE

The biological synthesis of the catecholamines is described in Chapter 25. The formation of dopamine and norepinephrine goes on in the brain, in sympathetic postganglionic nerves, and in the adrenal medulla. The transmethylation of norepinephrine to epinephrine is a more restricted process histologically; it seems to be reserved primarily for certain cells of the adrenal medulla, and is accomplished through the mediation of S-adenosylmethionine. Because of the difference in pharmacological properties of norepinephrine and epinephrine (see Table 25-1) it is conceivable that a significant alteration in the rate at which S-adenosylmethionine is formed or the rate at which its S-methyl group is transferred could have serious consequences for the functioning of the sympathetic nervous system. However, there is no direct information available on this matter of sensitivity of epinephrine synthesis to a deficiency of methyl groups.

Speculation on the basis of the adrenochrome hypothesis has predicted a further consequence of an altered norepinephrine : epinephrine ratio. This extension begins with the proposed hallucinogenic action of adrenochrome and the hypothesis that this or some closely related substance is a causative agent in schizophrenia. If the formation of adrenochrome from epinephrine can be minimized, the argument goes, then a specific curative action will have been achieved. As an alternative to reducing the rate of oxidation of epinephrine to adrenochrome, the research group in Saskatchewan who have proposed the hypothesis have attempted to hinder the prior process, $i.e.$, the methylation of norepinephrine. No specific inhibitors of transmethylases are yet known. However, nicotinic acid was introduced as an agent which, given in sufficiently large amounts, would compete with norepinephrine for available methyl groups. The competing processes are shown in Reactions 8-7 and 8-8:

$$\text{Norepinephrine} \rightarrow \text{Epinephrine} \qquad (8\text{-}7)$$

$$\text{Nicotinic acid} \rightarrow \text{Nicotinamide} \rightarrow \text{N-Methylnicotinamide} \quad (8\text{-}8)$$

Inasmuch as the methyl group of N-methylnicotinamide is not transferable, excessive formation of this product would cause other methylation reactions to suffer. But more far-reaching effects could also be expected, because for every gram of nicotinic acid methylated 1.2 gm. of methionine are effectively neutralized. When it is considered that the recommended allowance of L-methionine is a little over 2 gm. per day it can be appreciated that a substantial degree of methylation of the administered nicotinamide could have significant consequences for protein synthesis (growth, repair of tissue), phospholipide metabolism, creatine formation, and other fundamental processes of the body.

In addition to the problem of the priority held by the N-methylation of norepinephrine in this series of reactions, there must be taken into account the fact that the catecholamines also undergo O-methylation at the *meta* phenolic group. This methylation applies to both epinephrine and norepinephrine, and it accounts for the major portion of the metabolism of these compounds. Thus, it is a quantitatively greater process than the N-methylation. For this reason, the changes postulated to occur in N-methylation of norepinephrine could, in the present state of our knowledge, just as well be expected to occur in O-methylation of this compound and epinephrine. Without specific studies designed to measure the changes, if any, in the extent of methylation at these two sites it is speculation of a high order to predict that administration of an alternative methyl acceptor will ultimately result in diminution of a substance (adrenochrome) whose formation *in vivo* is possible, but unproved.

## METHIONINE SULFOXIMINE

Until about 15 years ago nitrogen trichloride (agene) was one of the bleaching agents used industrially in the processing of wheat flour. It was then found that flour treated in this way acquires convulsant properties for some mammalian species. The induced seizures are actually due to the sulfoximine of methionine which is formed by the action of the agene upon the amino acid in the wheat protein (4). The reaction can be represented as follows:

$$CH_3 \cdot S \cdot CH_2CH_2CH(NH_2)COOH + NCl_3 \rightarrow$$
$$Cl_2 + CH_3 \cdot S(=NCl)CH_2CH_2 \underset{\underset{COOH}{|}}{CH(NH_2)} \quad (8\text{-}9)$$

|           L-Methionine                          Methionine sulfoximine

The mechanism of the convulsant action of methionine sulfoximine has been related to various processes, based upon its antimetabolite action in bacterial and mammalian experiments toward both methionine and glutamic acid. The seizures can be prevented, moreover, by large doses of asparagine or of methionine (4). Methionine sulfoximine inhibits the synthesis of glutamine in brain (5, 6); the only experimental treatment thus far found which antagonizes this effect is the addition of methionine and ammonium chloride to the medium in which are incubated slices of cerebral cortex from animals whose seizures have been induced by this agent (6). It is noteworthy that under other conditions convulsions can be produced by excessive amounts of ammonia, or by carbonyl agents which diminish the production of cerebral γ-aminobutyric acid.

Another action of methionine sulfoximine *in vivo* is its inhibition of the incorporation of methionine into brain proteins (7). Hence, the action of this convulsant appears to be based upon disturbance of the balance of intermediary metabolic reactions involving glutamic acid, methionine, and ammonia.

## Behavioral Effects of Methionine

Pollin et al. (8) tested large doses of L-methionine in chronic schizophrenic patients, receiving iproniazid. In some patients the daily administration of 20 gm. of the amino acid led to considerable verbalization, as well as increased anxiety and motor activity. These and other changes led to the conclusion that methionine had brought about some improvement in the clinical state of the patients who had reacted to the amino acid. Methionine has also been tested in hepatic coma (p. 117).

# References

1. MILLER, D. S., and D. J. NAISMITH. *Nature 182:*1786, 1958.
2. EDOZIEN, J. C. *Nature 184:*1150, 1959.
3. GAITONDE, M. K., and D. RICHTER. *In Metabolism of the Nervous System,* *ed.* D. RICHTER, London, Pergamon Press, 1957.
4. REINER, L., F. MISANI, and P. WEISS. *Arch. Biochem. Biophys. 25:*447, 1950.
5. PACE, J., and E. E. McDERMOTT. *Nature 169:*415, 1952.
6. PETERS, E. L., and D. B. TOWER. *J. Neurochem. 5:*80, 1959.
7. KOLOUSEK, J., and Z. LODIN. *Physiol. Bohemosloven. 8:*129, 1959.
8. POLLIN, W., P. V. CARDON, JR., and S. S. KETY. *Science 133:*105, 1961.

# 9

# AMINES, NITRILES, AND
# AMMONIA

## Formation and Metabolism of Amines

Amines have the general structure $R \cdot NH_2$, where $R$ signifies a carbon chain of one or more —$CH_2$— units, or a ring structure. The biogenic amines are derived by the decarboxylation of L-amino acids either in the intestinal lumen, through the action of bacteria, or in the tissues. Some of the amines encountered in organs and body fluids are shown in Table 9-1. Pyridoxal phosphate, the phosphorylated form of vitamin $B_6$, is required for the conversion of amino acids to the corresponding amines.

### METABOLISM OF AMINES (1)

The main metabolic pathway pursued by the amines is the oxidative one, in which ammonia is released and an aldehyde is formed. Some of these aldehydes have an action on brain metabolism and systemically they may show pharmacodynamic activity. But information about the biological activity of many aldehydes of special interest, such as those corresponding to the indolylethylamines and the catecholamines, is unfortunately lacking, for these particular compounds are difficult to prepare and to preserve in quantities sufficient for this purpose. Several types of enzyme occur in mammalian tissues which oxidize amines: their substrate specifi-

TABLE 9-1

| Precursor | Amine Derivative |
|---|---|
| Alanine | Ethylamine |
| Arginine | Agmatine |
| Aspartic acid | $\beta$-Alanine |
| Cysteic acid | Taurine |
| Cysteine | Cysteamine |
| Dihydroxyphenylalanine (Dopa) | Dopamine and other catecholamines |
| Glycine; sarcosine; creatine; epinephrine; metanephrine | Methylamine |
| Glutamic acid | $\gamma$-Aminobutyric acid |
| Histidine | Histamine |
| 5-Hydroxytryptophan | 5-Hydroxytryptamine (serotonin); bufotenine; melatonin |
| Kynurenine | Kynurenamine (kynuramine) |
| Leucine | Isoamylamine |
| Lysine | Cadaverine (pentamethylenediamine); piperidine |
| Ornithine (also arginine and citrulline) | Putrescine (butanediamine) |
| Ornithine + Methionine | Spermine; spermidine |
| Pyrimidine | $\beta$-Alanine |
| Serine | Ethanolamine (colamine); choline |
| Serine + fatty acid or aldehyde | Sphingosine |
| Tryptophan | Tryptamine |
| Tyrosine ($p$-Tyrosine) | Tyramine, dopamine |
| $m$-Tyrosine | $m$-Tyramine, dopamine |
| Valine | Isobutylamine |

cities differ, but the chemical reaction they catalyze is the same Reaction 9-1).

$$RCH_2NH_2 + O_2 + H_2O \rightarrow RCHO + H_2O_2 + NH_3 \qquad (9\text{-}1)$$

These amine oxidases were early classified into two groups on the basis of their activity toward certain biogenic and related amines. One type of enzyme acts upon aliphatic and phenylethyl amines; these substrates, possessing but one amine group, suggested the name monoamine oxidase. The other type of enzyme attacks some short-chain aliphatic diamines, a fact that has given rise to the generic name diamine oxidase. Later studies have shown that histamine and other types of amine also serve as substrates.

The two enzymes are otherwise distinguished from one another. Diamine oxidase is inhibited by carbonyl reagents which attack its co-enzyme, pyridoxal phosphate; monoamine oxidase is not so affected. Diamine oxidase employs flavin adenine dinucleotide as an auxiliary coenzyme; to the present time no coenzyme requirement has been established for monoamine oxidase. Diamine oxidase is found as a soluble constituent of the cell; monoamine oxidase is associated with the mito-chondria and is peptized only with difficulty. The two enzymes are affected by specific inhibitors: monoamine oxidase by octanol and iproniazid, diamine oxidase by semicarbazide and aminoguanidine.

The names for these enzymes are now recognized to carry inaccurate connotations. The physiological substrate of diamine oxidase is regarded as histamine, but this is not a diamine; furthermore, its methyl derivative is not a substrate for this enzyme *in vivo*. Mescaline, a monoamine derivative of the phenylethylamine series, is oxidized not by monoamine oxidase, but by diamine oxidase. These and other exceptions to the terminology originally proposed by Zeller do not detract from the established usefulness of the classification, as long as the development of studies on these enzymes is kept in mind.

The monoamine and diamine oxidases occur in many tissues. A third enzyme, which has been found in plasma of ruminant species, oxidizes an array of amines, notably spermine; its function has been little investigated. An oxidase in plants converts lysine to a piperidine derivative, but thus far an analogous enzyme has not been detected in animal tissues. Indeed, the distal amino group of compounds such as $\gamma$-aminobutyric acid and lysine is metabolized in animal tissues not through oxidation, but by transamination.

A reaction of amines described recently is incorporation into proteins, presumably through the formation of an amide linkage (2). It has been suggested that this may be one manner in which amines exert their biological action.

## AMINES, BRAIN DAMAGE, AND MENTAL DISEASE

*It seems to me that the primary seat of insanity generally is in the region of the stomach and intestines, and it is from that centre that the disorder of intelligence propagates itself as by a species of irradiation.—Pinel, writing in 1807. [Quoted by Watson (3).]*

For many years the most widely promulgated biochemical theory of mental disease has claimed that an endogenously formed toxin is the cause of the psychoses. The toxin has been presumed to originate in the intestine or other free mucous surfaces of the body, being formed there by bacterial action. The toxin-producing organisms may not occur in healthy persons but if they do, then—according to the hypothesis—the product of their action is detoxified in the liver shortly after its absorption. In other individuals the material gets into the general circulation either because of the hepatic dysfunction which it causes, among its many presumed actions, or because of pre-existing (and predisposing) liver damage. The potent biological activity of amines has for years thrown suspicion upon them as causative agents in mental diseases, and it is clear from the roster in Table 9-1 that many of those which can be formed in animal tissues have specific and potent pharmacodynamic actions; perhaps other, as yet unrecognized, amines occur which have actions upon the central nervous system. Among the earliest experimental evidence favoring the theory of "cerebrotoxic amines" was that of Quastel and Wheatley (4) and Pugh and Quastel (cf. Chapter 3, "The Hippuric Acid Test of Liver Function"). This evidence indicated that substances normally produced in the body from tyrosine and tryptophan may affect oxidative processes of the brain in the same way as narcotics do. If biogenic amines were to appear in the blood stream in excessive concentration then, it was held, they could cause an anoxia which might be partly responsible for psychotic manifestations in mental diseases. The depression of cerebral respiration occasioned by the addition of such amines to brain slices in vitro is by no means specific to this group of compounds, for it occurs with many other substances including alcohols, aldehydes, barbiturates, and other drugs, but it is nevertheless true that many of the active compounds with this action are chemically related to the phenylethyl amines and to the indoles (4, 5). Amphetamine is a case in point. It inhibits the respiration of separated cerebral tissue and affects the brain in vivo as an excitant and as an addiction former. If depression of cerebral oxidations and, consequently, reduction of the brain's energy supply are of etiological significance in mental diseases then this factor may well play a role in the psychosis attendant upon habituation to amphetamine.

In spite of the attractiveness of the hypothesis of autointoxication by amines coming from the intestinal flora, substantial evidence in its favor has not been forthcoming. That a defect in liver function may allow some toxic metabolite(s) to enter the general circulation and to reach the brain is indicated by the observations of Baker (6). He found that in many patients with liver disease there are perivascular changes in all regions of the brain, with damage to the cell bodies as well as demyelination. Indeed, some amines may directly attack and alter the myelin structure. On the other hand, histopathological examination of the brains of schizophrenics has not revealed any changes which can be described as characteristic of the disease. Furthermore, the type of toxic demyelination seen in the experimental animal is not the same as the changes in demyelinating diseases to which man is subject (7).

The other part of the amine hypothesis, namely, the claim that schizophrenics harbor large amounts of some toxic substance in their body fluids, has been asserted many times (*cf.* 8). The evidence offered in its support has never been adequately or consistently confirmed. Attempts to detect excessive amounts of amines in blood drawn from schizophrenic subjects have been unsuccessful thus far (9). With the very sensitive paper chromatographic and fluorometric methods for amines now becoming available (10) it should be possible to devise investigations which will contribute useful information about the levels of various amines occurring in the blood and cerebrospinal fluid of the mentally ill. Indeed continuing investigations along these lines are going on in several centers (*e.g.,* 11). Application of knowledge of intermediary metabolism and of the enzymology of humans will also lead to the introduction of tests for determining the activity of specific processes in the formation  and catabolism of amines. At present some of the tests available are crude in the sense that they measure the over-all activity of the body, when what is wanted is really the activity of particular enzymes in the brain (or other organ). For example, monoamine oxidase activity can be measured by the metabolic conversion *in vivo* of orally administered 5-hydroxytryptamine to 5-hydroxyindoleacetic acid (12). Decarboxylase activity, representing the immediate process resulting in the formation of amines, is measured by the amount of amine excreted following the intravenous or oral administration of an amino acid. In one of the tryptophan-load tests these and other enzymes are measured as a metabolic group, by determining 5-hydroxyindoleacetic acid in the urine; as already described (page 81), the results from such tests have been inconclusive and contradictory. The most refined tests—metabolic balance studies with isotopically labeled amines—have as yet had little currency, but it has been shown already by this means that the metabolism of epinephrine is normal in schizophrenic patients. The growth of knowledge of intermediary metabolism and the enzymology of humans will also lead to the introduction of tests for determining the activity of specific processes in the formation and catabolism of amines.

## Nitriles

These are compounds with the general structure $RCH_2CN$. Nitriles do not occur as metabolites but they are of interest for their pharmacological actions. The aliphatic nitriles seem to be oxidized in the body to organic acids with the splitting off of the nitrilo (—CN) group. The cyanide which is formed is converted in the tissues, through the intervention of the enzyme rhodanese and an appropriate sulfur donor, to thiocyanate (—SCN).

Two compounds of this series are of special interest. These are malononitrile $CH_2(CN)_2$ and $\beta,\beta$-iminodipropionitrile (IDPN), NH-$(CH_2CH_2CN)_2$. The first of these was studied by Hyden and Hartelius (13). Given intravenously to 66 mental patients in whom therapy had failed or was contraindicated, in repeated doses of 3 to 6 mg./kg. of body weight, the drug caused tachycardia, facial vasodilatation, peripheral vasoconstriction, and malaise. Each treatment consisted of an injection of malononitrile followed one hour later by sodium thiosulfate, administered as an antidote. This combination caused euphoria and spontaneity in those patients who were depressed. There was increased contact in the schizophrenic group. In a further study with smaller doses of malononitrile injected slowly, Hartelius again reported positive results; the beneficial effects were said to persist in about half the patients (14).

The rationale for trying malononitrile was its experimental action in the rabbit in increasing the ribonucleic acid (RNA) content of the ganglion cells of the central nervous system. This action was associated with the evidence obtained by Hyden and Hartelius that the protein and RNA content of certain ganglion cells of lobotomy tissue removed from schizophrenics was lower than in similar tissue taken from normal subjects shortly after accidental death. These findings have not been confirmed. Malononitrile has been tested in other hospitals but without the same beneficial results.

IDPN was first studied in 1952–53 by Delay and Thuillier (15). They reported that its injection causes permanent damage in experimental animals, resulting in a syndrome characterized by hyperactivity, turning, choreoathetotic movements, motor incoordination, and defective equilibrium. Other investigators have made similar findings (16, 17). The chronic administration of IDPN causes extreme necrosis of motor neurones of the spinal cord involving the tracts (18). The toxicity of IDPN is not accounted for by the slow release of the nitrilo group as HCN. Pretreatment of animals with thyroxine protects them against this nitrile (17).

The closely related compound $\beta$-aminopropionitrile ($H_2NCH_2CH_2$-CN) does not have these neurotoxic actions. By contrast its predominant action is on the mesenchymal tissues where it causes changes in bony development and leads to dissecting aneurysm of the aorta, degenerative arthritis, and other effects (19, 20). $\beta$-Aminopropionitrile has been isolated from *Lathyrus odoratus*. The consumption of this legume as a major part of the diet causes "odoratism" in man. The disease can be produced experimentally by the addition of small amounts of the pure compound (1 to 2 gm./kg.) to an otherwise normal diet.

These experimental and clinical findings raise the question of the origin of lathyrism in man. Clinically, lathyrism is a motor spastic paraplegia, with progressive crippling, and occurs after long-continued consumption of large amounts of chick peas (*L. sativus*) (19, 21). It is conceivable that chronic intoxication with IDPN or with an IDPN-like material in this plant is responsible for this disease, in the same way as $\beta$-aminopropionitrile appears to cause odoratism. However, it should be emphasized that the causative agent of lathyrism has not yet been identified.

## Formation and Metabolism of Ammonia

### SOURCES (22–24)

The ammonia with which the body must cope is derived in large measure from the action of the intestinal flora. Of the remainder, which is formed in mammalian tissues, probably the most important source, quantitatively is L-glutamic acid. This amino acid is deaminated by a specific enzyme (Reactions 2-2 and 2-3) and can be resynthesized through the action of transaminases, which facilitate the transfer of the amino group of other amino acids to $\alpha$-ketoglutaric acid, to form glutamic acid once again. In this way the nitrogen of many of the naturally occurring amino acids is ultimately converted into ammonia by the succession of Reactions 4-4, 2-2, and 2-3. There are riboflavin-containing enzymes in the body which oxidize L-amino acids directly to the corresponding keto acid, but these do not have great activity. The acute administration of large amounts of an amino acid may have a lethal effect, both the L- and D-forms being toxic in experimental animals. The toxicity is probably due not only to the ammonia which is formed *in vivo,* but also to the accumulation of the deaminated carbon skeleton of the amino acid (25).

Some ammonia is formed by the action of amine oxidases. (Methylamine, $CH_3NH_2$, is a product of the action of monoamine oxidase on epinephrine and metanephrine.) Other sources of ammonia are the deamidation of proteins and the deamination of adenylic acid to form inosinic acid.

## METABOLIC TRANSFER OF AMMONIA

Not all the ammonia that is produced in the body is excreted in the urine as ammonium salts or urea. Small amounts enter other metabolic pathways before proceeding to these terminal ones. For example, glutamine and asparagine are formed by the amidation of the corresponding amino acids, with the participation of adenosine triphosphate (ATP) as a source of energy. The amide of glycine is formed in the course of biosynthesis of the purines and neurohypophyseal hormones.

The original work of Krebs and Henseleit on the mechanism of urea formation (26) has been amplified in recent years by new data. Urea is synthesized in the liver through a series of reactions involving four amino acids. In the first step ammonia and carbon dioxide, as carbamic acid, $H_2N \cdot COOH$, are phosphorylated by the agency of ATP to carbamyl phosphate. This very reactive compound then combines with ornithine. The citrulline which is formed condenses with L-aspartic acid to yield argininosuccinic acid, from which L-arginine and fumaric acid are derived. Finally, arginase catalyzes the hydrolysis of arginine to urea, at the same time regenerating ornithine which can be utilized once more in the urea cycle.

A new form of mental deficiency has been described in two siblings who excreted very large amounts of argininosuccinic acid in the urine (27). A grossly abnormal electroencephalogram was manifested clinically in epileptiform attacks. An unusual feature was the high concentration of the urea cycle intermediate in the cerebrospinal fluid relative to the plasma. In spite of the large amount of this intermediate lost in the urine the urea levels in plasma and urine were normal.

Proline also contributes to the ornithine pool. This amino acid is metabolized (*a*) by deamination and oxidation to glutamic acid, and (*b*) by α-decarboxylation to putrescine, a diamine. Arginine is cleaved in at least one other way than stated for the production of urea. Its amidine group can be transferred to glycine (Reaction 3-4), yielding ornithine and guanidoacetic acid (glycocyamine). Guanidoacetic acid is trans-methylated by S-adenosylmethionine, with the formation of creatine and homocysteine (Reaction 3-5). The phosphorylated form of creatine plays an important role in the tissues, especially in muscle, as a means of storing energy. In this respect it serves as an auxiliary to the adenylic acid system (Reaction 9-2).

Phosphocreatine + Adenosine diphosphate ⇌ Creatine
$$+ \text{ Adenosine triphosphate} \quad (9\text{-}2)$$

Production of ammonia in the body amounts to about 8 gm. per day. Of this, approximately 1 gm. is excreted as ammonium salts and ammonia, the remainder in the form of urea. The balance between the various mechanisms for the formation of ammonia and for its removal from the body results in the persistence of small amounts of ammonia in the peripheral blood (28). The best estimates indicate that there is substantially less than 1 $\mu$g./ml. in the circulating peripheral blood, but investigators disagree about the correct value to be assigned to this, probably because of differences in their technique of measurement. The estimation may be readily vitiated if shed blood is allowed to stand for any length of time, for then oxidative deamination of certain endogenous substrates, particularly the adenine nucleotides, contributes additional ammonia.

Under experimental conditions in which large amounts of ammonium acetate are infused, toxic consequences can be prevented by the prior treatment of the animals with one of the amino acids of the urea cycle (29). Doses of L-arginine that are lower than those required to achieve this protection can synergize effectively with many compounds, including glutamic and aspartic acids (and some of their derivatives) as well as alanine, pyruvic acid, glucose and sodium chloride. This wide variety of protective agents indicates that other significant accessory detoxification mechanisms are available to the organism for the removal of ammonia besides urea formation (30).

### HEPATIC COMA (22, 31–34)

Liver disease is sometimes complicated by neurological and mental symptoms which presage the appearance of coma (31, 32, 35). The neurological disturbances include absent or abnormal reflexes, exaggerated knee jerk and ankle clonus, dilated pupils, choreiform movements of the arms with grasping actions (flapping tremor) and "lead pipe" or "cogwheel" rigidity (31). There may be changes in the electroencephalo-gram. Psychologically, the patient is withdrawn and shows changes in personality, affect, and intellect. He slips from a state of clouded con-sciousness and confusion into coma. The odor of the breath and urine is characteristic (fetor hepaticus). This type of coma can develop on the basis of rather different degrees of hepatocellular function; it may occur in acute hepatitis or in the course of chronic cirrhosis of the liver. In some of the latter cases the collateral circulation expands between the intestine and the systemic vessels, thus permitting some blood coming from the intestinal tract to by-pass the liver. The neuropsychiatric symp-toms of this group have been termed portal-systemic encephalopathy (33). Some light has been thrown on these phenomena by reference to the pharmacological actions of ammonia and ammonium salts. Small amounts of ammonia stimulate the medullary regulatory centers and spinal neurones; large doses cause convulsions which are of the spinal rather than the epileptiform type (36). But the toxicity of ammonium salts shows up in a particularly marked fashion in patients with liver disease. The administration of such salts to patients with advanced hepatic cirrhosis initiates a syndrome very much like that seen in impend-ing hepatic coma: the patient is agitated, does not recognize the people around him, has difficulty in answering questions, wears a vacant expres-sion on his face, and suffers from tremor of the limbs (37). Other substances are also capable of generating this syndrome in patients with liver disease, or of exacerbating it when it is already present. Among these substances are the ammonium-containing ion exchange resins, urea, methionine, and glutamine, but not glutamic acid (32, 38). Increased dietary protein also elevates ammonia production, but proteins differ in the amounts of ammonia that they can release into the blood stream. The proteins of blood are especially effective in this regard (24). The actions of urea and methionine mentioned above can be clinically neutral-ized by supplying an antibiotic; this demonstrates that the toxicity of these compounds depends upon their transformation to other substances by bacteria. Urea gives rise to ammonia (urease action) but the toxic products of methionine metabolism are not known (but see p. 117). The use of antibiotic therapy does not affect the rise in blood ammonia stemming from the ingestion of protein or glutamine (23).

Another agent which can precipitate coma in patients with liver cirrhosis is the carbonic anhydrase inhibitor acetazoleamide (34). This drug may interfere with utilization of carbon dioxide for the formation of carbamic acid and carbamyl phosphate, the first steps in the conversion of ammonia to urea. In fact, following treatment with acetazoleamide there is a rise in the ammonia concentration in the blood (34).

At one time there was considerable debate regarding the primary change in liver disease that would account satisfactorily for the ammonemia. One view held that the high blood ammonia in these patients is due to an impaired ability of the liver to convert ammonia into urea (39), but this became untenable when it was found that partially hepatectomized animals can dispose of ammonia at a normal rate. A contrary view explained the rise in the blood level of ammonia as a consequence of the altered hepatic circulation, that is, reduction in the portal flow and diversion of much of the circulation coming from the intestinal tract into the systemic circulation (22, 37); in this way, the ammonia formed by the gut flora by-passes the liver and its urea-forming system of enzymes. In experimental animals, portacaval anastomosis completely shunting the portal blood away from the liver (Eck's fistula) has some features analogous to those observed in patients veering toward hepatic coma. Dogs operated in this way are susceptible to the so-called meat intoxication which is accompanied by elevated blood ammonia concentrations (40) and by frank disturbance of the nervous system (41). The animals do not survive for more than a year beyond the operation. It has been shown that the Eck fistula is essentially equivalent to hepatectomy on the basis of biochemical and electroencephalographic studies (42). The symptoms of anorexia, weight loss, stupor, and coma appear to depend upon a complete and persistent portacaval shunt, for they do not occur in animals with a portal-systemic collateral circulation; such animals survive the operation indefinitely (42). Hence, other factors besides the main diversion of portal circulation (and with it, diversion of toxic products into the systemic circulation) must be taken into account before the explanation of the course of events following Eck's operation can be considered complete.

**Blood Chemistry of Hepatic Coma.** Quantitative changes occur in a number of important blood constituents, but none in so characteristic a fashion that it can be correlated unequivocally with the severity of the clinical state. For example, bilirubin concentration of the serum is above the normal range, but its degree of elevation is variable. Certainly the most characteristic change is the rise in blood ammonia (43, 44): at the same time this is the clearest of biochemical danger signals. Ammonia begins to pass into the cerebral tissue, as shown by measurements of the arteriovenous difference, as soon as the blood level exceeds $1 \mu$ g./ml.

(44). The important question as to whether the ammonia level of the blood reflects directly the degree of neurological or mental involvement in hepatic coma has been the subject of widespread discussion. Some investigators have found a rough proportionality between the ammonia concentration in the blood and the depth of coma (44). But most measurements of the ammonia level have been made on venous blood, and therefore do not give what may be the critical information, i.e., the level in the arterial blood arriving at the brain.

Besides the elevated ammonia and bilirubin there are tendencies toward raised concentrations of keto acids (pyruvic, α-ketoglutaric, acetoacetic) in the blood (45, 46, 47) and lowered ester cholesterol (38) and serum albumin. The amino acids are present in their normal concentrations, except for methionine, which may be raised (45, 48). The glutamine content of the plasma is unaffected (49).

***The Biochemical Defect.*** Two closely related questions regarding hepatic coma are biochemical in nature. These relate to the underlying chemical pathology and to the nature of the toxic agent acting on the brain. Precise answers have not yet been given in either case but, on the basis of the available evidence, several hypotheses have been proposed to explain the biochemical changes and have logically led to trials of various therapeutic measures.

In the first place, the disturbances in ammonia and amino acid metabolism have drawn the attention of many investigators. For example, in one of his early metabolic studies of this condition Walshe (31) considered that changes in the amino acid pattern of the blood, as a consequence of the liver disease, affect brain metabolism even to the extent of interfering with glutamic acid formation there. In this way a defect in the cerebral ammonia-binding mechanism was presumed to be at fault. In fact, this is not inconsistent with the elevated blood ammonia concentration in liver disease, including hepatic necrosis, and with the recognized toxicity of ammonia and its salts. Walshe's interest in the amino acid changes led to his distinction between two types of hepatic change: (1) liver injury developing insidiously, usually in older persons, and following a more prolonged course with severe jaundice, usually negative flocculation tests, and essentially normal amino acid excretion; and (2) acute hepatitis occurring in the young adult, exhibiting some degree of generalized aminoaciduria (50). Bessman and Bessman have looked at the ammonia problem in another light.

They postulate that ammonia exerts its toxicity by acting as trap for a tricarboxylic acid cycle intermediate in the brain (44). This hypothesis is based upon the finding that $\alpha$-ketoglutaric acid is converted to glutamic acid in the presence of high ammonium concentrations. A biochemical defect of this kind would interrupt cerebral oxidations by diverting a key intermediate, through overly active binding of ammonia. Data on the cerebral metabolic rate in hepatic coma are in accord with this view (51). However, the concentration of blood ammonia required to achieve a reduction of the observed order under experimental conditions is much greater than those found clinically. Hence, other factors must be sought.

Of course, the major ammonia-binding mechanism of the body is the urea cycle, and if ammonia is not removed at the normal rate it would be natural to look for some defect in this direction, but there does not seem to be any information on the activity of the enzymes of this cycle in the diseased liver.

Takahashi and his colleagues claim that agmatine, the decarboxylation product of arginine, occurs in the urine of patients with hepatic coma (52). Agmatine is not a usual urinary product, nor is it known to be formed by the action of enzymes in mammalian tissues. Its formation probably results from the action of microorganisms in the intestine. This aspect of arginine metabolism requires clarification.

Another specific derangement of amino acid metabolism in hepatic coma centers around the sulfur-containing compound, methionine (Chapter 8). Because of its association with the normal functioning of the liver through lipotropic and other actions methionine has been tested in hepatic disturbances as a potential therapeutic agent. In many cases it has been beneficial, but the administration of this amino acid to patients with hepatic cirrhosis aggravates their condition, with deterioration in the neurological and mental state (48, 53, 54, 55). The mechanism of the toxic action of methionine has not yet been discovered; there may be an unusually great release of ammonia or some other product such as methylsulfide, $CH_3SH$. This compound has been isolated from the urine of a patient whose jaundice eventually led to hepatic coma (56). It may contribute to the characteristic odor of the breath and urine of patients with this condition. A nitrogenous base has also been implicated as the fetor hepaticus (57). The toxic substance derived from methionine results from bacterial action, for the suppression of the intestinal flora by antibiotics protects those patients who are especially sensitive to oral methionine (53, 55). Occasional cases of hepatic coma are encountered with elevated serum methionine levels.

*Therapeutic Agents.* Because of its ammonia-binding capacity glutamic acid has had numerous trials in this disorder. There have been occasional successes with it, but the results have been generally disappointing (35, 58). Bessman, Shear, and Fitzgerald (24) suggest that some patients have an increased complement of the glutamine-forming enzyme system, through adaptation to the chronically elevated ammonia level in the blood, and that this provides a substitute for the arginine cycle. Walshe (45) has recognized the variable response to glutamic acid and thinks that it may be more useful as a medicament in selected cases, particularly in those in which the coma is precipitated by hemorrhage. As already pointed out, the proteins of blood are ammonia-releasers in the intestinal tract.

On theoretical grounds α-ketoglutaric acid would seem to be a highly suitable candidate for binding brain (as well as extracerebral) ammonia, but its elevated concentration in the blood in cirrhosis of the liver suggests that there is already some impairment in its utilization. Moreover, it is not certain that this acid is capable of passing readily from the blood into the brain tissue.

L-Arginine has also been tested as a means of depressing the ammonia levels in hepatic coma. When given intravenously it not only protects animals from the toxic action of ammonia but also has some efficacy in clinical trials (59, 60). Thus, in patients infused with large amounts of glycine, a measure which otherwise results in serious ammonemia, the prior administration of arginine prevents this increase (60). In those who have an elevated blood ammonia concentration by reason of liver disease the injection of arginine causes, after a latent period of some hours, a decrease in the blood ammonia, without a change in the glutamine or α-ketoglutarate levels. On this basis glutamic acid and arginine may be useful in combination, the first for its immediate effects, and the second for its longer-lasting action by removing ammonia from the tissues as urea. Arginine is also undergoing trial in poisoning by ammonia inhalation and by ingestion of ammonium chloride.

In some contrast to the viewpoints thus far described the mechanism of cerebral toxicity in hepatic coma has been differently interpreted by Sherlock and her colleagues (35). They have pointed out that, because ammonia is the only toxic agent thus far found, it is not necessarily the only one in liver disease. They have postulated instead that a toxin is formed from an amino acid by intestinal bacteria, and that this toxin—which may or may not be ammonia—is absorbed and passes into the systemic circulation unchanged; detoxication fails because of some metabolic derangement in the parenchymal cells of the liver or because of the presence of the collateral vessels. As a result the toxic substance eventually reaches the brain and exerts its action there. The therapy which Sherlock employs is based upon this hypothesis. Treatment consists in (*a*) the withdrawal of protein from the diet in order to reduce drastically the nitrogenous precursor of the toxin; and (*b*) the use of antibiotic therapy to decrease the intestinal flora producing the toxin (55). The combination of low-protein diet with antibiotic has been found useful in patients with impending coma; the treatment is continued until the critical stage has passed. Previously, McDermott and Adams used sulfonamides successfully to reduce the ammonia-forming organisms of the gut in hepatic coma (61).

# References

1. SOURKES, T. L. *Rev. Can. Biol. 17:*328, 1958.
2. SARKAR, N. K., D. D. CLARKE, and H. WAELSCH. *Biochim. et Biophys. Acta 25:*451, 1957.
3. WATSON, C. *J. Ment. Sci. 69:*52, 1923.
4. QUASTEL, J. H., and A. M. H. WHEATLEY. *Biochem. J. 27:*1609, 1933.
5. WALSHE, J. M., L. DE CARLI, and C. S. DAVIDSON. *Clin. Sci. 17:*11, 1958.
6. BAKER, A. B. *J. Neuropath. Exp. Neurol. 8:*283, 1949.
7. WOLF, A. *Acta Neurol. et Psychiat. Belg. 9:*633, 1954.
8. McGEER, E. G., and P. L. McGEER. *J. Ment. Sci. 105:*1, 1959.
9. RICHTER, D., and M. LEE. *J. Ment. Sci. 88:*127, 1942; MUNKVAD, I. *Acta Psychiat. et Neurol. 25:*89, 1950.
10. SJOERDSMA, A., W. LOVENBERG, J. A. OATES, J. R. CROUT, and S. UDEN-FRIEND. *Science 130:*225, 1959; ASATOOR, A. M., and C. E. DALGLIESH. *Biochem. J. 73:*26P, 1959; ASATOOR, A. M., and D. N. S. KERR. *Clin. Chim. Acta 6:*149, 1961.
11. GEORGI, F., C. G. HONEGGER, D. JORDAN, H. P. RIEDER, and M. ROTTEN-BERG. *Klin. Wochschr. 34:*799, 1956.
12. SJOERDSMA, A., L. GILLESPIE, and S. UDENFRIEND. *Lancet ii:*159, 1958.
13. HYDEN, H., and H. HARTELIUS. *Acta Psychiat. et Neurol. Suppl.* 48, 1948.
14. HARTELIUS, H. *Am. J. Psychiat. 107:*95, 1950.
15. DELAY, J., P. PICHOT, J. THUILLIER, and J. MARQUISET. *Compt. Rend. Soc. Biol. 146:*533, 1952; THUILLIER, J., A. BURGER, and P. MOUILLE. *ibid. 147:*1052, 1953.

16. HARTMANN, H. A., and H. F. STICH. *Science 125*:445, 1957; AZIMA, H., and B. GRAD. *Can. Psychiat. Assoc. J. 2*:147, 1957.

17. SELYE, H. *J. Clin. Exp. Psychopathol. 19*:97, 1958.

18. HARTMANN, H. A., J. J. LALICH, and K. AKERT. *J. Neuropath. Exp. Neurol. 17*:298, 1958.

19. STRONG, F. M. *Nutrition Rev. 14*:65, 1956.

20. SELYE, H. *Rev. Can. de Biol. 16*:1, 1957.

21. DASTUR, D. K., and C. G. S. IYER. *Nutrition Rev. 17*:33, 1959.

22. KIRK, E. *Acta Med. Scand. Suppl.* 77, 1936.

23. WEBSTER, L. T., JR., C. S. DAVIDSON, and G. J. GABUZDA. *J. Lab. Clin. Med. 52*:501, 1958.

24. BESSMAN, A. N., G. S. MIRICK, and R. HAWKINS. *J. Clin. Invest. 37*:990, 1958.

25. GULLINO, P., M. WINITZ, S. M. BIRNBAUM, J. CORNFIELD, M. C. OTEY, and J. P. GREENSTEIN. *Arch. Biochem. Biophys. 64*:319, 1956.

26. KREBS, H. A., and K. HENSELEIT. *Z. physiol. Chem. 210*:33, 1932.

27. ALLAN, J. D., D. C. CUSWORTH, C. E. DENT, and V. K. WILSON. *Lancet i*:182, 1958; WESTALL, R. G. *Biochem. J. 77*:135, 1960.

28. PARNAS, J. K., and A. KLISIECKI. *Biochem. Z. 169*:255, 1926.

29. GREENSTEIN, J. P., M. WINITZ, P. GULLINO, S. M. BIRNBAUM, and M. C. OTEY. *Arch. Biochem. Biophys. 64*:342, 1956; FAHEY, J. L., R. S. PERRY, and P. F. McCOY. *Am. J. Physiol. 192*:311, 1958.

30. WINITZ, M., J. P. DU RUISSEAU, M. C. OTEY, S. M. BIRNBAUM, and J. P. GREENSTEIN. *Arch. Biochem. Biophys. 64*:368, 1956.

31. WALSHE, J. M. *Quart. J. Med. 20*:421, 1951.

32. PHILLIPS, G. B., R. SCHWARTZ, G. M. GABUZDA, and C. S. DAVIDSON. *New England J. Med. 247*:239, 1952.

33. SUMMERSKILL, W. H. J., E. A. DAVIDSON, S. SHERLOCK, and R. E. STEINER. *Quart. J. Med. n. s. 25*:245, 1956.

34. KUEHN, H. A. *Deut. Med. Wochschr. 83*:658, 1958.

35. SHERLOCK, S., W. H. J. SUMMERSKILL, and A. M. DAWSON. *Lancet ii*:689, 1956.

36. AJMONE-MARSAN, C., M. G. F. FUORTES, and F. MAROSSERO. *EEG Clin. Neurophysiol. 1*:291, 1949.

37. VAN CAULAERT, C., and C. DEVILLER. *Compt. Rend. Soc. Biol. 111*:50, 1932; VAN CAULAERT, C., C. DEVILLER, and M. HALFF. *Presse Médicale 41*:217, 1933.

38. CHAIKIN, N. W., and M. S. KONIGSBERG. *Am. J. Gastroenterol. 27*:266, 1957.

39. FULD, H. *Klin. Wochschr. 12*:1364, 1933.

40. MONGUIO, J., and F. KRAUSE. *Klin. Wochschr. 13*:1142, 1934.

41. HAHN, M., O. MASSEN, M. NENCKI, and J. PAVLOV. *Arch. Exp. Path. u. Pharmakol. 32*:161, 1893.

42. BOLLMAN, J. L., E. V. FLOCK, J. H. GRINDLAY, R. G. BICKFORD, and F. R. LICHTENHELD. *A. M. A. Arch. Surgery 75*:405, 1957

43. WHITE, L. P., E. A. PHEAR, W. H. J. SUMMERSKILL, and S. SHERLOCK. *J. Clin. Invest. 34*:158, 1955.

44. BESSMAN, S. P., and A. N. BESSMAN. *J. Clin. Invest. 34:*622, 1955; TYOR, M. P., and H. O. SIEKER. *Am. J. Med. 37:*50, 1959.

45. WALSHE, J. M. *Lancet i:*1235, 1955.

46. SELIGSON, D., G. J. McCORMICK, and V. SBOROV. *J. Clin. Invest. 31:*661, 1952.

47. SUMMERSKILL, W. H. J., S. J. WOLFE, and C. S. DAVIDSON. *J. Clin. Invest. 36:*361, 1957.

48. KINSELL, L. W., H. A. HARPER, G. K. GIESE, S. MORGEN, D. P. McCALLIE, and J. R. HESS. *J. Clin. Invest. 28:*1439, 1949.

49. SEEGMILLER, J. E., R. SCHWARTZ, and C. S. DAVIDSON. *J. Clin. Invest. 33:* 984, 1954.

50. WALSHE, J. M. *Quart. J. Med. 22:*483, 1953.

51. FAZEKAS, J. F., H. E. TICKTIN, W. R. EHRMANTRAUT, and R. W. ALMAN. *Am. J. Med. 21:*843, 1956.

52. TAKAHASHI, K., H. ENOMOTO, and H. MOMUJAMA. *Igaku to Seibutsugaka 32:*81, 1954; *seen in Chem. Abstr. 51:*18283i, 1957.

53. WEBSTER, L. T., JR., and G. J. GABUZDA. *J. Lab. Clin. Med. 50:*426, 1957.

54. SINGH, I. D., J. A. BARCLAY, and W. T. COOKE. *Lancet i:*1004, 1954.

55. PHEAR, E. A., B. RUEBNER, S. SHERLOCK, and W. H. J. SUMMERSKILL. *Clin. Sci. 15:*93, 1956.

56. CHALLENGER, F., and J. M. WALSHE. *Biochem. J. 59:*372, 1955; *Lancet i:* 1239, 1955.

57. BUTT, H. R., and H. L. MASON. *Gastroenterology 26:*829, 1954.

58. IBER, F. L., and T. C. CHALMERS. *J. Clin. Invest. 36:*706, 1957.

59. FAZEKAS, J. F., H. E. TICKTIN, and J. G. SHEA. *Am. J. Med. Sci. 234:*462, 1957; McDERMOTT, W. V., JR., D. H. HENNEMAN, and C. LAUMONT. *J. Clin. Invest. 36:*913, 1957; YOUNG, W. K., J. V. V. JOHNSON, H. E. TICKTIN, and J. F. FAZEKAS. *Am. J. Med. Sci. 238:*60, 1959.

60. FAHEY, J. L. *J. Clin. Invest. 36:*1647, 1957.

61. McDERMOTT, W. V., JR., and R. D. ADAMS. *J. Clin. Invest. 33:*1, 1954.

# 10

# NUCLEOTIDES AND NUCLEIC ACIDS

## Nucleotides

The simplest nucleotides consist of a purine or pyrimidine base linked to a phosphorylated sugar. A nucleoside results when a phosphate residue is hydrolyzed from the molecule. The first nucleotides studied by biochemists were obtained by the breakdown of the high-molecular-weight nucleic acids, and these were shown to have the following organic components:

> Purines: adenine and guanine
> Pyrimidines: uracil, cytosine, and thymine
> Carbohydrates: ribose and 2-deoxyribose

The polynucleotides or nucleic acids as they exist in the cell were recognized to be of two types, depending upon the nature of the sugar component. Those containing ribose were termed ribonucleic acid (RNA) or pentosenucleic acid (PNA), the others deoxyribonucleic acid (DNA, DRNA). Nucleic acid entities containing both sugars are not known. In addition to the simple nucleotides that constitute the basic units of the nucleic acids, a number of compounds of related structure have come to light in metabolic studies, and these compounds are encompassed within a slight extension of the above definition: some are dinucleotides in which the two component nucleotides are linked through their phosphate groups; some possess two or three phosphate groups; one (riboflavin phosphate) contains a pentitol (ribitol) instead of an aldose. These are described in Table 10-1, together with their known functions in metabolism. The variegated list includes nucleotides that serve as structural components of RNA and DNA; and those which are precursors of the purines and pyrimidines; participants in energy transfer and storage; constituents of the yellow enzymes and of vitamin $B_{12}$; and cofactors in acylation reactions (*i.e.,* transfer of compounds possessing the acidic function), protein synthesis, carbohydrate transformations, and phospholipide biosynthesis. The special importance of the two ribosides, uridine and cytidine, in brain metabolism has been described by Geiger (1).

The amounts of the different nucleotides in the tissues are variable. In the brain the major nucleotide components are the compounds of adenine (2–4). The other nucleotides that have been detected are present in smaller concentrations. These are the guanine phosphates, the uridine phosphates, inosinic acid, and pyridine nucleotides (3, 5). Of the nucleic acids RNA is present in greater concentration than DNA in the brain (2, 6, 7). The latter attains its highest concentrations in the cerebellar cortex and hypothalamus; the greatest amounts of RNA are in the hypothalamus, in the cerebellar and cerebral cortices, and in the basal ganglia. The lowest concentrations of both types are present in the spinal cord (6).

Following electroshock the RNA concentration decreases in all parts of the brain, but the DNA remains essentially unchanged (8). The increased activity of ribonuclease suggested by this result has been reported some time ago to occur in the cerebrospinal fluid of psychotic patients (9).

## METABOLISM OF PURINES

The purines are synthesized in the body as nucleotides, and the free bases usually occur only in the course of degradative processes leading to their terminal metabolism. The complexity of the synthetic reactions can be gauged from Figure 10-1, which indicates the metabolic origin of the nitrogen and carbon atoms of inosinic acid (hypoxanthine riboside). It will be noted that four amino acids are involved in this synthesis. They are glutamine, glycine, serine, and aspartic acid.

Inosinic acid is the initial purine nucleotide formed, and it is

TABLE 10-1. COMPOSITION AND FUNCTIONS OF NUCLEOTIDES

| Nucleotide | Nitrogen Base | Metabolic Role |
|---|---|---|
| *Amino Acid Amides* | | |
| Glycinamide ribotide | Glycinamide | Purine precursor |
| 4-Amino-5-imidazole-carboxamide ribotide | 4-Amino-5-imidazole-carboxamide | Purine precursor |
| Succino-aminoimidazole carboxamide ribotide | 5-Aminoimidazole-4-carboxamide | Purine precursor ($C_6$-donor) |
| *Purines* | | |
| Inosinic acid (inosine monophosphate; IMP) | Hypoxanthine | Precursor of adenylic acid |
| Inosine triphosphate (ITP) | Hypoxanthine | Involved in formation of phosphoenolpyruvic acid from oxaloacetic acid |
| Adenylic acid (adenosine monophosphate, AMP) | Adenine | RNA; DNA*; coenzymes |
| Adenosine triphosphate (ATP) | Adenine | Transfer and storage of energy; activation of acyl groups, sulfate, phosphate, and $CO_2$ |
| Adenosine-3′,5′-monophosphate (cyclic AMP) | Adenine | Activation of phosphorylase, corticosteroidogenesis |
| Xanthosine monophosphate | Xanthine | Precursor of guanylic and uric acids |
| Guanylic acid (guanosine monophosphate, GMP) | Guanine | RNA; DNA |
| Guanosine triphosphate (GTP) | Guanine | Protein synthesis; regeneration of ATP |
| *Pyrimidines* | | |
| Orotidine monophosphate | Orotic acid | Precursor of pyrimidines |

TABLE 10-1 *(Continued)*

| Nucleotide | Nitrogen Base | Metabolic Role |
|---|---|---|
| Uridylic acid (uridine monophosphate, UMP) | Uracil | RNA; carbohydrate transformations as uridine diphosphoglycosides |
| Uridine triphosphate (UTP) | Uracil | Formation of uridine diphosphoglucose, -galactose, -glucosamine, etc. |
| Cytidylic acid (cytidine monophosphate, CMP) | Cytosine | DNA; RNA |
| Cytidine triphosphate (CTP) | Cytosine | Phospholipide synthesis |
| Cytidinemonophospho-N-acetyl-neuraminic acid | Cytosine | Synthesis of sialic acid polymers |
| Thymidylic acid (thymidine monophosphate) | Thymine | DNA |

*Coenzymes*

| | | |
|---|---|---|
| Flavin monophosphate (FMN; flavin mononucleotide) | Isoalloxazine | Coenzyme of L-amino acid oxidase; precursor of FAD |
| Flavin adenine dinucleotide (FAD) | Isoalloxazine and adenine | Coenzyme of many oxidases and cytochrome reductases |
| Benzimidazole ribotide | 5,6-Dimethylbenzimidazole | Erythropoiesis, as part of vitamin $B_{12}$ molecule |
| Diphosphopyridine nucleotide (DPN; Coenzyme I; NAD) | Nicotinamide and adenine | Coenzyme of many dehydrogenases |
| Triphosphopyridine nucleotide (TPN; Coenzyme II; NADP) | Nicotinamide and adenine | Coenzyme of some dehydrogenases and hydroxylases |
| Adenosine diphospho-pantothenyl-$\beta$-mercapto-ethylamine (coenzyme A) | Adenine | Acetylation and other acylation reactions |

* Contains the deoxypentose sugar.

converted into adenine and guanine nucleotides through Reactions 10-1 to 10-3. Reaction 10-1 requires magnesium ions and guanosine triphos-

$$\text{Inosinic acid} + \text{L-Aspartic acid} \rightarrow \text{Adenylosuccinic acid ribotide} \rightarrow$$
$$\text{Adenylic acid} + \text{Fumaric acid} \quad (10\text{-}1)$$

$$\text{Inosinic acid} + \text{DPN}^+ + \text{H}_2\text{O} \rightarrow \text{Xanthosine monophosphate}$$
$$+ \text{DPNH} + \text{H}^+ \quad (10\text{-}2)$$

$$\text{Xanthosine monophosphate} \rightarrow \text{Guanylic acid} \quad (10\text{-}3)$$

phate as cofactors. Reaction 10-3 also requires magnesium, together with adenosine triphosphate; glutamine supplies the necessary amino group. Some tissues, especially muscle, have a very active deaminase

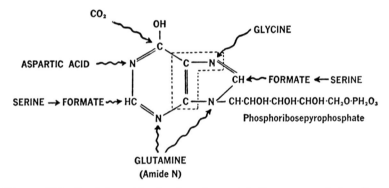

Figure 10-1. Inosinic acid, showing the metabolic sources of its nitrogen and carbon atoms.

acting specifically upon adenylic acid to form inosinic acid and ammonia. The substrate is regenerated as shown in Reaction 10-1.

In the breakdown of nucleotides the purine is cleaved from the pentosephosphate and is enzymically oxidized to uric acid, the terminal metabolic product in man. This occurs in several stages. Adenine is first deaminated through the action of adenase to hypoxanthine; the latter is successively oxidized in tissues containing xanthine oxidase to xanthine and then uric acid. Guanine is deaminated by a different enzyme (guanase), forming xanthine.

The uric acid is excreted through the kidney. Little is held at any given time in the blood and tissues, the body pool of uric acid amounting only to about 1 gm., a quantity that is turned over every 2 days or less. In gout the size of the body pool increases sharply, and uric acid, which is a poorly soluble compound in physiological fluids, crystallizes out in the tissues as monosodium urate.

The metabolism of the purines in man and some other primates follows the pattern described above, but in lower mammals an enzyme known as uricase is present that oxidizes uric acid to allantoin, and in these species allantoin represents the terminus of purine metabolism.

## METABOLISM OF PYRIMIDINES

The mode of biosynthesis of the pyrimidines is not as well understood as is that of the purines. However, the main steps have been established (10). The first of these is the transfer of the carbamate group of carbamyl phosphate, $H_2NCOO \cdot PH_2O_3$, to L-aspartic acid. This molecule is dehydrogenated (and cyclized) in a stepwise fashion to orotic acid (2,6-dioxy-4-carboxypyrimidine; uracil-4-carboxylic acid). The pyrimidines found in nucleic acids are then formed from this precursor, as shown in Reactions 10-4 and 10-5. Uracil arises by de-

$$\text{Orotic acid} \rightarrow \text{Uracil} + CO_2 \qquad (10\text{-}4)$$

$$\text{Uridine triphosphate} + NH_3 \rightarrow \text{Cytidine triphosphate} + H_2O \qquad (10\text{-}5)$$

carboxylation of orotic acid, and cytosine is formed from uracil when the latter is in the form of its nucleoside triphosphate (UTP). Reaction 10-5 has a more complex mechanism than is shown and, in fact, requires adenosine triphosphate as a cofactor. Thymine, or 5-methyluracil, is probably formed by the hydroxymethylation of uracil, followed by reduction of the hydroxyl group. Unlike cytosine and the purine bases, which occur in nature with both ribose and deoxyribose, uracil is found in combination only with ribose, and thymine only with deoxyribose. This means that RNA is characterized by the presence of uracil, and DNA by its content of thymine.

The breakdown of the pyrimidines leads to the formation of two amino acids which are not found among the constituents of proteins. The uracil ring is reduced and hydrolyzed to give ammonia, carbon dioxide, and $\beta$-alanine. Cytosine follows the same pathway, after deamination to uracil. Thymine is also metabolized according to this pattern, but in its case the amino acid formed is $\beta$-aminoisobutyric acid. The rate of excretion of this compound appears to be under genetic control (11). This would imply that the actual process controlled lies even further back, at the stage of breakdown of DNA or of thymine.

## URIC ACID AND INTELLIGENCE

Uric acid is 2,6,8-trioxypurine. It is chemically related to the xanthine alkaloids, caffeine, theobromine, and theophylline. The first of these alkaloids is 1,3,7-trimethyl-2,6-dioxypurine. Orowan has made the interesting suggestion that uric acid, like caffeine and theobromine may have some stimulating action on the central nervous system and that the primates, which have lost uricase from their complement of enzymes in the course of evolution and which now carry about 4 to 5 mg. of uric acid per 100 milliliters of plasma, have benefited from this endogenous cortical stimulant, in the development of the highest levels of intelligence (12). Haldane suggested two consequences of Orowan's hypothesis, which might be tested experimentally: (a) that hyperuricemic persons are, on the average, more intelligent or less easily fatigued than others; and (b), because of the constant low-level stimulation from the endogenous uric acid, that exogenously administered caffeine alkaloid would have less effect on them (13). Since these proposals were made the first suggestion has been tested. Stetten and Hearon have amassed data on over 800 army inductees, specifically on their serum uric acid concentration and their score on U.S. Army intelligence tests. The correlation coefficient between these two variables was found to be $+0.0759$, with a probability of 0.015. This indicates a significant but extremely low level of positive correlation (14). Obviously it does not indicate a causative relation. Stetten (15) has evaluated Orowan's suggestion in a discussion of the frequent association of high intellectual attainment with the hyperuricemic condition, gout.

## Nucleic Acids

The nucleic acids have been studied for almost 100 years. Their constituent units—the nitrogen bases, sugar, and phosphoric acid—have long been known but the manner in which the nucleotides are linked together has thus far been described with some precision only for RNA. Although both RNA and DNA possess the polynucleotide structure, they differ markedly in chemical and physical properties. This is attributable to some known factors such as the difference in the sugar component and the different pair of pyrimidines (cytosine and uracil in RNA; cytosine and thymine in DNA); probably macromolecular differences in the configuration of the polynucleotide strands are also responsible for the variation in properties. These differences show up, in solubility, which is so important a consideration in the extraction of the nucleic acids from the tissues. RNA dissolves in dilute salt solutions, but DNA does not; the latter is, however, extractable with strong sodium chloride solutions. RNA is also very susceptible to the action of alkali which depolymerizes it, but DNA is quite stable under the same conditions. The presence of a very active ribonuclease in many tissues introduces difficulties when the aim of extraction is to obtain a high-molecular-weight preparation of RNA.

The distribution of nitrogen bases differs also in the two types of nucleic acid. In DNA the ratios of adenine to thymine and of guanine to cytosine (therefore, also, of purines to pyrimidines) are very near unity, but in RNA these ratios are inconstant. On the other hand, the ratio of (adenine + cytosine) to (uracil + guanine) is approximately 1.0 in RNA.

## FUNCTIONS OF THE NUCLEIC ACIDS

The ribonucleic acids from different organs are variable in composition, and signify an organ-specific function of these compounds. By contrast, DNA appears to have the same composition in the various organs of a given species, and is reasonably constant in amount in the nucleus, except at cell division and some other occasions when it is formed. These facts are in keeping with the evidence that DNA is the principal genetic material. The identification of DNA as the functional constituent of the chromosomes necessarily assigns to it the dual role (a) of delivering specific substances to the cytoplasm, which initiate the regulation of cellular events, and (b) of duplicating itself to maintain the hereditary continuity through cell division. A great deal of attention has been focused on the macrostructure of DNA—its molecular shape and fiber size—as well as its microstructure, i.e., the arrangement of nucleotides along its strands. Indeed, it is the detailed order of the nucleotides, or rather their nitrogen bases, in the molecule that provides the "code" for exact replication of the DNA molecule itself as well as for synthesis of those others controlled by DNA. Several models have been constructed of the DNA molecule in the attempt to explain the facts of self-duplication and of coding. The former has been accounted for, on the basis of physical measurements, by representing the molecule as made up of two strands of polydeoxyribonucleotide wound around one another in the form of an elongated double helix. The model of this fibrous molecule has the purine of one chain juxtaposed to a pyrimidine of the other, the two being held together by hydrogen bonds. The order of the nitrogen bases and their specific pairing constitute the physical basis of the genetic code, according to this hypothesis. In cellular division one strand goes to each of the two daughter cells and constitutes the template upon which a new partner chain is synthesized.

The pairing of adenine with thymine and of guanine with cytosine has been shown to be compatible with molecular geometry.

RNA is associated with protein synthesis in the cell. This is based upon the observation that the RNA content of tissues increases in cells that are actively synthesizing protein (*cf.* Reference 16, also pp. 16, 24). However, more evidence is required to establish this RNA-protein relationship. Although a two-stranded structure with a specific combination of bases would also help explain the role of RNA in protein synthesis, no satisfactory configuration of the RNA molecule has been yet proposed. According to one view of the problem the arrangement of nitrogen bases, projecting outward from the skeleton of the RNA molecule, specifies the order in which amino acids condense together to form polypeptides. Others regard the ribonucleoprotein molecule as a whole as the template for formation of new protein.

Most of the RNA of the cell is of very high molecular weight, and is found associated with microsomes in the cell cytoplasm. Another portion of the RNA is present in the cytoplasm and is of much smaller molecular size. This soluble RNA (SRNA) has the role of carrying amino acids which have been activated by cytoplasmic enzymes to the template—microsomal RNA—upon which the peptide chains are presumed to be synthesized. Further discussion of the relation of nucleic acids to protein synthesis may be found in various reviews (*e.g.,* Ref. 17).

On the basis of the projected role of RNA in protein synthesis, Hyden has advanced a hypothesis of the intracellular processes involved in learning and recall in the central nervous system (18). The problem in essence is the translation of electrical (neuronal) information into a long-lasting biochemical code which can be broken, *i.e.,* repeatedly interpreted under appropriate conditions in the nervous system. Hyden suggests that the modulated frequency of impulses in the neuronal circuit affects the ionic equilibrium of the cytoplasm, and this, in turn, affects the stability of a nitrogenous base at a specific site in the RNA molecule. An exchange reaction takes place with another base substituting for the original one. The formation of RNA and protein attendant upon the neuronal activity allows the altered molecule to specify the structure of the newly formed molecules in terms of the sequence of structural components (nucleotides or amino acids). In the course of metabolism the specified protein evokes the complementary molecule at the next point in the neuronal circuit. Ultimately, this results in the release of the transmitter substance. The response pattern to the particular modulated frequency of stimulation is then guaranteed through this molecular mechanism.

The degree of variation in protein structure which RNA may endow is very high. Although differences between various RNA molecules originate in the order of arrangement of but four nitrogenous bases, adenine, guanine, cytosine and uracil, it has been estimated that these could give rise to about $10^{15}$ different arrangements. Hyden estimates that this is the probable number of items of information encoded during the life of a human being (18).

A test of biological activity of RNA has been made in aged patients suffering from failure of memory retention. Some beneficial effects were noted (18A).

The application of information theory to neurophysiological activity can be expected to depend more and more upon knowledge of the specific structure of the nucleic acids and their protein components, and how these polymeric molecules are put together. Very important advances have been made in the enzymatic mechanisms through which the nucleic acids are formed, particularly in the laboratories of Ochoa (19) and Kornberg (20). Just as there are differences in structure and composition of RNA and DNA, so do their modes of synthesis differ. In the case of RNA, specific enzymes catalyze the condensation of ribonucleoside diphosphates either singly or in combination to form a product which is not dissimilar from the natural RNA. The synthesis is shown in Reaction 10-6. (N = nitrogen base, R = ribose, P = phos-

$$\text{n NRPP} \rightleftarrows (\text{NRP})_n + \text{nPi} \tag{10-6}$$

phoric acid, Pi = inorganic phosphate.) Ochoa has called the enzyme catalyzing this reaction polynucleotide phosphorylase.

The enzymatic synthesis of DNA is somewhat different. The enzymes from bacterial as well as mammalian sources act upon the deoxynucleoside triphosphates in this case, and a mixture of these must serve as the substrate of Reaction 10-7 (dR = deoxyribose, P—P = in-

$$\text{n NdRPPP} \rightleftarrows (\text{NdRP})_n + \text{nP—P} \tag{10-7}$$

organic pyrophosphate). Both nucleotide phosphorylase and deoxynucleotide pyrophosphorylase require magnesium ions for activity. The reaction has to be primed with a small amount of the corresponding nucleic acid. In the synthetic reaction the nucleotide residues are added onto the primer or are constructed according to its model. The reverse reactions require inorganic phosphate or pyrophosphate, respectively.

## CHROMOSOMAL ABNORMALITIES (TABLE 10–2)

Chromosomal changes are of several kinds. According to current concepts a mutation is an alteration in the structure of a particular DNA molecule at some point along the axis of a chromosome. On the basis of what has been said above, the new structure provides the metabolizing cell with correspondingly new information based upon the altered molecular code. This may have far-reaching consequences in the cell because of a difference in the complement of enzymes that are formed. Among the present concepts of biochemical genetics is the view that enzyme formation is under genetic control (21). Changes, such as a loss of a particular enzymic activity (thereby producing a metabolic block), have been related to homozygosity for a recessive pair of genes. Examples of this are being discovered on an increasing scale in man as the study of human genetics progresses, and a number of the resulting phenotypes, *i.e.,* characteristic syndromes such as phenylketonuria and galactosemia, are discussed elsewhere in this book. Present knowledge does not permit us to say whether the enzyme is missing or whether it is actually formed with, let us say, an abnormal sequence of amino acids. If it is the latter, then the abnormality of structure would be serious enough to render the protein inactive as a catalyst. This would represent a state which Pauling describes as a molecular disease (p. 193).

Cytological studies of human tissues have recently revealed other types of chromosomal change: an increase or a decrease in the chromosome number (22). This may come about through the phenomenon of nondisjunction (23). Böök and Santesson have detected triploidy in a patient with a malformation syndrome (24), but abnormalities also arise from failure of individual chromosomes to separate completely at meiosis (23) or from translocation of material. In the case of the female sex chromosome this would result in two ova, both possessing the normal number of autosomes, but one without an X-chromosome, and the other with two of them. At fertilization four combinations would then be possible. One of these, YO, is nonviable, and another (XXX) has been recognized in *Drosophila* (the superfemale) and in man. The type with but a single X-chromosome and no partner (XO) is associated with gonadal dysgenesis (Turner's syndrome). In this condition the ovaries are absent or rudimentary. The

TABLE 10-2. CHROMOSOMAL DISORDERS AND BIOCHEMICAL DEFECTS

A. *Gross chromosomal disorders*
  1. Polyploidy: triploidy in a case of malformation syndrome
  2. Unit changes in chromosome numbers
     *a.* Non-disjunction at meiosis
        I. Autosomes
           i. mongolism; acute leukemia (n = 47)
           ii. low I.Q. associated with polydyspondylism (n = 45)
           iii. mongolism + Klinefelter's syndrome (n = 48)
        II. Sex chromatin
           i.   YO: nonviable
           ii.  XXX: *Drosophila* superfemale; weak female phenotype recognized clinically
           iii. XO: gonadal dysgenesis (Turner's syndrome)
           iv.  XXY: Klinefelter's syndrome (weak male phenotype)
     *b.* Mosaicism = nondisjunction at mitosis after first division. *e.g.*, Klinefelter's syndrome with some XXY cells, some XX
B. *Presumed microchanges in the chromosome* *
  1. Detected by the presence of abnormal molecules
     *a.* abnormal structures: Hemoglobin S
     *b.* Abnormal distributions of serum haptoglobins, transferrin, $\gamma$-globulins, etc.
  2. Detected by loss of specific enzymatic activity or characterized by a distinct biochemical feature
     *a.* In carbohydrate metabolism
        I. Glucose-6-phosphate dehydrogenase deficiency (sensitivity to primaquine, naphthalene, fava beans, etc.)
        II. Fructosuria (benign)
        III. Galactosemia (deficiency of galactose-1-phosphate uridyl transferase)
        IV. Glycogen storage diseases
        V. Post-prandial hypoglycemia; idiopathic hypoglycemia (sensitivity to leucine)
        VI. Pentosuria (benign)
        VII. Hunter-Hurler syndrome (deposit of acidic mucopolysaccharides)
     *b.* In lipide metabolism
        I. Idiopathic hyperlipemia (deficiency of lipase?)
        II. "Lipogranulomatosis" (storage of lipoglycoproteins)
        III. Sphingolipidoses: amaurotic family idiocy (infantile form = Tay-Sachs' disease); reticular and histiocytic sphingomyelinosis (Niemann-Pick's disease); Gaucher's disease

TABLE 10-2 (*Continued*)

---

   *c.* In protein metabolism
      I. Ceruloplasmin deficiency (hepatolenticular degeneration)
     II. Analbuminemia
    III. Agammaglobulinemia
    IV. Afibrinogenemia
     V. Idiopathic hemochromatosis
    VI. Acatalasemia
   *d.* In amino acid metabolism
      I. Primary hyperoxaluria (defect in glycine metabolism)
     II. Cystathioninuria
    III. Cystinuria
    IV. Maple-syrup urine disease (absence of enzymes catalyzing breakdown of keto acids derived from the branched-chain amino acids: valine, leucine, and isoleucine)
     V. Argininosuccinuria
    VI. Hartnup disease (defect in tryptophan absorption)
   VII. Phenylketonuria (lack of phenylalanine hydroxylase)
  VIII. Alcaptonuria (lack of homogentisicase)
    IX. Albinism (lack of tyrosinase)
   *e.* Other biochemical defects
      I. Isoniazid inactivation (slow and rapid detoxifiers)
     II. Hypophosphatasia (deficiency of serum and tissue alkaline phosphatase)
    III. Hyperkalemic familial periodic paralysis
    IV. T-substance anomaly (excretion of alloxanlike substance)
     V. Serum pseudocholinesterase deficiency (succinyldicholine sensitivity)
    VI. Erythrocyte acetylcholinesterase deficiency (paroxysmal nocturnal hemoglobinuria)

---

\* Selected examples are given. A genetic basis has been described for only some of the listed syndromes.

patient usually comes to the physician's attention when pubertal changes fail to occur. Ford and his colleagues describe the XO patient with gonadal dysgenesis as having the female phenotype with an abnormal genotype (23). The fourth possibility, the XXY type, has also been characterized in man (25); it is found in Klinefelter's syndrome, a disease characterized by a weak male phenotype.

Of great interest in this regard is the detection of a supernumerary autosome in persons with mongolism (25, 26) and in another syndrome of multiple abnormalities (27). Whereas the normal chromosome number is 46, the patients with these conditions have 47. The mechanism of action of this extra chromosome in initiating the changes that result in the mongoloid state is unknown. It may be that extra or abnormal enzymes are formed or that the additional chromosome interferes in some way with the directive action of the others upon the metabolic activities of the cell. Whatever the mechanism, the finding of a chromosomal basis to mongolism certainly warrants a concerted search for specific metabolic deviations in this disease.

# References

1. GEIGER, A., and S. YAMASAKI. *J. Neurochem. 1*:93, 1956; GEIGER, A. *Physiol. Revs. 38*:1, 1958.

2. MCILWAIN, H. *In Metabolism of the Nervous System, ed.* RICHTER, D., London, Pergamon Press, 1957.

3. KORANSKY, W. *Arch. exp. Path. u. Pharmakol. 234*:46, 1958.

4. MANDEL, P., and S. HARTH. *J. de Physiol. 52*:166, 1960.

5. SCHMITZ, H., V. R. POTTER, R. B. HURLBERT, and D. M. WHITE. *Cancer Res. 14*:66, 1954.

6. MIHAILOVIC, L., B. D. JANKOVIC, M. PETKOVIC, and D. MANCIC. *Experientia 14*:9, 1958.

7. MAY, L., and R. G. GRENELL. *Proc. Soc. Exp. Biol. Med. 102*:235, 1959.

8. MIHAILOVIC, L., B. D. JANKOVIC, M. PETKOVIC, and K. ISAKOVIC. *Experientia 14*:144, 1958.

9. SPIEGEL-ADOLF, M., P. H. WILCOX, and E. A. SPIEGEL. *Am. J. Psychiat. 104*:697, 1948.

10. SMITH, L. H., JR., and F. A. BAKER. *J. Clin. Invest. 38*:798, 1959.

11. BLUMBERG, B. S., and S. M. GARTLER. *Nature 184*:1990, 1959.

12. OROWAN, E. *Nature 175*:683, 1955.

13. HALDANE, J. B. S. *Nature 176*:169, 1955.

14. STETTEN, D., JR., and J. Z. HEARON. *Science 129*:1737, 1959.

15. STETTEN, D., JR. *Perspectives in Biol. Med. 2*:185, 1959.

16. HYDEN, H. *In Neurochemistry, ed.* ELLIOTT, K. A. C., I. H. PAGE, and J. H. QUASTEL, Springfield, Ill., Charles C Thomas, 1955.

17. WILKINS, M. H. F. *In Biochemical Society Symposium No. 14, ed.* CROOK, E. M. New York, Cambridge University Press, 1957; RICH, A. *Ann. N.Y. Acad. Sci. 81*:709, 1959.

18. HYDEN, H. *In Proceedings IVth International Congress on Biochemistry,* Vienna, 1958, Vol. 3, London, Pergamon Press, 1959.

18A. CAMERON, D. E., and L. SOLYOM. *Geriatrics 16*:74, 1961.

19. GRUNBERG-MANAGO, M., and S. OCHOA. *J. Am. Chem. Soc. 77*:3165, 1955; OCHOA, S. *Ann. N.Y. Acad. Sci. 81*:690, 1959.

20. KORNBERG, A. *Science 131*:1503, 1960.

21. BEADLE, G. W. *Chem. Rev. 37*:15, 1945.

22. BARR, M. L. *Science 130*:679, 1959.
23. FORD, C. E., K. W. JONES, P. E. POLANI, J. C. DE ALMEIDA, and J. H. BRIGGS. *Lancet i*:711, 1959.
24. BÖÖK, J. A., and B. SANTESSON. *Lancet i*:858, 1960.
25. FORD, C. E., K. W. JONES, O. J. MILLER, U. MITTWOCH, L. S. PENROSE, M. RIDLER, and A. SHAPIRO. *Lancet i*:709, 1959.
26. LEJEUNE, L., M. GAUTHIER, and R. TURPIN. *Compt. Rend. Acad. Sci. Paris 248*:602, 1959; JACOBS, P. A., A. G. BAIKIE, W. M. C. BROWN, and J. A. STRONG. *Lancet i*:710, 1959.
27. EDWARDS, J. H., D. G. HARNDEN, A. H. CAMERON, V. M. CROSSE, and O. H. WOLFF. *Lancet i*:787, 1960; SMITH, D. W., K. PATAU, E. THERMAN, and S. L. INHORN. *J. Pediat. 56*:338, 1960.

# 11

# CARBOHYDRATES

## Chemistry and Classification

The carbohydrates constitute only a small fraction of the weight of the mammalian organism, but their functional importance is recognizable in almost every physiological activity: in energy metabolism (glucose, glycogen, the pentoses), in preserving the stability of the blood (heparin), in maintaining normal connective tissue metabolism (the mucopolysaccharides, ascorbic acid), in specificity reactions (blood group substances, glycoproteins), in detoxication processes (glucuronic acid), in the structure of nucleic acids (ribose, deoxyribose), and in neuronal metabolism (galactose, glucosamine, galactosamine, neuraminic acid, gangliosides).

The simplest carbohydrates possess the empirical formula $(CH_2O)_n$. The first member of the series $(n = 1)$ is formaldehyde and, although this compound is not generally classified as a carbohydrate, it is certainly an important one in several metabolic sequences, even perhaps playing a role in the biosynthesis of trioses (*i.e.*, 3-carbon sugars). Higher members of the series, up to the heptuloses (7-carbon sugars), have been detected in animal metabolism. These are the monosaccharide units condensed together in glycosidic linkage; examples of these are lactose (consisting of glucose and galactose), sucrose (glucose and fructose), and maltose (two glucose units). Polysaccharides are made up of large numbers of the smaller units; the best known in the animal kingdom is glycogen, and in the plant world starch.

The empirical formula shows that the carbohydrates are polyhydroxylated carbon compounds. One or more additional functional groups serve to classify them. Thus, the common *aldoses* possess a terminal aldehyde group (*e.g.,* glucose, galactose, mannose, ribose); the ketoses, a ketonic group (*e.g.,* fructose, sedoheptulose, ribulose); the amino sugars, an amino group as well as the carbonyl function (*e.g.,* glucosamine, galactosamine, neuraminic acid). There are also sugar acids, in which one of the terminal carbons has been oxidized: in glucuronic acid it is the primary alcoholic group which has been converted to the carboxyl; in ascorbic acid, the aldehyde has been oxidized to the corresponding acid. Partially reduced sugars also occur (deoxyribose, fucose). The polymeric carbohydrates, or polysaccharides, consist of but one sugar, such as glucose in glycogen or in starch, or of several, as in the mucopolysaccharides. Some of these contain hexosamine, galactose, mannose, fucose, and sialic acid (N-acylneuraminic acid), and have a more or less neutral reaction. The acidic mucopolysaccharides contain hexuronic acid, N-acetylhexosamine, and sulfuric acid; they are represented by the chondroitin sulfates, heparins, and hyaluronic acid. Some mucopolysaccharides are linked to protein. Sugar-containing lipides (cerebrosides, gangliosides) are well-known compounds in nervous tissue.

Neuraminic acid and compounds containing it are discussed in Chapter 12.

## Digestion, Absorption, Assimilation (1)

Carbohydrates are absorbed from the small intestine as monosaccharides. Digestion of starch to the disaccharide stage begins early under the influence of salivary amylase. Disaccharidases occur in the small intestine and their action completes the prerequisites for the absorptive process. The sugars are absorbed at differential rates, glucose uptake being relatively rapid.

For half a century sugar-tolerance tests have been employed to estimate the individual's ability to absorb and assimilate orally administered sugar. Criteria have been established regarding the height of the venous blood sugar concentration and the time taken for it to return to preingestion level. Subjects in whom the hyperglycemia is abnormally great or in whom it persists for long are said to have low tolerance. Brief-lasting hyperglycemia or a mildly elevated blood sugar concentration is a mark of high tolerance. Older subjects, even those in good health, may show abnormally low glucose tolerance, and this fact must be taken into account in studies of psychiatric patients. Many variations of the tolerance test have been described, including the substitution of fructose, galactose, or xylose for the more commonly employed glucose.

Absorbed sugar passes from the intestinal lumen into the parenchymal tissue, and thence into the circulating blood. It reaches the liver where it is phosphorylated by the enzyme, hexokinase (Reaction 11-1) to glucose-6-phosphate (glucose-6-P). The product is isomerized enzymatically (Reaction 11-2) to glucose-1-P (P representing ester phosphate). This compound, the Cori ester, is linked in Reaction 11-3 to

$$\text{Glucose} + \text{ATP} \rightarrow \text{Glucose-6-P} + \text{ADP} \qquad (11\text{-}1)$$

$$\text{Glucose-6-P} \rightleftarrows \text{Glucose-1-P} \qquad (11\text{-}2)$$

$$\underset{\substack{\text{Uridine}\\\text{triphosphate}}}{\text{Glucose-1-P} + \text{UTP}} \rightarrow \underset{\substack{\text{Uridine diphosphate}\\\text{glucose}}}{\text{UDPG}} + \underset{\text{Pyrophosphate}}{\text{PP}} \qquad (11\text{-}3)$$

uridylic acid, with the formation of uridine diphosphate glucose (UDPG) and it is this product which is the substrate for glycogen-synthesizing enzymes. Other glycogen-forming sugars must first be converted to UDPG. For example, absorbed fructose is phosphorylated and isomerized to glucose-6-P as the first stage in its utilization.

The action of phosphorylase permits the reformation of glucose-1-P (Reaction 11-4) and glucose-6-P. This process occurs under conditions

$$\text{Glycogen} + \text{n } H_3PO_4 \rightleftarrows \text{n Glucose-1-P} \qquad (11\text{-}4)$$

favoring the formation of blood sugar, as in hypoglycemia. A glucose-6-phosphatase in liver completes the sequence by hydrolytically releasing glucose and inorganic phosphate.

## Pathways of Intermediary Metabolism

The dissimilation of glucose is one of the prime energy-yielding processes in metabolism. The first major process of carbohydrate metabolism to be discovered in mammalian and many other tissues is known as the Meyerhof-Embden pathway of glycolysis. It consists of the breakdown of the sugar to triose phosphates and thence to pyruvic acid ($C_6 \rightarrow 2C_3$). Parallel reactions divert a portion of the sugar into the so-called monophosphate shunt or pentose phosphate pathway, in which 5-carbon sugars are formed $(C_6 \rightarrow C_5 + CO_2)$. Pentoses which have been absorbed from the diet can be converted into hexose sugars (via the triose phosphates) by additional "shunt" enzymes (*cf.* Figure 11-1).

The terminal oxidation of carbohydrate commences with the oxidative decarboxylation of pyruvic acid and the simultaneous thio-esterification of the product to form acetylcoenzyme A. The next stage is the condensation of acetylcoenzyme A with oxaloacetic acid to form citric

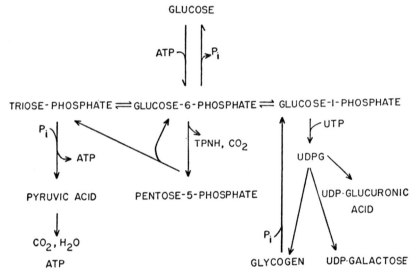

Figure 11-1. Alternate pathways of metabolism of glucose.

acid (and free coenzyme A). In this way, the pyruvic acid molecule formed in glycolysis loses one of its carbons as carbon dioxide and is prepared for complete combustion in the citric acid cycle (2). This cycle consists of a group of enzymes whose consecutive operation results in the degradation of the citric acid to oxaloacetic acid with the formation of carbon dioxide from two of the citric acid carbons $(C_2 + C_4 \rightarrow C_6 \rightarrow C_4 + 2CO_2)$. It is also called the tricarboxylic acid cycle because in its initial stages several such acids are formed, in succession. Later on, dicarboxylic acids (among them, oxaloacetic) appear. Krebs has formulated a unifying concept of intermediary metabolism, in which this cycle of reaction plays a central role in the terminal oxidation of numerous metabolites. Three acids are focal points, in this respect: (*a*) acetic (in the form of its coenzyme A thioester) is derived from carbohydrate, fatty acids, glycine, and certain other amino acids; (*b*) α-ketoglutaric acid (see below) is formed from glutamic acid, proline, histidine, and arginine; (*c*) oxaloacetic acid is derived from aspartic acid, tryptophan, phenylalanine, and tyrosine (*cf.* Figure 11-2).

## GLYCOLYSIS

The initial reactions in the breakdown of glycogen have been presented above (Reactions 11-4 and 11-2). Dissimilation of the sugar

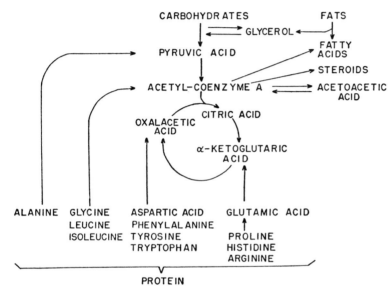

Figure 11-2. Interrelationships of metabolic paths of carbohydrates, fats, and protein.

to pyruvic (or lactic) acid then proceeds as shown in Reactions 11-5 to 11-10. Reaction 11-7 provides the substrate for the dehydrogenation

$$\text{Glucose-6-P} \rightleftarrows \text{Fructose-6-P} \qquad (11\text{-}5)$$

$$\text{Fructose-6-P} + \text{ATP} \rightarrow \text{Fructose-1,6-diphosphate} + \text{ADP} \qquad (11\text{-}6)$$

$$\text{Fructose diphosphate} \rightleftarrows 2 \text{ Triose-3-P} \qquad (11\text{-}7)$$

$$\text{Triose-3-P} + P_i + \text{DPN}^+ \rightleftarrows \text{1,3-Diphosphoglyceric acid} + \text{DPNH} + \text{H}^+ \qquad (11\text{-}8)$$

$$\text{1,3-Diphosphoglyceric acid} + 2\text{ADP} \rightarrow \text{Pyruvic acid} + 2 \text{ ATP} \qquad (11\text{-}9)$$

$$\text{Pyruvic acid} + \text{DPNH} + \text{H}^+ \rightleftarrows \text{Lactic acid} + \text{DPN}^+ \qquad (11\text{-}10)$$

reaction in which DPN participates (*i.e.,* Reaction 11-8). Diphosphogly-cerate is transformed, with the contribution of its phosphate groups to ADP, into pyruvic acid (Reaction 11-9). Under aerobic conditions the reduced coenzyme (DPNH) of Reaction 11-8 is reoxidized to $DPN^+$ but, when the supply of oxygen is limited as in conditions of continued muscular activity or deficient blood supply, the pyruvate, which constitutes the terminus of the glycolytic pathway, is itself reduced to lactate by the reduced coenzyme (Reaction 11-10). In this way, two mols of triose phosphate yield four mols of high energy phosphate in the course of the stepwise conversion to pyruvate. The carbohydrate from which the triose phosphate originates makes use of two such bonds in order to bring it to the triose phosphate stage. This means that there is a net gain of useful energy (stored in the form of ATP) resulting from the oxidative step in glycolysis. Fructose, galactose, and mannose, three other dietary sugars, can be phosphorylated and brought into the glycolytic pathway also.

## METABOLISM OF PYRUVIC ACID

The further metabolism of pyruvic acid is mediated by a complex combination of enzymes and coenzymes whose action may be represented by Reactions 11-11 to 11-16. The mechanism of Reaction 11-11 is

$$\text{Pyruvic acid} + \text{Coenzyme A} \rightarrow \text{Acetyl-coenzyme A} + CO_2 \tag{11-11}$$

$$\text{Pyruvic acid} + CO_2 \rightleftarrows \text{Oxaloacetic acid} \tag{11-12}$$

$$\text{Oxaloacetic acid} + \text{Acetyl-coenzyme A} \rightleftarrows \text{Citric acid} + \text{Coenzyme A} \tag{11-13}$$

$$2 \text{ Acetyl-coenzyme A} \rightarrow \text{Acetoacetyl-coenzyme A} + \text{Coenzyme A} \tag{11-14}$$

$$\text{Acetoacetyl-coenzyme A} + H_2O \rightarrow \text{Acetoacetic acid} + \text{Coenzyme A} \tag{11-15}$$

$$2 \text{ Pyruvic acid} \rightarrow 2CO_2 + \text{Acetoin (Acetylmethylcarbinol)} \tag{11-16}$$

very complex, for not only is coenzyme A involved as a direct reactant, but diphosphothiamine, DPN, and lipoic acid are also needed as co-factors (3). Quantitatively speaking the citrate condensation (Reaction 11-13) is the most important reaction of pyruvic acid and leads ultimately to its complete oxidation.

The formation of hexoses and glycogen from pyruvic acid does not simply entail a reversal of reactions previously described. The pyruvic acid must be phosphorylated and converted to 3-phosphoglyceric acid. Additional phosphorylation yields 1,3-diphosphoglyceric acid, the metabolism of which can be traced to hexose in reactions already described.

The carboxylation of pyruvic acid (Reaction 11-12) maintains a steady supply of oxaloacetic acid for citrate formation. In thiamine deficiency acetyl-coenzyme A synthesis from pyruvic acid is limited because of the reduced concentration of DPT; hence, pyruvic acid accumulates in the body fluids. When glucose metabolism is depressed and pyruvic acid formation is reduced the equilibrium relationships normally obtaining among the various reactions in which pyruvic acid is utilized are upset and minor paths of metabolism, normally accounting for very little of the pyruvic acid which is dissimilated, are now thrown into prominence. Thus, reduction in glycolytic rate may be so great as to reduce appreciably the oxaloacetate level in the tissues and, therefore, the rate of entrance of pyruvic acid as acetyl-coenzyme A, into the tricarboxylic acid cycle. Because of this, acetoacetic acid (and other ketone bodies) begin to accumulate (Reactions 11-14 and 11-15) at a faster rate than the peripheral tissues can metabolize them.

Some circumstances have been found in which minor metabolites such as acetoin (Reaction 11-16) and its reduction product butane-2,3-diol, increase in the body fluids. Clinically, this is seen in some severe cases of diabetes. Experimentally, the injection of pyruvate causes increased amounts of acetoin to appear in the blood.

Methylglyoxal (pyruvic aldehyde) is sometimes found in mammalian tissues. Although its specific precursor is not known, it is probably of carbohydrate origin. There are enzymes in the liver and elsewhere which convert it to lactic acid; one of them utilizes glutathione (GSH) as its coenzyme (Reaction 11-17). Pyruvic acid is then formed through Reaction 11-10.

$$\text{Methylglyoxal} \longrightarrow \text{Lactic acid} \qquad (11\text{-}17)$$
$$\text{CH}_3\text{COCHO} + \text{H}_2\text{O} \xrightarrow{\text{(GSH)}} \text{CH}_3\text{CHOHCOOH}$$

## THE TRICARBOXYLIC ACID CYCLE

The first tricarboxylic acid in the terminal oxidative cycle, citric acid, is rearranged enzymatically to isocitric acid and this compound is oxidized to α-ketoglutaric acid (Reaction 11-18). α-Ketoglutaric

Isocitric acid + TPN$^+$ → $\alpha$-Ketoglutaric acid

$$+ CO_2 + TPNH + H^+ \quad (11\text{-}18)$$

acid undergoes dehydrogenation, along with a loss of $CO_2$. The dicarboxylic acid, succinic, is formed and ultimately gives rise to oxaloacetic acid (Reactions 11-19 to 11-22).

$\alpha$-Ketoglutaric acid + TPN$^+$ + Coenzyme A $\rightleftarrows$ $CO_2$

$$+ \text{Succinyl-coenzyme A} + TPNH + H^+ \quad (11\text{-}19)$$

$$\text{Succinic acid} \rightleftarrows \text{Fumaric acid} + 2H \quad (11\text{-}20)$$

$$\text{Fumaric acid} + H_2O \rightleftarrows \text{Malic acid} \quad (11\text{-}21)$$

$$\text{Malic acid} + DPN^+ \rightleftarrows \text{Oxaloacetic acid} + DPNH + H^+ \quad (11\text{-}22)$$

## THE PENTOSE PHOSPHATE PATHWAY

Besides the glycolytic pathway glucose-6-P can be metabolized through a second series of reactions, more important than the subsidiary significance implied in the name monophosphate shunt. This series is initiated by the dehydrogenation of the 6-ester (Reaction 11-23) and proceeds as shown in Reactions 11-24 to 11-26. In the transketolation

Glucose-6-P + TPN$^+$ $\rightleftarrows$ 6-Phosphogluconic acid + TPNH

$$+ H^+ \quad (11\text{-}23)$$

6-Phosphogluconic acid + TPN$^+$ $\rightleftarrows$ Ribulose-5-P + $CO_2$ + TPNH

$$+ H^+ \quad (11\text{-}24)$$

$$\text{Xylulose-5-P} \rightleftarrows \text{Ribulose-5-P} \rightleftarrows \text{Ribose-5-P} \rightleftarrows \text{Ribose-1-P} \quad (11\text{-}25)$$

Ribulose-5-P + Ribose-5-P $\rightleftarrows$ Glyceraldehyde-3-P

$$+ \text{Sedoheptulose-7-P} \quad (11\text{-}26)$$

represented in Reaction 11-26 ($C_5 + C_5 \rightleftarrows C_3 + C_7$) the ribulose-5-P molecule is split to yield the 3-carbon sugar formed in glycolysis (*cf.* Reaction 11-7) and active glycoaldehyde, the 2-carbon fragment which is transferred to ribose-5-P. This reaction is catalyzed by an enzyme requiring DPT as coenzyme. Hexose phosphate can be regenerated by transaldolation (Reactions 11-27 and 11-28). As already discussed,

Sedoheptulose-7-P + Glyceraldehyde-3-P $\rightleftarrows$ Tetrose-4-P

$$+ \text{Fructose-6-P} \quad (11\text{-}27)$$

Pentose-5-P + Tetrose-4-P $\rightleftarrows$ Glyceraldehyde-3-P

$$+ \text{Fructose-6-P} \quad (11\text{-}28)$$

glyceraldehyde-3-P (triose phosphate) and fructose-6-P can be converted into glucose phosphates. Reactions 11-23 to 11-28 illustrate how sugars of different chain lengths can be formed in the body. Other reactions of the same kind extend the scope of this carbohydrate arithmetic and of the types of sugars formed.

## OTHER REACTIONS OF CARBOHYDRATES

The formation of glycolaldehyde ($HOCH_2CHO$) in the active (*i.e.*, readily transferable) form occurs not only when ribose-5-P is the donor (Reaction 11-26) but with other keto sugars too. Furthermore, it is formed enzymatically by the decarboxylation of hydroxypyruvic acid ($HOCH_2COCOOH$). One of the sources of hydroxypyruvic acid is through the transamination of L-serine (Reaction 11-29). Although

$$HOCH_2CH(NH_2)COOH + CH_3COCOOH \rightarrow HOCH_2COCOOH$$
$$+ CH_3CH(NH_2)COOH \quad (11\text{-}29)$$

glycolaldehyde is best known as a transient intermediate in transketolation, at least a small portion appears to enter another metabolic route after its release from the bound form. The free compound readily undergoes oxidation to the corresponding acid, glycollic acid, which may also originate from the amino acid glycine through the action of an oxidase (Reaction 11-30) and a pyridine nucleotide-linked dehydrogenase (Reaction 11-31).

Glycine                      Glyoxylic acid     Ammonia
$$H_2NCH_2COOH + H_2O + O_2 \rightarrow HCOCOOH + NH_3 + H_2O_2$$
$$(11\text{-}30)$$

Glyoxylic acid                       Glycollic acid
$$CHOCOOH + DPNH + H^+ \rightleftarrows HOCH_2COOH + DPN^+ \quad (11\text{-}31)$$

Glucuronic acid is an important conjugating agent in metabolism for both specific endogenous substances (*e.g.*, adrenal cortical hormones, bilirubin) and some drugs. Combination with glucuronic acid renders the compound considerably more water-soluble. The process requires uridine triphosphate (UTP) and comes about as shown in Reactions 11-3, 11-32, and 11-33 (see also Figure 11-1).

$$UDPG + 2DPN^+ + H_2O \rightarrow UDPGlucuronide + 2DPNH + 2H^+$$
$$(11\text{-}32)$$

$$UDPGlucuronide + Bilirubin \rightarrow Bilirubin\ glucuronide + UDP \quad (11\text{-}33)$$

The oxidation of glucose to glucuronic acid may be the preliminary step in many species toward the formation of L-ascorbic acid, or vitamin C. D-Galactose has also been proposed as the natural starting material for this biosynthesis. In either case the intermediary steps lead to the formation of L-gulono- or L-galactonolactone, respectively; both compounds yield L-ascorbic acid upon oxidation by a specific dehydrogenase. The absence of this L-galactonolactone dehydrogenase from the tissues of the guinea pig determines the dietary requirement of this species for vitamin C. Presumably the same enzymatic defect in man is responsible for the human requirement for this vitamin also.

Glucuronic acid represents an important constituent of mucopolysaccharides such as hyaluronic and chondroitinsulfuric acids. UDP-glucuronic acid plays a key role in the biosynthesis of these substances.

Amino sugars can be formed with the participation of glutamine; the phosphorylated amino sugars serve as substrate for acetylation (Reactions 11-34 and 11-35). Through the action of a phosphoglucomutase-like enzyme the phosphoryl radical is transposed to the first carbon atom

$$\text{Hexose-6-P} + \text{Glutamine} \rightarrow \text{Hexosamine-6-P}$$
$$+ \text{Glutamic acid} \quad (11\text{-}34)$$

$$\text{Glucosamine-6-P} + \text{Acetyl-coenzyme A} \rightarrow \text{N-Acetylglucosamine-6-P}$$
$$+ \text{Coenzyme A} \quad (11\text{-}35)$$

$$\text{N-Acetylglucosamine-1-P} + \text{UTP} \rightarrow \text{UDP-N-Acetylglucosamine}$$
$$+ \text{PP} \quad (11\text{-}36)$$

of the sugar derivative, and then incorporation of this molecule takes place into a uridine diphosphonucleotide. It is the UDP ester in Reaction 11-36 which is concerned with the introduction of acetylhexosamine into gangliosides and mucopolysaccharides.

## Hormonal and Nervous Regulation of Carbohydrate Metabolism

The maintenance of normal carbohydrate metabolism is a complex process under the control of several endocrine glands as well as the nervous system. Our knowledge about the latter mechanisms is much less complete than about the humoral ones.

The diet provides the major supply of carbohydrate, but some is also derived in metabolism from proteins, and this process of gluconeogenesis (synthesis of carbohydrate from noncarbohydrate sources) plays an important role under many conditions. It is accelerated by the adrenal cortical hormones.

Shifts in carbohydrate from one organ to another occur during muscular exercise. In mild activity the pyruvic acid generated in glycolysis is readily catabolized through the tricarboxylic acid cycle. When the work output increases pyruvic acid is formed in greater quantities, the oxygen supply to the muscle fibers is insufficient to metabolize it all, and then lactic acid is formed (Reaction 11-10). This lactic acid circulates to the liver where it is resynthesized into glycogen. Blood sugar, which is formed from this glycogen, can then return to the muscle and other peripheral tissues.

These general processes of carbohydrate metabolism: glucose uptake by the tissues, gluconeogenesis, glycolysis, oxidation, and the lactic acid cycle, are all influenzed by the secretions of a number of endocrine glands, chief among which is the pancreas. Excision of this organ is followed by diabetes mellitus, the metabolic sequelae of which are reversed by the administration of insulin. In spite of our extensive and detailed knowledge of the intermediary steps in the breakdown of glucose and in the formation of glycogen the specific metabolic or enzymatic defect in this disorder is unknown. It has been shown experimentally that insulin favors the entrance of monosaccharides into cells and the phosphorylation of glucose there. The opposite state of affairs in insulin deficiency consists of an elevated blood sugar and reduced rate of glycolysis. It is possible that in diabetes there is also an enhanced activity of glucose-6-phosphatase in the liver so that more glucose-6-P is diverted from the glycolytic pathway into the free glucose pool than is normally the case. The decrease in the breakdown of sugar leads inevitably to a reduction in the amount of pyruvic acid going to form oxaloacetic acid by way of Reaction 11-12 and, thereby, to a reduction in the level of the polycarboxylic acids which catalyze terminal combustion. Specifically, there is a deficiency of oxaloacetic acid available for condensation with acetyl-coenzyme A (formed in Reaction 11-11). The chief alternate route followed by the acetyl-coenzyme A is that of self-condensation (Reaction 11-14) with the formation of acetoacetic acid (Reaction 11-15). It is, hence, possible to explain the major biochemical alterations in diabetes mellitus, but it must be kept in mind that this is a syndrome with various etiologies and that its course is profoundly affected by many endocrine, constitutional, and hereditary factors.

In addition to the defective utilization of carbohydrate in diabetes there is also a relative overproduction of carbohydrate by gluconeogenesis. This too, is restored to normal by the administration of insulin.

The release of insulin from the $\beta$-cells of the islets of Langerhans is under a fine homeostatic control. The concentration of glucose in the blood directly influences the secretory activity of the islets so that an elevation of the blood sugar is countered by the release of insulin into the blood stream. The Exton-Rose glucose-tolerance test represents one means of testing this homeostatic mechanism. Two portions of glucose are consumed in this form of the test; these are taken 30 minutes apart. The blood sugar concentration is estimated in samples drawn just before each dose and 30 minutes after the second. Normally, the first portion of glucose evokes the release of sufficient insulin to avoid any secondary increase in the blood sugar level following the consumption of the second dose. In some adult diabetics this type of regulation falters; then the release of insulin can be stimulated by the so-called oral insulins such as the sulfonylureas. Juvenile diabetics, by contrast, suffer from a lack of insulin in the islet tissue and the sulfonylureas are ineffective in their cases. The mechanism of action of these oral insulins is not understood.

Experimental diabetes can also be produced by the administration of excessive amounts of adrenal cortical hormones. Conversely, removal of the adrenal cortices renders the animal hypersensitive to insulin and, in fact, ameliorates pancreatic diabetes. How the anti-insulin action comes about is not known. A suggestion made some years ago that the adrenal cortical hormones potentiate the inhibition of hexokinase by anterior pituitary extracts has not been confirmed.

The anterior pituitary gland modulates carbohydrate metabolism through at least two of its secretions. One of these, corticotropin, acts through the adrenal cortex. It favors gluconeogenesis, causes glycogen deposition, raises the blood sugar, and reverses hypoglycemia induced by insulin. The other important secretion in this regard is the growth hormone. The type of result obtained with it depends upon many factors, chief among which is the chronicity of treatment. In acute experiments growth hormone causes the secretion of insulin, but after repeated injections its diabetogenic action is in evidence, perhaps as a result of exhaustion of the $\beta$-cells of the islets of Langerhans (4). The contrainsulin effects of growth hormone have been demonstrated on various test systems: blood sugar level, glucose utilization by isolated skeletal muscle, and others. Treatment with growth hormone is accompanied by the appearance in the plasma of an anti-insulin factor (4, 5). The titer of this factor is much higher in insulin-resistant subjects than in normal persons or insulin-sensitive diabetics.

Epinephrine exerts its contrainsulin action by catalyzing the conversion of phosphorylase into its active form. As a result more glycogen is broken down and more glucose-6-P is made available within the cell for maintenance of the blood sugar and for glycolysis. The effects of epinephrine on carbohydrate metabolism are demonstrable in isolated tissue, such as strips of rat diaphragm. The release of epinephrine from the adrenal medulla is under nervous control through fibers carried in the splanchnic nerves. This function of the sympathoadrenal system is constantly kept in play in making the minor adjustments of homeostasis, in effecting the greater ones embraced in Cannon's concept of emergency reactions, and in the expression of emotions. The efferent postganglionic fibers of the sympathetic nervous system release norepinephrine as the neuroeffector agent, but this hormone is considerably less active than epinephrine in bringing about the breakdown of glycogen.

The actions of a second pancreatic hormone, glucagon, provide some contrast to those of insulin. Glucagon displays hyperglycemic, glycogenolytic, and gluconeogenic functions, none of which appears to be mediated through a simple direct antagonism of insulin. It is synthesized in the $\alpha$-cells of the islet tissue (see Chapter 27).

An anti-insulin factor in serum has already been mentioned (5). It combines with insulin to form an inactive complex. Haavaldsen and his colleagues (6) have associated this type of action with a member of the $\alpha_1$-globulin fraction of the plasma. They consider that some schizophrenics produce more than normal amounts of this substance. Their evidence for this is based upon the finding that plasma from such subjects can inhibit the uptake of glucose by skeletal muscle *in vitro,* or at least cause a reduction in the amount of glucose taken up in the presence of normal serum. This phenomenon has also been observed by Streifler and Kornblueth (7) who used rat retina respiring in a glucose-containing medium as the test system. The glucose utilization by this tissue, some of whose metabolic characteristics resemble those of the brain, was significantly lower in the presence of serum of schizophrenics than that of healthy persons. Frohman et al. have described similar evidence for a plasma factor in schizophrenic patients (8). Haavaldsen, too, noted that the plasma of some schizophrenic subjects lacks a factor which is normally present and which stimulates glucose uptake.

It was Claude Bernard who first demonstrated the role of the nervous system in carbohydrate metabolism through his experiments associating glucosuria with damage to medullary centers (piqûre). Hypothalamic lesions may also cause diabetes. This subject is of growing significance in endocrinological studies as illustrated in the relationships which have already been worked out between hypothalamic and endocrine (*e.g.,* adenohypophyseal) functions (Chapter 23).

## Carbohydrate Metabolism of Brain and Nerve (9)

The maintenance of the activities of the brain depends ultimately upon the continuous metabolism of substances in that organ to provide the necessary energy. This energy is utilized (a) in preserving the integrity and function of cellular membranes; (b) in the transfer of certain materials across membranes; and (c) in nervous transmission. These are some of the prerequisites for the complex neurophysiological-psychological functions of the brain. It is now well appreciated that the primary fuel whose combustion liberates this energy is carbohydrate. In slices of cerebral tissue incubated in buffered media the greatest stimulation of oxygen uptake is occasioned by the addition of glucose or pyruvic acid. Although other carbohydrates, such as fructose and lactic acid, support respiration (i.e., the utilization of oxygen), they must be added to the media in relatively high concentrations. However, these compounds all have one feature in common: they support respiration and they permit it to increase when the isolated slices are artificially stimulated by electrical pulses. This feature stands in contrast to the action of other carbohydrates and carbohydrate-like materials, such as tricarboxylic acid cycle intermediates, which can stimulate respiration but which cannot raise the rate of respiration to a higher level when electrical impulses are passed.

As might be expected, the range of carbohydrates capable of supporting the oxidative activity of the brain *in vivo* (studied both by perfusion and by infusion experiments) is even more limited, for now there are additional rate-limiting reactions to contend with. Permeability is more selective; the nutrient must pass through the membrane of the cerebral cell as well as the vascular epithelium. Moreover, metabolites which support respiratory activity of the cerebral tissue *in vitro* may not be sufficiently active in this respect or may not be converted to utilizable nutrients at a sufficiently rapid rate to maintain this respiration *in situ* along with all the other functions of the brain which are based upon it. Fructose, lactic acid, and pyruvic acid belong in this category; they cannot substitute for glucose *in vivo*.

Several groups have investigated the respiratory quotient of the brain and have found it to be very nearly 1.0. This result indicates that carbohydrate is the main substrate *in vivo*. The fraction of the oxygen consumption and carbon dioxide production not accounted for by combustion of glucose is but a small proportion of the total, but this portion represents the extent to which noncarbohydrate substances (*e.g.*, glutamic and other amino acids) are utilized normally.

# Spontaneous Hypoglycemia (10, 11)

There are many diverse causes of spontaneous hypoglycemia (for their classification see Reference 10) and only a few types will be discussed here. Conn has emphasized the great importance of the differential diagnosis of the syndrome, inasmuch as some of the symptoms may falsely direct attention to "brain tumor, epilepsy, acute alcoholism, encephalitis, neurocirculatory asthenia, cardiac neurosis, various psychoses, atypical angina pectoris and peptic ulcer."

## FUNCTIONAL HYPOGLYCEMIA

This is a form of autonomic imbalance showing up in the erratic control of the blood sugar level. It has also been called physiological or neurogenic hypoglycemia and functional hyperinsulinism. Even on diets containing adequate carbohydrate the patient suffers from spontaneous episodes of hypoglycemia. For example, after a meal the blood sugar does not become stabilized at the normal level but drops below the preprandial concentration, to about 50 to 60 mg. percent. The hypoglycemia does not occur during the night or early morning, thus excluding an effect of fasting. The patient is frequently under physical or emotional strain. Conn regards susceptible individuals as "hyperreactors in general, manifesting instability of the vegetative nervous system in many ways" such as through vasomotor fluctuations or gastric hyperacidity. The symptoms of hypoglycemia are usually referable to brain function, perhaps because of the reduction in the supply of sugar to this organ. The hypoglycemia probably represents the result of excessive release of insulin from the pancreas by the preceding meal; by the time the blood sugar has dropped to normal levels insulin action is still present. The restriction of carbohydrate in the diet has a salutary effect upon the condition.

Broberger et al. (12) have used an insulin-tolerance test in cases of idiopathic hypoglycemia. In contrast to healthy children given insulin, these patients respond with a greater fall in the blood sugar and without an increase in the urinary excretion of epinephrine.

## FAMILIAL HYPOGLYCEMIA (13, 14)

This disease has been called "idiopathic spontaneous hypoglycemia of infants." The repeated occurrence of epileptiform seizures in the untreated child results in irreparable damage to the brain and, even though the incidence of seizures declines with age, a residue of mental deterioration and neurological defect may persist. The condition is usually recognized before the child is two years old, but its onset may come later than this. There is a strong familial basis.

A beginning has been made in eludicating this type of hypoglycemia. In certain cases, protein feeding has a potent hypoglycemic action (14). L-Leucine and its metabolic derivatives α-ketoisocaproic and isovaleric acids are active in reducing the blood sugar (14, 15) but other amino acids do not do this (15). Indeed, leucine administration specifically causes the release of insulin (16).

## GLYCOGENOSES

In contrast to diabetes, the glycogenoses are characterized by a tendency to hypoglycemia, especially upon fasting. The inability to maintain the blood sugar derives from one or another enzymatic defect in the formation of glycogen, in its hydrolysis, or in the dephosphorylation of the glucose phosphate ester which is formed. Glycogen is a branched-chain polymer of glucose units, for whose breakdown and synthesis the coordinated action of several important enzymes is required. (a) The enzyme phosphorylase (Reaction 11-4) appears to be concerned with the phosphorolysis of glycogen to glucose-1-P. It exists in active and inactive forms; epinephrine and, perhaps, glucagon aid in the conversion of the latter to the enzymatically effective type. (b) As mentioned above, UDPG serves as the source of glucose for the synthesis of glycogen. The main type of glucosidic linkage in this carbohydrate is the 1:4-linkage. (c) In addition to these enzymes, amylotransglucosidase initiates branching along the polymeric chain by inserting a 1:6-linked glucose unit at intervals. Enzymatic lengthening of the chain then continues along this branch, through 1:4-linkages. In this way the polymeric molecule is built up. Normally, the initial steps in the formation of blood sugar from glycogen require the action of phosphorylase in the presence of inorganic phosphate. Glucose-1-P units are split from the glycogen, but the action of phosphorylase ceases when a branching point is reached. (d) Here another enzyme, amylo-1,6-glucosidase, hydrolyzes the molecule; the debranched fragment of glycogen is subjected once more to the action of phosphorylase, and the process repeats itself. The glucose-1-P formed in these reactions is isomerized to the 6-ester (Reaction 11-2), and the latter is then hydrolyzed by glucose-6-phosphatase an enzyme occurring in the liver and some other tissues, but not in muscle.

Until our knowledge of glycogen expanded sufficiently to include details of its structure and metabolism, the glycogenoses could only be described as storage diseases. With the aid of advanced enzymatic and physicochemical techniques they have been reclassified as diseases traceable to an enzymatic defect. In the glycogen disease as described classically by von Giercke, it has been found that the glycogen structure is normal but that glucose-6-phosphatase is deficient in the liver. A rarer form of the condition entails a deficiency of the debranching enzyme; the consequence of this is that the polysaccharide assumes an abnormal structure, bearing numerous short side chains. The same defect occurs in those cases of glycogenosis with the main deposits of the polysaccharide in the skeletal muscle fibers. An analogous disease has been postulated in which the concentration of the branching enzyme is low. This would result in abnormally long side chains in the glycogen molecule.

Other clinical entities are found in this group of diseases; in one of them the glycogen content of all tissues is high; in another this substance is especially high in the heart. The glycogen in these cases is normal in structure, and the enzymatic defect is unknown.

Some individuals afflicted with glycogenosis achieve adulthood in apparent good health, but for those with other types of the disorder there is an early and fatal outcome.

## CONGENITAL GALACTOSEMIA

Galactose is formed from glucose normally in small amounts in the tissues; it is utilized in the synthesis of the galactose-containing lipides, of acetylgalactosamine-containing polysaccharides and, during lactation, for the formation of lactose (milk sugar). The transformation of glucose begins with the epimerization of UDPG to UDP-galactose (UDPGal). Diphosphopyridine nucleotide is a cofactor in Reaction 11-37 and probably mediates a dehydrogenation-rehydrogenation reaction in which the fourth carbon of the glucose chain is converted to

$$\text{UDPG} \rightleftarrows \text{UDPGalactose} \qquad (11\text{-}37)$$

$$\text{Glucose-1-P} + \text{UTP} \rightarrow \text{UDPG} + \text{PP} \qquad (11\text{-}38)$$

$$\text{Galactose} + \text{ATP} \rightarrow \text{Galactose-1-P} + \text{ADP} \qquad (11\text{-}39)$$

$$\text{Galactose-1-P} + \text{UDPG} \rightleftarrows \text{Glucose-1-P} + \text{UDPGalactose} \qquad (11\text{-}40)$$

$$\text{UDPAcetylglucosamine} \rightleftarrows \text{UDPAcetylgalactosamine} \qquad (11\text{-}41)$$

its epimer; the UDPG is itself formed through a reaction of the Cori ester (Reaction 11-38). UDPGal is also formed when galactose is consumed, through the successive actions of galactokinase and galactose-1-P uridyl transferase (Reactions 11-39 and 11-40). UDPGal is the galactosylating agent which effects the incorporation of the sugar moiety into larger molecules. A reaction analogous to that in Reaction 11-37 probably accounts for the conversion of UDP-acetylglucosamine (*cf.* Reaction 11-36) into its galactose analog (Reaction 11-41).

Excessive amounts of galactose in the diet are toxic. This has been shown in experimental animals, and is now known for humans with a congenital defect in the enzymatic mechanisms for the utilization of this sugar. More than 10 to 15 percent of galactose in the diet ultimately brings about convulsions (quivering syndrome) in chicks (17). Another toxic action, cataract formation, is an important sequela in the rat just as it is in clinical galactosemia. The mode of action of galactose seems to be associated with its inhibition of glucose metabolism in the lens. A reduced rate of utilization of the latter sugar would introduce difficulties in the lens in the maintenance of the fund of energy or the supply of intermediates needed to preserve the structure and function of that organ. Similarly, interference with glucose metabolism in the brain may be responsible for the effects upon the nervous system. It is also possible, of course, that the absorption of large amounts of galactose leads to excessive incorporation of this sugar into the galactose-containing lipides of the brain, with deleterious consequences. Analysis of the brain of galactosemic individuals *postmortem* ought to yield direct information on this score. Such a mass action effect of galactose upon metabolism can actually occur, as has been found experimentally in galactose-fed chicks. The livers of such birds contain substantially increased amounts of UDPGal (17).

Clinically, galactose poisoning is observed in congenital galactosemia. The symptoms appear shortly after birth and progress to a fatal outcome unless treatment is instituted early. There is failure of normal growth and active development; jaundice and hepatosplenomegaly are characteristic features. In more advanced cases cataracts develop, the liver becomes cirrhotic, and the nervous system sustains damage as evidenced by mental retardation. Analysis of the urine shows the presence of protein, acetone, and galactose. The blood galactose level rises, and this sugar may replace some of the glucose, thereby causing hypoglucemia. The galactose tolerance test is quite abnormal. As soon as the child is taken off milk-containing foods or foods with galactose-containing plant oligosaccharides the blood galactose falls and the glycosuria disappears. If this is done early enough, the damage to the lens, brain, and other organs can be avoided.

Kalckar and his colleagues (18, 19) have been able to identify the specific enzymatic defect in some cases of congenital galactosemia by examination of the red blood cells and liver biopsy specimens. They find that Reaction 11-39 proceeds normally, but Reaction 11-40 is blocked because of gross deficiency of the liver enzyme which catalyzes it, galactose-1-P uridyl transferase. Inasmuch as the enzymes catalyzing the transformation of galactose (Reactions 11-37, 11-39, 11-40) are all present in the erythrocyte it is possible to diagnose the condition when its appearance is suspected or anticipated by an enzymatic assay performed on blood. A positive test on cord blood could obviate having the infant ever ingest galactose (19).

### BLOOD SUGAR IN SENILE CONFUSIONAL STATES

Glucose infusions may have beneficial effects in some senile confusional states. Helps (20) studied 5 elderly diabetics with cerebral arteriosclerosis, three of whom had hypoglycemic-like attacks even though their blood sugar was elevated. In four of these patients the dosage of insulin used for the control of the diabetes was reduced. This was followed by the arrest or reversal of the mental deterioration. Helps's hypothesis is that the reduced cerebral blood flow resulting from the arteriosclerotic condition is countered by the adaptation of cerebral metabolism to a high blood sugar. When insulin is used the patient suffers from a relative hypoglycemic state insofar as the brain is concerned. For normoglycemic individuals exhibiting senile confusion glucagon, growth hormone, or adrenal cortical hormones may be useful in elevating the blood sugar.

Robinson (21) has used intravenous glucose successfully in the treatment of senile delirium.

## Carbohydrate Metabolism in the Psychoses

*What is the practical significance of blood sugar curves in connection with mental disorders? It is possible that they may be just one expression of a general causative disordered metabolism . . . and it is probable that with appropriate investigations further important metabolic defects may be discovered . . . . The feature of the blood sugar curve in the normal is its constancy, and treatment that brings the abnormal curve nearer to normal limits may be associated with clinical improvement.—S. A. Mann (22).*

The testing of the sugar tolerance of mental patients has been one of the most frequent bases of psychiatric research programs. Judging from the voluminous literature which has grown up since the beginning of this century, this work has also been among the most unimaginative. There are dozens of studies of sugar tolerance in the literature. The techniques employed in carrying out the tests have varied, as have the investigator's criteria for the classification of their patients into psychiatric groups. The results have usually been assessed in essentially qualitative terms, judged from the shape of the blood sugar curve, although there have been attempts (23) to quantify the data.

In spite of the extensive room for variability in test conditions, there is relatively good agreement among investigators that glucose tolerance is abnormal in psychotic patients. This abnormality takes the form of low tolerance in catatonia (24), manic-depressive psychosis (depressive phase) (23, 24, 25, 26), endogenous depression (27, 28), and schizophrenia (23, 25, 27). In the manic phase of manic-depressive psychosis the glucose tolerance has been reported to be abnormally high (23, 24, 27), that is, the curves tend to be low and flat. Normal tolerance was exhibited by psychoneurotic patients (24).

It is not meant by this brief summary to imply that results of sugar tolerance studies have been uniform, but rather to indicate broadly the area of agreement. For example, Mann was not able to correlate the abnormality in the glucose test and the form of psychosis. Others have also failed to note any major differentiation among the psychoses they studied. To offset this lack of specificity as well as spurious or incidental factors contributing to the abnormal carbohydrate metabolism some investigators have performed the test on their patients on several occasions. In these cases a significant correlation between the results of the test and the patient's psychiatric condition has been seen (22, 23, 26, 29): as the patients improve the tolerance curves return to normal.

One of the most striking features about these endeavors is their imitative character: many of the studies have failed to reach out for new aspects of the abnormal carbohydrate tolerances that preceding studies had elaborated. The abiding conclusions were already drawn by S. A. Mann in the paper which he published in 1925 and in which he outlined the three general points of agreement among his own cases and those others which he had reviewed: (a) "In a large proportion of early and chronic mental cases there is a disordered carbohydrate metabolism as shown by a sustained hyperglycemia following glucose ingestion." (b) "This abnormality cannot be associated in particular with any mental condition, but it is generally accepted that its frequency is greater in those associated with melancholia and especially stupor."

(c) The third point is made in the paragraph quoted at the head of this section, namely, the association of clinical improvement and normalization of the glucose tolerance curve. In spite of Mann's clear statement similar studies have been repeatedly undertaken since then as is attested to by the review of McFarland and Goldstein in 1938 (30) and that of Altschule in 1953 (31).

If there has been any progress in this field of glucose tolerance studies in mental disorders, then it is in the etiology of the abnormality and in the specificity of the biochemical changes. What aspect of carbohydrate metabolism goes awry? Is it the absorption of sugar from the intestinal tract, alterations in the enzymatic machinery of the hepatic cells concerned with the conversion of glucose to glycogen, the activity of the insulin-producing system and of the contrainsulin mechanisms, or some other factor?

According to one theory there is a delayed or slowed absorption of the administered sugar from the intestine in the psychotic group, with the consequent reflection of this process in the blood levels over an inordinately long period of time. Because of the difficulty of studying the rate of intestinal absorption directly, it has been estimated in many studies by difference, *i.e.*, by comparing the tolerance curves obtained by oral and by intravenous administration of glucose. Although the results of such studies are far from unanimous, there are enough of them showing abnormal intravenous glucose tolerance curves to indicate that changes in the intestinal epithelium do not constitute a unitary explanation of the phenomena with which we are now concerned.

As already discussed in this chapter, several investigators have reported that the plasma of psychotic patients contains an anti-insulin factor or lacks some substance which favors glucose utilization by muscle and which is present in normal blood. These results lend support to the view that mental illness is accompanied by an altered state of hormonal balance, as reflected in the control of carbohydrate metabolism.

The hormonal imbalance theory does not exclude another approach which has been promulgated for many years and which takes into account the factor of autonomic regulation. Thus, Diethelm has emphasized the importance of noting "the type, depth, acuteness and duration of the emotions, the constitutional tendencies of emotional responsiveness and display, and the body response" (32). He proposed to interpret the results of sugar tolerance tests in terms of the functional opposition of a "vago-insulin system" and the sympathoadrenal apparatus, and thereby differentiate the emotional responses also (33). Freeman and Elmadjian have similarly stressed the influence of psychological factors upon glucose tolerance. They consider the low tolerance shown by schizophrenics to be nonspecific. "It is due to 'tension' since (a) there is some interrelationship with emotional disturbances as shown by the Rorschach test; (b) there is in some cases a 'normalization' of sugar tolerance with diminution of the psychotic behavior; (c) a normal glucose tolerance can be changed to an abnormal (reduced) tolerance by the administration of a stress procedure" (34). These views recommend the physiological approach in explaining deviations of sugar tolerance. This ultimately requires detailed investigation of events in the higher centers and the activity of both parts of the autonomic nervous system in their multiple influences upon metabolism.

Although great emphasis has been laid by many reviewers upon the glucose tolerance curve as an indicator of deviation from metabolic normalcy, other measures of metabolism have been made by a few investigators with results that fit the concept of a defect in the handling of carbohydrates. Great caution is required, however, in the interpretation of data in this field because of the effect of dietary adaptations (35). For example, a high carbohydrate diet favors the development of a high glucose tolerance and this influence is so pervasive that the glucose fed in succesive tests may be sufficient to improve the tolerance. Altschule has made the claim that glutathione, administered intravenously in a course of therapy over 9 to 12 days (in a total dose of 3 to 6.5 gm. of glutathione per kilogram body weight) potentiates the improvement in glucose tolerance occasioned by a high carbohydrate diet (36). This treatment-study, carried out with chronic schizophrenic and with depressive patients, led to only very slight and transitory changes in the mental picture.

Another adaptation is revealed by the insulin tolerance test. A proportion of mental patients exhibit a lowered response to intravenously administered insulin; the reduction in the blood sugar is less than in normal controls (37). However, the responsiveness returns to normal after the subjects have been on a high carbohydrate diet for some time.

Some of the carbohydrate intermediaries in the blood which have been measured in the attempt to elucidate the error in carbohydrate metabolism in psychotic patients are, among others, acetoin and the following acids: lactic, pyruvic, α-ketoglutaric, acetoacetic, and phosphoglycollic. Lactic acid tends to be elevated in psychotic subjects (38), especially after physical exercise (39), but this deviation from normal may be merely a function of training, another factor playing an important role in the carbohydrate economy of the body. $\alpha$-Ketoglutaric acid (fasting) levels in the plasma are also somewhat elevated, but there is great variation among individuals (38, 40). It has been stated that psychotic patients metabolize infused lactate more slowly than nonpsychotics, and that their blood $\alpha$-ketoglutarate remains elevated for an unduly long time (41).

Under certain conditions the concentration of ketone bodies in the blood is found to be elevated in schizophrenics (42); this also occurs in normal persons subjected to some significant emotional stress. This finding calls to mind the influence of hormonal and neurohumoral factors in controlling carbohydrate metabolism.

Acetoin levels in the blood are said to be high in patients with manic-depressive psychosis, but normal in psychoneurotics (43). The higher concentration in certain cases may reflect a disturbance in the normal utilization of glucose, for the blood acetoin is found to be high in poorly controlled diabetic patients.

Although its origin is at present uncertain, phosphoglycollic acid has been reported to occur in the erythrocytes of schizophrenic subjects in concentrations twice as high as normal (44). However, studies of the problem of phosphorylated intermediates in red cells, by Laity and by Dyfverman and Broman (45), failed to find differences between normal and schizophrenic subjects.

Sacks has measured the $CO_2$ derived from oxidation of isotopically labeled glucose in the brain substance *in vivo* (46). Less of this $CO_2$ appears in the immediate postinjection period in chronic psychotic patients as compared with normal subjects.

Changes in blood constituents help to consolidate the concept of a derangement of carbohydrate metabolism, already grounded in the glucose tolerance test results, but they do not reveal the cause of this derangement, its site in intermediary reactions, or the role of nutritional adaptive processes. From the glucose tolerance curve studies there appears to be a defect in the utilization of glucose itself. From the blood chemistry studies one may conclude that there is also present in some psychotic subjects an additional defect at the stage of pyruvic acid metabolism and even further on. This defect is occasionally reflected in an elevated lactic acid or acetoin concentration, or in the appearance of ketosis.

# Some Additional Abnormalities of
# Carbohydrate Metabolism

### THE HUNTER-HURLER SYNDROME

Abnormal deposition of two types of compound occurs in the Hunter-Hurler syndrome (also known as gargoylism and lipochondrodystrophy). Gangliosides accumulate in abnormal amounts in the gray matter of the brain in many cases; other lipide material is deposited in the cornea, creating the pathognomonic milky-white clouding. Actually the deformities of bone and cartilage are first noticed, inasmuch as they introduce the grotesque features for which the disease has been named. Later, progressive mental and physical deterioration are observed. These features have hitherto placed gargoylism among the lipidoses. Besides the gangliosides, an acidic mucopolysaccharide accumulates; Brante first found it in the liver and the brain meninges (47). It contains no lipide component and gives a color reaction with orcinol which is different from that observed with the gangliosides. Substances of this kind have been found in the urine of a patient with the syndrome. Thus, relatively large amounts of chondroitin sulfuric acid-B ($\beta$-heparin) are excreted along with a related compound, possibly heparin monosulfuric acid (48). Normally, only a very small amount of chondroitin sulfuric acid-A (the type found in cartilage) is excreted in the urine. The B type has been previously isolated from normal skin and, indeed, this tissue may be the source of the urinary compound in the Hunter-Hurler syndrome. Brante (47) has suggested that in this syndrome excessive production of hexosamine for the synthesis of the primary storage product, the mucopolysaccharide of connective tissue, is diverted into channels of ganglioside formation (*cf.* Chapter 12).

Yet another type of polysaccharidosis has been described by Craig and Uzman (49) in three cases. They describe it as a familial disorder with "hepatosplenomegaly, anemia, failure in physical development, susceptibility to respiratory infection, and no blood sugar response to epinephrine." The storage compound which these investigators isolated contained hexoses, hexuronic acid, and neuraminic acid.

### PENTOSURIA (50)

In the condition known as "essential pentosuria" L-xylulose is excreted in the urine in large amounts. Hiatt has noted a metabolic defect in one pentosuric individual in the conversion of D-glucuronolactone to D-ribose (51).

## GLUCOSE-6-P DEHYDROGENASE DEFICIENCY

One other enzymic defect in the metabolism of carbohydrate may be mentioned here although it is not associated with any mental or nervous abnormality, but with hemolytic anemia. This is the hereditary deficiency of glucose-6-phosphate dehydrogenase also known as primaquine-sensitivity of the erythrocytes (52). The mechanism whereby this enzyme (catalyzing Reaction 11-23) aids in preserving the erythrocytes intact is not clear, but it does so with the aid of glutathione. Thus, red cells taken from an individual with the hemolytic tendency lose their content of reduced glutathione (GSH) when incubated with a compound such as acetylphenylhydrazine. Normally GSH is maintained in the reduced state: that is to say, oxidized glutathione (GSSG) is reduced by the reduced triphosphopyridine nucleotide generated through the pentose phosphate pathway (Reactions 11-23 and 11-24). When the enzyme catalyzing Reaction 11-23 is missing from the erythrocytes the oxidation of glutathione is favored by default, and the hemolytic mechanism comes into play.

# References

1. PETERS, J. P., and D. D. VAN SLYKE. *Quantitative Clinical Chemistry,* Vol. I, 2d ed. Baltimore, Williams & Wilkins, 1946; SOURKES, T. L. *In Biochemistry and Physiology of Nutrition, ed.* BOURNE, G. H., and G. W. KIDDER, Vol. I, New York, Academic Press, 1953.
2. KREBS, H. A., and W. A. JOHNSON. *Enzymologia 4:*148, 1937.
3. LYNEN, F., U. HENNING, C. BUBLITZ, B. SORBO, and L. KRÖPLEIN-RUEFF. *Biochem. Z. 330:*269, 1958.
4. DE BODO, R. C., and N. ALTSZULER. *Physiol. Rev. 38:*389, 1958.
5. MARSH, J. B., and N. HAUGAARD. *J. Clin. Invest. 31:*107, 1952.
6. HAAVALDSEN, R., O. LINGJAERDE, and O. WALAAS. *Confin. Neurol. 18:*270, 1958.
7. STREIFLER, M., and W. KORNBLUETH. *In Chemical Concepts of Psychosis,* ed. RINKEL, M., and H. C. B. DENBER, New York, McDowell, Obolensky, 1958.
8. FROHMAN, C. E., N. P. CZAJKOWSKI, E. D. LUBY, J. S. GOTTLIEB, and R. SENF. *A. M. A. Arch. Gen. Psychiat. 2:*263, 1960.
9. HIMWICH, H. E. *Brain Metabolism and Cerebral Disorders.* Baltimore, Williams & Wilkins, 1951; MCILWAIN, H. *Biochemistry and the Central Nervous System.* London, J. & A. Churchill, 1955.

10. Conn, J. W. *J.A.M.A. 134:*130, 1947.
11. Skillern, P. G., and E. H. Rynearson. *J. Clin. Endocrinol. Metab. 13:* 587, 1953.
12. Broberger, O., I. Jungner, and R. Zetterstroem. *J. Pediatr. 55:*713, 1959.
13. McQuarrie, I. *Am. J. Dis. Child. 87:*399, 1954.
14. Cochrane, W. A., W. W. Payne, M. J. Simpkiss, and L. I. Woolf. *J. Clin. Invest. 35:*411, 1956.
15. Mabry, C. C., A. M. DiGeorge, and V. H. Auerbach. *J. Pediatr. 57:*526, 539, 1960.
16. DiGeorge, A. M., V. H. Auerbach, and C. C. Mabry. *Nature 188:*1036, 1960; Marrack, D., V. Marks, and F. C. Rose. *Lancet ii:* 1329, 1960.
17. Hansen, R. G., R. A. Freedland, and H. M. Scott. *J. Biol. Chem. 219:* 391, 1956.
18. Kalckar, H. *Science 125:*103, 1957; Isselbacher, K. J. *Am. J. Clin. Nutr. 5:*527, 1957.
19. Anderson, E. P., H. M. Kalckar, and K. J. Isselbacher, *Science 125:* 113, 1957.
20. Helps, E. P. W. *Lancet i:*138, 1957.
21. Robinson, G. W., Jr. *South. Med. J. 32:*479, 1939.
22. Mann, S. A. *J. Ment. Sci. 71:*443, 1925.
23. McCowan, P. K., and J. H. Quastel. *Lancet ii:*731, 1931; *idem, J. Ment. Sci. 77:*525, 1931.
24. Lorenz, W. F. *Arch. Neurol. Psychiat. 8:*184, 1922.
25. Raphael, T., and J. P. Parsons. *Arch. Neurol. Psychiat. 13:*743, 1925.
26. Raphael, T., W. Ferguson, and O. Searle. *Arch. Neurol. Psychiat. 19:* 120, 1928.
27. Henry, G. W., and E. Mangum. *Arch. Neurol. Psychiat. 13:*743, 1925.
28. Drury, K. K., and C. Farran-Ridge. *J. Ment. Sci. 71:*8, 1925.
29. Freeman, H., and R. N. Zaborenko. *Arch. Neurol. Psychiat. 61:*569, 1949.
30. McFarland, R. A., and H. Goldstein. *Am. J. Psychiat. 95:*509, 1938.
31. Altschule, M. D. *Bodily Physiology in Mental and Emotional Disorders.* New York, Grune & Stratton, 1953.
32. Diethelm, O. *Arch. Neurol. Psychiat. 36:*342, 1936.
33. Diethelm, O., E. J. Doty, and A. T. Milhorat. *Arch. Neurol. Psychiat. 54:*110, 1945.
34. Freeman, H., and F. Elmadjian. *Am. J. Psychiat. 106:*660, 1950.
35. Knox, W. E., V. H. Auerbach, and E. C. C. Lin. *Physiol. Rev. 36:*164, 1956.
36. Altschule, M. D., S. H. Henneman, P. D. Holliday, and R. M. Goncz. *A. M. A. Arch. Int. Med. 99:*22, 1957.
37. Lingjaerde, O. *Acta Psychiat. Neurol. Scand. Suppl. 80:*202, 1953.
38. Henneman, D. H., M. D. Altschule, and R. M. Goncz. *A. M. A. Arch. Int. Med. 94:*402, 1954.
39. Easterday, O. D., R. M. Featherstone, J. S. Gottlieb, M. L. Nusser, and R. V. Hogg. *A. M. A. Arch. Neurol. Psychiat. 68:*48, 1952.
40. Buscaino, G. A., and A. Rapisarda. *Acta Neurol. 3:*251, 1948.

41. PERRIN, G. M., M. D. ALTSCHULE, and P. D. HOLLIDAY. *A. M. A. Arch. Int. Med. 105:*752, 1960.

42. NORTHCOTE, M. L. M. *J. Ment. Sci. 78:*263, 1932; THOMPSON, J. W., and J. H. ASTE-SALAZAR. *Arch. Neurol. Psychiat. 41:*375, 1939; WORTIS, H., E. BUEDING, and W. E. WILSON. *Proc. Soc. Exp. Biol. Med. 43:*279, 1940; LÖFVENDAHL, H., and T. VALATIN. *Acta Med. Scand. 106:*70, 1941; KITAY, J. I., and M. D. ALTSCHULE. *A. M. A. Arch. Neurol. Psychiat. 68:*506, 1952.

43. DAWSON, J., R. P. HULLIN, and A. POOL. *J. Ment. Sci. 100:*536, 1954.

44. ÖRSTRÖM, A. *Arch. Biochem. Biophys. 33:*484, 1951.

45. LAITY, J. L. H. *Lancet ii:*422, 1958; DYFVERMAN, A., and L. BROMAN. *Scand. J. Clin. Lab. Invest. 9:*356, 1957.

46. SACKS, W. *J. Appl. Physiol. 14:*849, 1959.

47. BRANTE, G. *Scand. J. Clin. Lab. Invest. 4:*43, 1952.

48. DORFMAN, A., and A. E. LORINCZ. *Proc. Nat. Acad. Sci. (U.S.A.) 43:*443, 1957.

49. CRAY, J. M., and L. L. UZMAN. *Pediatrics 22:*20, 1958.

50. HOLLMANN, S. *Klin. Wochschr. 37:*737, 1959; TOUSTER, O. *Am. J. Med. 26:*724, 1959.

51. HIATT, H. H. *Biochim. et Biophys. Acta 28:*645, 1958.

52. GROSS, R. T., R. E. HURWITZ, and P. A. MARKS. *J. Clin. Invest. 37:*1176, 1958.

# 12

## LIPIDES

The term lipide includes many diverse groups of compounds having in common only a general similarity of solubility properties. Solubility in ether, alcohol, petroleum fractions, or the short-chain halogenated hydrocarbons such as chloroform and ethylene chloride—the so-called fat solvents—depends, of course, upon the molecular structure of the compound concerned and, because of the variety of lipides, no all-inclusive statements can be made other than to indicate that each type consists of, or possesses in its structure, a nonpolar unit which in many cases is a fatty acid. A drawback to discussion of the lipides is the excessively large number of trivial names that have grown up into the subject. Fortunately, our knowledge of the chemical composition of all lipide groups is becoming much more precise and it is often possible to dispense with the traditional names and to base nomenclature upon conventional rules. In practice, a compromise is frequently sought to obviate the use of unwieldy polyhyphenated chemical terms whilst preserving a precise meaning.

The metabolism of lipides is pertinent to the study of brain function for two reasons. In the first place 25 to 30 percent of the fresh weight of nervous tissue consists of these substances. (For reviews of the subject, see References 1, 2.) Anatomically they are found in the enclosing membranes around nerve cells and their axons. Hence, the highest concentrations are found in the white matter of the brain and in peripheral nerve, both rich in myelin. Contrary to earlier concepts that regarded the lipides simply as inert structural materials of the neurone, metabolic studies with isotopically labeled intermediates have revealed the dynamic changes they constantly undergo. For example, the molecular fragments of the phosphatides exchange with similar uncombined components in the surrounding medium; moreover, the turnover rates are quite different for the various fragments.

Lipide metabolism also bears upon brain function in the biochemical investigation of the lipidoses. Many of these lipide disorders are characterized by mental and physical deterioration of the patient, changes which are noted some time after a period of apparently normal development has occurred. In the lipidoses excessive amounts of specific lipides are deposited in the brain or visceral organs, but how these constituents accumulate is not known, nor is the mechanism of the disturbances in cerebral and visceral functions occasioned by the lipide deposits understood to any extent. Specific micromethods for lipides ought to aid in the early chemical detection of the changes in blood and CSF or, for that matter, in biopsy material, and should permit tracing the changes through the course of the disease. Some work of this nature with respect to neuraminic acid metabolism has already been done in amaurotic family idiocy.

A signal advance in understanding the metabolism of lipides has been the discovery through tracer studies that the unesterified ("free") fatty acids of plasma, quantitatively a minor portion of the lipides of that fluid, have a high turnover rate and, indeed, are the major means whereby fatty acids are transported in the body (3). The fatty acids are actually carried in a loose linkage to the plasma proteins, notably the albumins. Recent studies have clarified how this fraction responds to nervous and humoral influences.

## Chemical Structure of Lipides

*Glycerides:* Fats are esters of the trihydric alcohol glycerol with three molecules of fatty acid; these are, therefore, called triglycerides. Mono- and diglycerides have one or two fatty acid molecules, respectively, in ester linkage with glycerol. Phosphatidic acid is a diglyceride with the third hydroxyl group (in an α-position) esterified with phosphoric acid. Most of it occurs in combination, but a small amount occurs in the free state in the tissues (4).

*Phosphatides:* The compounds with which phosphatidic acid is combined to form a phosphoric acid di-ester are choline, ethanolamine, serine, and inositol. The structures of the first three types of these *phosphatides* are well understood, but the linkages in the *phosphoinositides* have not been entirely clarified. Brain diphosphoinositide, a calcium-magnesium salt, consists of inositol, phosphoric acid (two moles), fatty acid, and glycerol. Inositol also occurs in other types of brain lipides, the phosphatidopeptides (P:inositol = 2:1) and the triphosphoinositides (P:inositol = 3:1). The choline-containing phosphatides are known as *lecithins;* those containing ethanolamine or serine are the *cephalins.*

*Sphingolipides* (Table 12-1) are derivatives of sphingosine, a fatty alcohol bearing an amino group. Sphingosine is 1,3-dihydroxy-2-amino-4-

TABLE 12-1. PHOSPHOLIPIDES AND SPHINGOLIPIDES

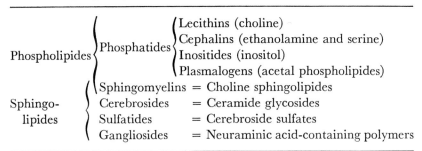

trans-octadecene. Its simplest derivatives are the *ceramides;* these are formed by the substitution of a fatty acid residue upon the amino group and are therefore amides. They have not been found free in the tissues. The *cerebrosides* are ceramide linked to a hexose sugar; well known examples are phrenosine and kerasine. In some cases the terminal constituent is a sulfuric acid ester of the sugar; these cerebrosides are known then as *sulfatides.* One of them is made up as follows: cerebronic acid-sphingosine-galactose-6-sulfate. Cerebrosides extracted from normal tissues contain some glucose, but galactose is the predominant sugar. *Sphingomyelins* are the sphingosine analogues of the phosphatidyl cholines, or lecithins. Their structure can be represented as: fatty acid-sphingosine-phosphoric acid-choline. The *gangliosides* are polymeric sphingolipides which actually first came to the attention of biochemists through investigations of the excessive lipide deposits in storage diseases such as Gaucher's and Tay-Sachs' diseases (5). They are normally present in the cells of the cerebral cortex, in small amounts. One of the simpler gangliosides, isolated by Egge (6), has a molecular weight of 1383, and consists of a cerebroside (ceramide-glucose), N-acetylgalactosamine, galactose, and N-acetylneuraminic acid.

Phosphatides and sphingomyelins are collectively known as *phospholipides*. *Plasmalogens*, or acetal phospholipides, are analogous compounds containing a long-chain aldehyde which takes the place of the fatty acid. These fatty aldehydes are known as *plasmals* (7); they form α,β-unsaturated ethers with the glycerol.

*Neuraminic acid* is a polyhydroxy amino acid whose structure resembles that of hexosamine having the mannosamine configuration, condensed with pyruvic acid (8). Acetyl and glycolyl derivatives of neuraminic acid also occur naturally and have the generic name *sialic acids* (9). These compounds have been detected in body fluids (serum, CSF, saliva, milk). The neuraminic acid of the serum is largely attached to proteins, and most of it is to the globulins (10, 11). It can be determined by Bial's orcinol reagent or by other methods after its precipitation with the proteins which bind it. By contrast, most of the neuraminic acid in CSF is readily dialyzable (12). Sialic acid of the serum is elevated above normal in active tuberculosis, advanced cancer, and parenchymatous liver disease (13). The serum neuraminic acid level is raised in amaurotic family idiocy and in the Hunter-Hurler syndrome (14).

Material isolated from brain, and termed *strandin,* is now considered to belong to the ganglioside group of compounds.

*α-Glyceryl ethers* occur in some tissues; their function is not known, although one of them has been reported to exert erythropoietic action. They consist of α-ethers of glycerol with long-chain alcohols. Examples are chimyl ($C_{16}$-chain) and batyl ($C_{18}$-chain) alcohols.

A few *hydrocarbons* are of physiological importance. Carotene, or provitamin A, is of plant origin, but it is converted in the intestinal tract into vitamin A. Squalene belongs to the terpene hydrocarbons; these substances are built up from isoprenoid ($C_5$) units. Squalene is an intermediary in the biosynthesis of cholesterol.

Many compounds belonging to the *steroid* group are found in animal tissues. About 30 have been isolated from the adrenal cortex alone, and others have been found in testis and ovary as well, where they are formed. Some steroids exert important hormonal actions. Cholesterol, a ubiquitous steroid, is the prototype possessing the basic structural pattern, that of the cyclopentanoperhydrophenanthrene nucleus. It is synthesized in many tissues, and most actively in the skin and liver. Although the brain of very young experimental animals can form it adult brain cannot do so (15). Two steroids, ergosterol and 7-dehydrocholesterol, are provitamins D; upon irradiation they are converted to vitamins $D_2$ and $D_3$, respectively.

The *lipoproteins* are now receiving much attention as indicators of lipide function. Among the substances which have been found in association with protein are phospholipides, cholesterol, and triglycerides.

# Intermediary Metabolism and Biosynthesis

## METABOLISM OF FATTY ACIDS

The fundamental structural unit in the biosynthesis and breakdown of fatty acids is the acetyl group. This two-carbon radical is split off enzymatically from these acids at a certain stage in their oxidation. Coenzyme A is one of the instruments of such transformation because it is, first of all, the recipient of the acetyl group transferred from the catenary linkage on the fatty acid and secondly, it is the subsequent donor of this metabolic fragment in other sequences. Examples of transfers in which acetyl-coenzyme A is active are (*a*) the synthesis of long chain members of the fatty acid series (by transfer of acetyl to an acceptor fatty acid molecule); (*b*) formation of ketone bodies (transfer to another acetyl group); (*c*) acetylation of natural substances (*e.g.*, glucosamine, neuraminic acid) or foreign amines, (*e.g.*, sulfanilamide); (*d*) condensation with oxaloacetic acid to form citric acid. Some of these have been discussed in Chapter 11 (*cf.* Figure 11-2).

When a glyceride undergoes breakdown it is initially hydrolyzed by lipase through successive steps to glycerol and fatty acids. The glycerol is phosphorylated to α-glycerophosphate and is then dehydrogenated to triose phosphate, in which form it enters the pathways of carbohydrate breakdown. The fatty acids are activated through the agency of adenosine triphosphate and coenzyme A, whereby fatty acyl-coenzyme A derivatives are formed. Other enzymes attack the acyl radical serially, producing the α,β-unsaturated derivative (by dehydrogenation), the β-hydroxy derivative (by addition of the elements of water across the double bond), and the α-keto derivative (by dehydrogenation of the alcoholic grouping). These transformations are shown in Reactions 12-1 to 12-3. The

$$R \cdot CH_2CH_2CH_2CO{-}SCoA \rightarrow R \cdot CH_2CH{=}CHCO{-}SCoA \rightarrow$$
$$R \cdot CH_2CHOHCH_2CO{-}SCoA \rightarrow R \cdot CH_2COCH_2CO{-}SCoA$$
$$(12\text{-}1\text{--}12\text{-}3)$$

β-keto-acyl-coenzyme A compound reacts with another molecule of the coenzyme, at the same time undergoing cleavage between the β and γ carbons. Acetyl-coenzyme A is now formed, along with the fatty acyl-coenzyme shorter by two carbons than the original one (Reaction 12-4).

$$R \cdot CH_2COCH_2CO\text{—SCoA} + HSCoA \rightarrow R \cdot CH_2CO\text{—SCoA} \\ + CH_3CO\text{—SCoA} \quad (12\text{-}4)$$

This process is repeated, resulting in the progressive shortening of the fatty acid and conversion of the fragments into the acetylated coenzyme. The synthesis of fatty acid molecules is essentially the reverse of the process just described. When fat is being laid down in the tissues some of the acetyl-coenzyme A formed from pyruvic acid (Chapter 11) follows the synthetic pathway to fatty acids as already described. Fat formation from carbohydrate is not infrequently a dominant metabolic process and is, in fact, cultivated in certain economic animals. Although there are pathways from fat to carbohydrate (e.g., through the incorporation of carbon atoms derived from fatty acid or acetate into tricarboxylic acid intermediates, conversion of oxaloacetate to phosphoenolpyruvate, and thence to glucose), there is no net increase in carbohydrate as a result of their operation (16).

In certain states (high fat feeding and diabetes) there is a diversion of acetyl-coenzyme A into the route of ketone body formation. Acetoacetic acid is first formed. This substance, together with the other ketone bodies, β-hydroxybutyric acid and acetone, can be further metabolized by peripheral tissues but not by the liver. Another path which drains off excess active acetate is the formation of cholesterol. This aspect of fat metabolism has been reviewed by Zilversmit (17).

## BIOSYNTHESIS OF TRIGLYCERIDES AND PHOSPHOLIPIDES

The resynthesis of triglycerides is a far more complicated process than their hydrolysis. Glycerol must first be phosphorylated by adenosine triphosphate. The product, α-glycerophosphate, may also originate from the glycolytic pathway, shown in Reaction 12-5. The two remaining

$$\text{Triose phosphate} + DPNH + H^+ \rightleftarrows \alpha\text{-Glycerophosphate} \\ + DPN^+ \quad (12\text{-}5)$$

$$\alpha\text{-Glycerophosphate} + 2 \text{ Fatty acyl-CoA} \rightleftarrows \text{Phosphatidic acid} + 2CoA \quad (12\text{-}6)$$

$$\text{Diglyceride} + \text{Fatty acyl-CoA} \rightarrow \text{Triglyceride} + CoA \quad (12\text{-}7)$$

hydroxyl positions on the glycerophosphate molecule are now substituted by fatty acids (Reaction 12-6). As soon as the phosphatidic acid has lost its phosphate group through the hydrolytic action of a phosphatase, the third fatty acid molecule can be esterified (Reaction 12-7). Compounds such as the lecithins are formed from two key intermediates, cytidine diphosphocholine and diglyceride. Their synthesis and mutual reaction serve as prototypic reactions in the formation of other phospholipides (Reactions 12-8–12-10). The nucleotide cytidine triphosphate (CTP) plays an important role here, as shown by enzymic studies with liver and brain. Ethanolamine phospholides are formed similarly.

$$\text{Choline} + \text{ATP} \rightarrow \text{Phosphorylcholine} \quad (12\text{-}8)$$

$$\text{Phosphorylcholine} + \text{CTP} \rightarrow \text{Cytidine diphosphocholine} + \text{Pyrophosphate} \quad (12\text{-}9)$$

$$\text{Cytidine diphosphocholine} + \text{Diglyceride} \rightarrow \text{Cytidine monophosphate} + \text{Phosphatidylcholine (lecithin)} \quad (12\text{-}10)$$

Another place for participation of cytidine diphosphocholine is in a reaction with ceramide, leading to the formation of sphingomyelins. Possibly the synthesis occurs as in Reaction 12-11. Many details of the

$$\text{Cytidine diphosphocholine} + \text{Ceramide} \rightarrow \text{Cytidine monophosphate} + \text{Sphingomyelin} \quad (12\text{-}11)$$

enzymatic processes described here may be found in the reviews by Kennedy (18).

## Lipide Composition of Normal Tissues and Body Fluids

A compilation of results of lipide analyses reported by various authors has been made in Table 12-2. These data have been obtained by a multiplicity of methods and, although the figures are generally consistent with one another, their heterogeneous origin with respect to methods and authorship should be taken into account in making comparisons. LeBaron and Folch have described the composition of lipides found in the brain (23).

The distribution of fatty acids in the lipides (according to chain length, degree of unsaturation) varies with species and with physiological state. The body cannot synthesize highly unsaturated fats and, therefore, these must be provided in the diet (essential fatty acids). When they are deficient, as in low-fat diets, there may be an increased susceptibility to infection and dermatitis.

TABLE 12-2. COMPOSITION OF HUMAN ORGANS AND BODY FLUIDS

| Organ | Plasma | Serum | Adult Brain Gray | Adult Brain White | Liver | Spleen | Kidney |
|---|---|---|---|---|---|---|---|
| | mg.% | mg.% | % of dry weight | | % of fresh weight | | |
| Total lipides | 570 | | 35 | 61 | | | |
| Total fatty acids | 180–950 | | | | 9–13 | 4–6 | 5–6 |
| Phospholipides | | 150–250 | 20 | 27 | 9–11 | 6–11 | 7–10 |
| Lecithin | | | 6–7 | 4–6 | 3–6 | 3–4 | 4–7 |
| Cephalin | | | 11 | 12–17 | 3–6 | 1–7 | 2–4 |
| Plasmalogens* | | 4 | | | | | |
| Sphingolipides | | | | | | | |
| Sphingomyelin | | 10–40 | 2–3 | 4–7 | 0.3–0.5 | 0.7–1.0 | 0.6–0.8 |
| Cerebrosides | 4.4† | | 4–6 | 16 | | 0.1–0.6 | |
| Gangliosides‡ | | | 4.6 | 2.6 | | | |
| Neuraminic acid§ | | 40–65 | | | | | |
| Cholesterol, total | 107–320 | 130–260 | 5–6 | 14 | 2.0–2.6 | 0.6–2.3 | 1.4–2.8 |
| Cholesterol, free | | 30–70 | | | 0.5 | 0.5–1.1 | 1 |
| Cholesterol, ester | | 100–190 | | | 1.5–2.2 | 0.2–1.2 | 0.5–1.7 |
| Main references | 21 | 22 | | 1 | 22 | 22 | 22 |

Additional data may be found as follows: *19; †20; ‡2; §10.

# Disturbances of Fat Metabolism in Relation to Mental Diseases

**SERUM CHOLESTEROL**

As a result of the search for metabolic parameters of the psychoses, the lipide substances have received their round of attention in the same way as have the carbohydrates, proteins, amino acids, and hormones. Much of this work is chronicled in the review by McFarland and Goldstein (24). To date it would seem that many of the relationships studied are of the second or even more distant order. The results of measurements of serum cholesterol exemplify this.

Cholesterol was one of the first lipides to be measured and was of special interest as an index of metabolic activity and, therefore, of thyroid function: if there were to be found a general metabolic deficiency in the psychoses then perhaps serum cholesterol would reveal evidence of it. As with many other blood constituents it has been established that the range of values of serum cholesterol in mental diseases is much wider than that found in groups of normal individuals. Schizophrenics may exhibit considerable variations from day to day, with occasional gross changes developing at a pace not observed normally (25). However, attempts to relate mean levels of cholesterol to diagnostic categories have met with little agreement, for the serum cholesterol level in schizophrenia may be elevated, reduced, or normal (21, 24). Some investigators have considered cholesterol to be low in early schizophrenia. Eaton and Muntz (26) agreed with this conclusion and extended it even further: "It is generally agreed that cholesterol levels tend to be high and frequently are above normal limits in manic-depressives, while values below normal limits are common in schizophrenics, though hypercholesteremia is found in some cases." Such cases have been noted in schizophrenics with an associated endocrine condition such as pubertal obesity, ovarian cysts, the puerperium, or hypophyseal eunuchoidism (27).

In the xanthomatoses cholesterol is deposited in the tissues through an unknown mechanism. Cholesterol need not be unusually elevated in the serum in this condition for the deposits to appear. The primary disorder is usually benign. The xanthomatoses of secondary origin are exemplified by essential lipemia.

There has been great interest in the relationship between serum cholesterol levels and coronary artery disease, and the further relation of these to personality factors. Friedman and Rosenman (28) have studied this problem and concluded that the mean serum cholesterol is much higher in men exhibiting "a behavior pattern primarily characterized by intense ambition, competitive 'drive,' constant preoccupation with occupational 'deadlines,' and a sense of time urgency" than in a group showing the converse pattern. Students writing university examinations experience an elevation in the serum cholesterol (29). Sloane et al. observed behavioral differences between two groups of students on controlled fat-free diets, the groups having been selected from those with high and low serum cholesterols, respectively (29A). The former exhibited greater competitiveness and conflict.

## SERUM LIPOPROTEINS

The development of ultracentrifugal techniques for the study of serum lipoproteins has permitted examination of this category of lipides in schizophrenic patients (30). Small deviations from the distribution of lipoproteins of high densities as found in normal persons have been encountered, but their cause and significance are not clear. These differences between the schizophrenic and normal groups do not apparently apply to the low density serum lipoproteins. In order to assess the significance of the changes noted it will be necessary to have, in the first place, information about the chemical nature of the lipides associated with the differentially sedimenting fractions.

Stepan and Hanzlicek have described a lipopeptide complex in the CSF which is increased in amount in chronic epilepsy and schizophrenia (30A).

## NEURAMINIC ACID

Although the gangliosides have been recognized as a chemical group for almost 20 years it is only within the last few years that their chemistry has been elucidated and methods for their determination worked out. This is also true in the case of neuraminic acid, and its relation to nervous and mental diseases can now be suitably assessed.

As was pointed out, the gangliosides are found in small amounts in cerebral cells, and one of their constituents, neuraminic acid, can be detected in the CSF. Bogoch considers that substances in brain and CSF which contain neuraminic acid in their structure have a function in the blood-brain barrier, and that this barrier may be inadequately developed in schizophrenics. He has based his view, in part, upon his finding that the neuraminic acid level of the CSF may be subnormal in schizophrenics (31). Papadopoulos et al. report normal neuraminic acid levels in this psychosis, but find elevated values in Parkinsonism (32). Volk et al. (11) have found that an increased proportion of serum neuraminic acid is combined with the globulin fraction in amaurotic family idiocy, and that there is actually a shift in the binding of neuraminic acid, from the $\alpha_1$-globulins to the $\alpha_2$- and $\beta$-globulin fractions.

## NEUTRAL FAT AND PHOSPHOLIPIDES

Lipodystrophy is characterized by the progressive loss of fat from the subcutaneous tissues of the face, neck, and upper part of the trunk. About two fifths of the cases exhibit psychological symptoms, and in many there is a history of emotional disturbance (33). The onset of symptoms may coincide with postencephalitic changes, cerebral concussion, grand mal epilepsy, or some other neurological disturbance. However, the etiology of the condition is unknown; endocrine and other hypotheses vie with neurological ones as a basis for it (33, 34). Gibson has found three cases of progressive lipodystrophy in a population of 400 mental defectives (35).

In multiple sclerosis the phospholipide content of the white matter decreases and esters of cholesterol are laid down. Neuraminic acid increases in concentration in the cortex. Biochemical problems in the demyelinating diseases and the demyelination process are discussed at length in reference (36).

In cephalin lipidosis patients exhibit splenomegaly, and physical and mental retardation; seizures also occur. Storage of a lipide considered to be cephalin occurs in the bone marrow, in the nerve cells of the cerebral cortex, and in the gray matter at other sites. This condition has thus far been described for two patients only, who were siblings (37). In these the cephalins of the blood were elevated but the cholesterol esters and the sphingomyelin level both tended to be low. Confirmation of the identity of the accumulated lipide as cephalin would constitute this as a new type of storage disease.

## LIPIDOSES

In the lipidoses a biochemical defect leads to abnormal storage of specific lipides. The biochemical relationships of these lipide disorders are shown in Table 12-3.

At least three diseases are characterized by the deposition of sphingosine-containing lipides: reticular and histiocytic sphingomyelinosis (Niemann-Pick's disease), the infantile form of amaurotic family idiocy (Tay-Sachs' disease), and Gaucher's disease. The first of these affects primarily the central nervous and reticuloendothelial systems. It is seen usually in children under the age of two, in whom physical and mental development has been noted to cease and then to pursue a retrograde course. There is hepatosplenomegaly, progressive wasting, enlargement of lymph nodes, pale-brown pigmentation of the skin, and macular degeneration. Chemical studies have revealed a marked increase in the concentration of sphingomyelin in visceral organs, but not in brain or serum. However, the ganglioside content of the brain may be slightly increased. Serum cholesterol is greatly elevated in some cases and is almost normal in others.

TABLE 12-3. DISEASES OF LIPIDE METABOLISM

| Name of Disorder | Lipide Affected | Changes Observed |
|---|---|---|
| Xanthomatoses | | |
| Primary | Cholesterol | Deposited widely in the tissues. Serum cholesterol is normal or elevated |
| Secondary | Cholesterol | Hypercholesterolemia |
| Cephalin lipidosis | Cephalins | Increased in viscera; lecithins decreased |
| Sphingolipidoses | Sphingolipides | Deposited in excess in certain tissues |
| Niemann-Pick disease | Sphingomyelin | Increased in some viscera; normal in brain and serum, but brain gangliosides may increase |
| Amaurotic family idiocy | Gangliosides | Increase in nerve cells; also appear in the glial cells; increase in cortical neuraminic acid |
| Gaucher's disease | Cerebrosides | Increase in cells of reticulo-endothelial system; glucocerebrosides also found |
| Congenital familial cerebral lipidosis | ? | Neuropathological changes like those in amaurotic family idiocy |
| Hunter-Hurler syndrome | Gangliosides and mucopolysaccharide | Increase in the nerve cells |
| Familial leucodystrophy | Gangliosides? | Increase in neuraminic acid of gray matter; gangliosides found in white matter |

Tay-Sachs' disease is similarly characterized by the deterioration of mental and physical attainments, beginning usually during the first year of life. The macular degeneration indicates the close relationship between this and Niemann-Pick's disease. However, the prominent chemical change in Tay-Sachs' disease is the increase in the ganglioside content of the neuronal cells and the appearance of this lipide in the glial cells; the latter normally do not contain any gangliosides. There is also an increase in the neuraminic acid concentration in the cortex (38) and in some cases an increase in its sphingomyelin content, although the total phospholipides decrease. Serum neuraminic acid is elevated in Tay-Sachs' disease (14).

Other forms of amaurotic family idiocy occur, and these are related to Tay-Sachs' disease in symptoms and pathology, but information about corresponding chemical changes is essentially lacking. In the rare late infantile form (Bielschowsky's disease) and in the juvenile form (Vogt-Spielmeyer's disease) there may be lipide infiltration of the visceral organs, but changes in the brain lipides have not been reported. Even less is known about the chemical components in Kuf's disease, a very unusual form of amaurotic family idiocy in which mental deterioration and extrapyramidal symptoms first appear in adulthood. In their review of the lipidoses Fog and Munkvad (39) point to the common denominator in the various types of amaurotic family idiocy, namely, the ballooning of the ganglion cells and their distension with lipide. A congenital familial cerebral lipidosis, resembling in its histopathology Tay-Sachs' disease, has been described (40).

The third sphingolipidosis, Gaucher's disease, shows accumulation of galacto- and glucocerebrosides within cells of the reticuloendothelial system. For example, kerasine may constitute up to 10 percent of the dry weight of the spleen. Normally, cerebrosides account for but a minute fraction of the tissue lipides other than in the nervous system; because of their unusual increase in this disease, Gaucher's has also been called "reticular and histiocytic cerebrosidosis." In the infantile form of the disease there is physical and mental deterioration along with the appearance of marked neurological changes, leading to an early and fatal termination. Degenerative changes in the cerebral cortex are seen on histological examination. In spite of these changes the cerebroside-laden reticular Gaucher cells are not found in the brain nor is there any increase in the cerebroside content of this organ. In adults Gaucher's disease follows a chronic course and seldom affects the central nervous system.

Under the category of leucodystrophy Pfeiffer and Hirsch (41) include all cases of primary, noninflammatory diffuse sclerosis. The disease is hereditary and is accompanied by muscular weakness and spasticity, amaurosis and mental deficiency. Histological observation shows deposition of metachromatic-staining lipide breakdown products in the white matter as well as in some of the basal ganglia (41, 42). By chemical extraction procedures it has been shown that the accumulated lipide consists of gangliosides, substances which do not occur normally in the myelin sheath where the major histological changes are seen (42). The neuraminic acid concentration of the cortex also increases, as it does in Tay-Sachs' disease and in multiple sclerosis (38).

## Relation Between Lipide Metabolism and Nervous and Mental Function (43)

Among the disorders of lipide metabolism discussed above, some are characterized by nervous and mental symptoms of a deteriorative character, and thereby illustrate the close relationship between chemical composition of the brain (or specific parts of it) and its functional activity. Until recently the mechanisms involved in this relationship had hardly been explored although, as Wertheimer and Shapiro pointed out (44) in 1948, intact nervous connections are required for normal fat metabolism. These authors even suggested then that nervous influence on adipose tissue may be of considerable importance in the etiology of obesity and leanness (44). This has since been borne out even more generally for the lipide group of compounds. Reduced sensory input in mice affects the turnover of cerebral phospholipides (45). The stress of university examinations is associated with an increase in the low-density serum lipoproteins (46) and unpleasant emotional arousal causes a rise in the fatty acid level of the plasma (47).

Lipide metabolism is under hormonal control also. The plasma fatty acids are increased by the injection of growth hormone, triiodothyronine, epinephrine, and norepinephrine; they are decreased by the administration of insulin or glucose. The posterior pituitary contains an agent which causes shifts of triglycerides from the omental and mesenteric stores to the liver (lipide mobilizer) (48). The effects of injection of catecholamines (43, 49) are matched by those of adrenergic stimulation, so that tilting an individual to induce vasopressor adjustments causes a rise in plasma norepinephrine accompanied by an increase in the plasma fatty acids (50). The response to epinephrine injection is dependent upon intact hypophyseal and adrenal glands; and in animals deprived of these organs, treatment with cortisone restores the response (51).

The precise mechanism of lipide changes as a result of affective experience or of adrenergic stimulation awaits clarification by further experiments. However, there is reason to think that the autonomic nervous system contains the nervous components responsible, together with the anterior pituitary-adrenal cortical axis, for the observed metabolic effects.

# References

1. BRANTE, G. *Acta Physiol. Scand. 18:*Suppl. 63, 1949; JOHNSON, A. C., A. R. McNAB, and R. J. ROSSITER. *Biochem. J. 44:*494, 1949.
2. SLOANE-STANLEY, G. H. *In Biochemical Society Symposium No. 8,* New York, Cambridge University Press, 1952.
3. FREDERICKSON, D. S. *J.A.M.A. 164:*1895, 1957.
4. MARINETTI, G. V., R. F. WITTER, and E. STOTZ. *J. Biol. Chem. 226:*475, 1957; HOKIN, L. E., and M. R. HOKIN. *J. Biol. Chem. 233:*800, 1958.
5. KLENK, E. *Z. physiol. Chem. 273:*76, 1942.
6. KUHN, R., H. EGGE, A. GAUHE, P. KLESSE, W. LOCHINGER, E. RÖHM, H. TRISCHMAN, and D. TSCHAMPEL. *Angewandte Chem. 72:*805, 1960.
7. OSTER, K. A. *Exp. Med. Surg. 5:*219, 1947.
8. CORNFORTH, J. W., M. E. FIRTH, and A. GOTTSCHALK. *Biochem. J. 68:*57, 1958; KLENK, E. *In Chemistry and Biology of Mucopolysaccharides,* ed. WOLSTENHOLME, G. E. W., and M. CONNOR, London, J. and A. Churchill, 1958.
9. GOTTSCHALK, A. *The Chemistry and Biology of Sialic Acids and Related Substances,* New York, Cambridge University Press, 1960.
10. BÖHM, P., S. DAUBER, and L. BAUMEISTER. *Klin. Wochschr. 32:*289, 1954.
11. VOLK, B. W., S. M. ARONSON, and A. SAIFER. *J. Lab. Clin. Med. 50:*26, 1957.
12. UZMAN, L. L., and M. K. RUMLEY. *Proc. Soc. Exp. Biol. Med. 93:*497, 1956; ROSS, J., and P. BÖHM. *Klin. Wochschr. 35:*351, 1957.
13. WINZLER, R. J. *Methods of Biochemical Analysis,* Vol. 2, New York, Interscience, 1955.
14. SAIFER, A., S. M. ARONSON, M. C. ZYMARIS, and B. W. VOLK. *Proc. Soc. Exp. Biol. Med. 91:*394, 1956.
15. SRERE, P. A., I. L. CHAIKOFF, S. S. TREITMAN, and L. S. BURSTEIN. *J. Biol. Chem. 182:*629, 1950.
16. WEINMAN, E. O., E. H. STRISOWER, and I. L. CHAIKOFF. *Physiol. Rev. 37:*252, 1957.
17. ZILVERSMIT, D. B. *Am. J. Med. 23:*120, 1957.
18. KENNEDY, E. P. *Can. J. Biochem. Physiol. 34:*334, 1956; *idem, Federation Proc. 16:*847, 1957.
19. STAMMLER, A. *Arch. Psychiat. u. Nervenkrankh. 192:*556, 1954.
20. SVENNERHOLM, E., and L. SVENNERHOLM. *Scand. J. Clin. Lab. Invest. 10:* 97, 1958.
21. PETERS, J. P., and D. D. VAN SLYKE. *Quantitative Clinical Chemistry, Interpretations,* Vol. I. 2d ed., Baltimore, Williams and Wilkins, 1946.
22. THANNHAUSER, S. J. *In Biochemical Disorders in Human Disease,* ed. THOMPSON, R. H. S., and E. J. KING, New York, Academic Press, 1957.
23. LEBARON, F. N., and J. FOLCH. *Physiol. Rev. 37:*539, 1957.
24. McFARLAND, R. A., and H. GOLDSTEIN. *Am. J. Psychiat. 95:*509, 1938.
25. LARUE, G. H., C. A. PAINCHAUD, and G. NADEAU. *Can. Med. Assoc. J. 62:* 581, 1950; NADEAU, G., and G. H. LARUE. *ibid. 66:*320, 1952.

26. EATON, M. T., JR., and H. M. MUNTZ. *Am. J. Psychiat. 104:*315, 1947.
27. FLEISCHHACKER, H. H., and F. N. BULLOCK. *J. Ment. Sci. 98:*466, 1952.
28. FRIEDMAN, M., and R. H. ROSENMAN. *J.A.M.A. 169:*1286, 1959.
29. WERTLAKE, P. T., A. A. WILCOX, M. I. HALEY, and J. E. PETERSON. *Proc. Soc. Exp. Biol. Med. 97:*163, 1958.
29A. SLOANE, R. B., A. HABIB, M. B. EVESON, and R. W. PAYNE. *J. Psychosom. Res. 5:*183, 1961.
30. STRISOWER, E. H., O. DE LALLA, J. W. GOFMAN, and B. STRISOWER. *Am. J. Psychiat. 114:*263, 1957.
30A. STEPAN, J., and L. HANZLICEK. *Psychiat et Neurol. 141:*59, 1961.
31. BOGOCH, S. *Am. J. Psychiat. 114:*172, 1957; BOGOCH, S., K. T. DUSSIK, and P. G. LEVER. *A. M. A. Arch. Gen. Psychiat. 1:*441, 1959.
32. PAPADOPOULOS, N. M., J. E. MCLANE, D. O'DOHERTY, and W. C. HESS. *J. Nerv. Ment. Dis. 128:*450, 1959.
33. MURRAY, I. *Brit. Med. J. ii:*1236, 1952.
34. WARIN, R. P., and J. T. INGRAM. *Lancet ii:*55, 1950.
35. GIBSON, R. *Can. Med. Assoc. J. 77:*217, 1957.
36. EDGAR, G. W. F. *Proceedings VIth International Congress of Neurology,* 1957. Brussels, Editions Acta Medica Belgica, 1957; SCHUMACHER, G. A. *New England J. Med. 262:*1019, 1960.
37. BAAR, H. S., and E. M. HICKMANS. *Acta Med. Scand. 155:*49, 1956.
38. CUMINGS, J. N. *Brain 78:*554, 1955.
39. FOG, T., and I. MUNKVAD. *Acta Psychiat. Neurol. Scand. 30:*197, 1955.
40. BROWN, N. J., B. D. CORNER, and M. C. H. DODGSON. *Arch. Dis. Childh. 29:*48, 1954.
41. PFEIFFER, J., and V. HIRSCH. *Excerpta Medica 8:*Section 7, 802, 1955.
42. EDGAR, G. W. F. *Excerpta Medica 8:*Section 7, 801, 1955.
43. BOGDONOFF, M. D. *A. M. A. Arch. Intl. Med. 105:*505, 1960.
44. WERTHEIMER, E., and B. SHAPIRO. *Physiol. Rev. 28:*451, 1948.
45. WASE, A. W., and J. CHRISTENSEN. *A. M. A. Arch. Gen. Psychiat. 2:*171, 1960.
46. GRUNDY, S. M., and A. C. GRIFFIN. *J.A.M.A. 171:*1794, 1959.
47. BOGDONOFF, M. D., E. H. ESTES, JR., and D. TROUT. *Proc. Soc. Exp. Biol. Med. 100:*503, 1959.
48. HASHIM, S. A. *Diabetes 9:*135, 1960.
49. HAVEL, R. J., and A. GOLDFIEN. *J. Lipid Res. 1:*102, 1959.
50. HAMLIN, J. T., R. B. HICKLER, and R. G. HOSKINS. *J. Clin. Invest. 39:*606, 1960.
51. SHAFRIR, E., and D. STEINBERG. *J. Clin. Invest. 39:*310, 1960.

# 13

## ALCOHOL

### Physiological and Nutritional Aspects ( 1 )

The absorption of ingested alcohol begins in the stomach and continues into the small intestine. Many factors affect its rate of absorption or, what is actually of first interest clinically and legally, the concentration of alcohol in the blood. The blood level increases in proportion to the quantity of alcohol consumed and its concentration, but it also depends upon the rate of ingestion. For example, alcohol consumed over a protracted period of time results in lower blood values than when it is taken quickly. The absorptive rate is also diminished if food is present in the stomach. Because absorption of ethanol from the gastrointestinal tract proceeds faster than its metabolism in the tissues, it is not difficult to achieve pharmacologically significant concentrations in the blood. Levels of 0.05 to 0.10 percent cause the first signs of inebriety, and as the ethanol concentration in the blood rises the effects upon mental and physical performance become progressively more serious, with depression not only of cortical but also of lower centers. At 0.5 percent the subject is "dead drunk," and any further elevation in concentration signals impending death.

The most important mechanism for reduction of tissue levels of ethanol is its oxidation. In experiments with radioactive ethanol, Casier found about one third of the administered dose to be converted to respiratory carbon dioxide in the first half-hour. A substantial portion was rapidly fixed in the tissues as fatty acids and cholesterol (2). Excretion of alcohol by way of the kidneys, lungs, and skin account for one tenth or less of the amount ingested. However, there is a maximal rate at which alcohol can be metabolized, and this is of the order of 300 gm. per day. The alcoholic habitué does not metabolize alcohol more rapidly than the novice, but his nervous system has developed a tolerance to the drug. Hence he can function quasi-normally at higher blood levels of alcohol.

When alcohol is oxidized, seven calories become available per gram. This energy serves the body just as well as calories derived from other foodstuffs so that on energetic considerations alone alcohol substitutes for fat, carbohydrate, and protein. However, it cannot replace protein entirely because of the body's requirement for essential amino acids. The substantial fuel value of alcohol guarantees that even modest amounts of it taken as an adjunct to a normal diet contributes significantly to the caloric content of the diet.

The alcohol consumed substitutes for other foods with which are usually associated such important nutrients as vitamins, proteins, and minerals; none of these is included in distilled beverages but beers contain some water-soluble components of value, e.g., vitamins and minerals. In other words, alcohol consumption has the positive effect of providing calories, but the negative one of displacing other important nutrients from the diet, at the same time. In this way the liberal use of alcoholic beverages supplants essential nutrients from the diet; this practice may (and does) lead to the development of vitamin deficiencies and mineral imbalances.

There is a converse problem in the effect of quality of the diet upon the consumption of alcohol. It has been reported that animals given a nutritionally unsatisfactory diet consume more ethanol in self-selection experiments than do animals on a complete regime. Basing himself upon results of this type Williams (3) has developed a working hypothesis about alcoholism in man, namely, that the tendency to alcoholism is in some individuals associated with unusually high requirements for certain nutrients, and unless these above-average requirements are met by substantial dietary supplementation a deficiency syndrome is set in motion, which leads to the choosing of alcohol. He considers the exceptional dietary requirements and, consequently, the alcoholism to be derived from the genetic make-up of the individual. However, other animal experiments show that simply raising the carbohydrate content of an already adequate diet, or adding fat or saccharin to it, will bring about a reduction of alcohol consumption (4). The postulated association of high requirements for certain essential nutrients and the "tendency to alcoholism" have, therefore, not been demonstrated in animals, not to speak of man. Moreover, this hypothesis runs counter to the main current of clinical thought that alcoholism is a chronic disease or disorder of behavior.

# Biochemical Aspects

## METABOLISM OF ALCOHOL

The oxidation of alcohol is initiated through the action of a specific dehydrogenase, a pyridine nucleotide-linked and zinc-containing enzyme (Reaction 13-1). The product, acetaldehyde, has potent actions on the

$$CH_3CH_2OH + DPN^+ \rightleftarrows CH_3CHO + DPNH + H^+ \quad (13\text{-}1)$$
$$\text{Ethanol} \qquad\qquad \text{Acetaldehyde}$$

cardiovascular system (5) but, fortunately, its further conversion in metabolism proceeds faster than its formation from ethanol.

Several enzymes are known to act upon acetaldehyde, but their relative quantitative roles in the body are not known. Oxidation to acetic acid is mediated by dehydrogenases (Reactions 13-2 and 13-3) and by an oxidase (Reaction 13-4). The product in Reaction 13-3, acetyl-coenzyme A, is ready for entry into the terminal oxidative pathway, the tricarboxylic acid cycle.

$$CH_3CHO + DPN^+ + H_2O \rightleftarrows CH_3COOH + DPNH + H^+ \quad (13\text{-}2)$$
$$\text{Acetaldehyde} \qquad\qquad \text{Acetic acid}$$

$$CH_3CHO + DPN^+ + \underset{\text{Coenzyme A}}{HSCoA} \rightleftarrows \underset{\text{Acetyl-coenzyme A}}{CH_3COSCoA} + DPNH + H^+$$

$$(13\text{-}3)$$

$$CH_3CHO + O_2 + H_2O \rightleftarrows CH_3COOH + H_2O_2 \quad (13\text{-}4)$$
$$\text{Acetic acid}$$

A minor pathway of carbohydrate metabolism is represented in Reaction 13-5. This is dimerization to acetoin (acetylmethylcarbinol). A final Reaction (13-6) has been achieved thus far only with bacterial

$$2CH_3CHO \rightleftarrows CH_3CHOHCOCH_3$$
$$\text{Acetoin}$$

$$(13\text{-}5)$$

$$CH_3CHO + OCH \cdot CHOH \cdot CH_2O \cdot H_2PO_3 \rightleftarrows \text{Deoxypentose phosphate}$$
$$\text{Triose phosphate}$$

$$(13\text{-}6)$$

enzymes and has not yet been demonstrated for animals. This is the aldolase-catalyzed condensation of acetaldehyde with D-glyceraldehyde-3-phosphate. The product, 2-deoxy-D-ribose-5-phosphate, is a constituent of deoxyribonucleic acids. Possibily, this sugar phosphate undergoes degradative reactions, other than by a reversal of Reaction 13-6, which result in a net removal of acetaldehyde from the body.

The liver is the main organ involved in the metabolism of alcohol but it is aided, once acetaldehyde is formed, by enzymes in some of the other viscera and by peripheral tissues, especially skeletal muscle. Among the several products that are judged to be potentially derived from acetaldehyde *in vivo* on the basis of enzymatic studies, acetoin seems to be formed in appreciable amounts only in the hepatectomized animal.

In the treatment of ethanol poisoning one desideratum is a technique for accelerating the metabolism of the drug. As already pointed out, the mechanisms for oxidizing acetaldehyde are rapid enough, but the dehydrogenation of the ethanol to the acetaldehyde is the slow reaction. The infusion of glucose and other carbohydrates appears to be an efficacious measure in this regard. Perhaps some moiety formed in the metabolism of carbohydrates combines with the acetaldehyde as it is formed and allows Reaction 13-1 to proceed faster. Insulin administration has also been advocated. Although there is some evidence in the literature for an acceleration of alcohol oxidation by insulin (6) the clinical results have been equivocal. Perhaps any value reported for it lies in its mobilization of carbohydrate. The oxidation of acetaldehyde to form acetyl-coenzyme A offers the possibility of complete oxidation to carbon dioxide and water, as already mentioned, or synthesis to fatty acids. The quantitative significance of these reactions requires investigation.

Vitamin $B_6$ has been tested in a few studies on alcoholic intoxication as an antidote. Wordsworth's brief but enthusiastic claim (7) for a sobering action of the vitamin has not been substantiated (8). Pyridoxine, moreover, does not accelerate the metabolism of alcohol (9) although it should be tested in the treatment of the alcohol-withdrawal syndrome ("rum fits"). A study of five patients experiencing this syndrome showed that three of them were deficient in vitamin $B_6$ by the xanthurenic acid excretion test. Deficiency of this vitamin may play a role in the etiology of the convulsive episode (10). Presumably the withdrawal fits can begin as the central depressant action of alcohol begins to wear off.

Rogers and Pelton claim (11) that supplements of glutamine aid in the medical rehabilitation of alcoholics.

## METABOLIC DERANGEMENTS IN ALCOHOLISM

The imbalances in the alcoholic's diet lead to nutritional deficiencies and these may progress to frank clinical symptoms. This places alcohol in the role of a "conditioning agent rather than a primary or precipitating cause" of the complications of alcoholism (12). Two of the more common vitamin deficiency syndromes met with in alcoholism are those of thiamine, resulting in Wernicke's syndrome, and nicotinic acid, leading to the nicotinic acid encephalopathy described by Jolliffe and his colleagues. Measurement of the serum vitamin $B_{12}$ concentration shows that it is abnormally low in some alcoholics. Pyridoxine deficiency has been mentioned above. Some authors have suggested that a subnormal intake of choline or of other donors of labile methyl groups, contributes to the hepatic cirrhosis met with in alcoholics.

Mineral and water balance are also upset in the chronic alcoholic. The seriously drunk individual requires measures to combat salt depletion and dehydration. Not only must sodium be supplied but also magnesium, whose importance in this respect has been recognized in recent years. Plasma magnesium is reduced by 10 to 35 percent in more than half of cases presenting with delirium tremens, and erythrocyte magnesium is abnormally low in all cases examined (13). This loss of magnesium may assume some significance because of the important role of the ion at various stages in the intermediary metabolism of carbohydrates. Patients with postalcoholic cirrhosis have a lowered serum zinc content and, in addition, exhibit zincuria. At post-mortem the zinc content of the liver is substantially below normal (14).

Altschule and his colleagues have found in chronic alcoholics normal concentrations of various carbohydrate intermediates in the blood. However, following the administration of glucose in a standard tolerance test the level of some of these compounds in the blood undergoes changes that are not seen in normal subjects. In fact, it is claimed that the changes exhibit the type of abnormality seen in similar circumstances in the psychoses and in multiple sclerosis (15).

# Drugs Causing Intolerance to Alcohol

In 1914 Koelsch first described a toxic syndrome among workers handling cyanamide (carbimide) in the manufacturing and fertilizer industries (16). The symptoms included flushing, headache and vertigo, tachycardia and tachypnea; the nervous system was not notably affected, for the sensorium remained clear and reflexes were normal. The remarkable feature of this syndrome was the fact that cyanamide induced it only when alcohol was consumed. Others recognized the same picture later, not only with cyanamide, but more recently with tetraethylthiuramdisulfide, or disulfiram (17). A constituent of the mushroom *Coprinus atramentarius* similarly affects the metabolism of alcohol; its composition is unknown.

Disulfiram has the structure $(C_2H_5)_2N-C(=S)-S-S-C(=S)-N(C_2H_5)_2$. When alcohol is ingested acetaldehyde accumulates, as shown by blood analyses (18) and the elevated levels of the latter compound in the circulating fluids are associated with the appearance of the syndrome described by Koelsch. The symptoms, including prominent cardiovascular and respiratory ones, exhibit a severity that depends upon the amount of alcohol consumed—a minimum of 5 to 10 gm. is required—and upon individual differences in tolerance. Although the pharmacological actions of acetaldehyde resemble those of the disulfiram-ethanol combination, the correlation of symptoms with blood acetaldehyde concentrations is not very good and has brought the suggestion (19) that disulfiram also affects other enzymes whose inhibition becomes apparent when ethanol and acetaldehyde are present in the tissues. Physiological interactions have been recognized and it is possible that one action of disulfiram is in altering vascular sensitivity to acetaldehyde. Other agents may contribute to the syndrome. Among them are carbon disulfide, formed from disulfiram normally, but in increased amounts when alcohol is also taken, and diethylamine, which has been detected in the blood after the administration of disulfiram and ethanol (2). The extremely unpleasant subjective effects have led to the use of this drug in the psychological treatment of alcoholism. The cooperative patient taking the drug is made aware of the sequence of events awaiting him should he consume an alcoholic beverage.

Because of the dangers inherent in the use of disulfiram, its side reactions, and the unpredictability of its action on ethanol metabolism, a search has been made for other drugs whose action is similar, but milder, and is more rapidly reversed upon withdrawal. Tests of various carbimides have shown favorable results for the calcium salt, $CaNCN$, in combination with citric acid (20). This drug causes a considerably shorter period of intolerance to alcohol which is, of course advantageous in control of medication.

## METHANOL

Methanol ($CH_3OH$) has less depressant action on the central nervous system than ethanol, but is much more toxic. The toxic dose is quite variable among individuals, and extends over a hundredfold range. Untreated cases of mild poisoning may recover completely or be left with a residuum of blindness; severe toxicity entails widely distributed symptoms which can end in death. At post-mortem there are degenerative changes in the visual apparatus and in other cerebral areas, as well as in the heart and viscera.

Methanol is oxidized in the tissues to formaldehyde ($HCHO$), and this in turn to formic acid ($HCOOH$), but the mechanism of these reactions is not known. The products, especially the latter, can be detected long after the methanol has been ingested. They cause a marked excretion of various organic acidic metabolites, associated with a severe acidosis. A necessary specific measure in the treatment of methanol poisoning is the replacement of this loss of the alkali reserve (21) with sodium citrate or sodium bicarbonate. Röe (22) has recommended the use of ethanol infusions, claiming that this compound inhibits the oxidation of the methanol and restricts appreciably the formation of the highly toxic aldehyde and acid. However, clinical trials by others have not yet demonstrated a clear benefit from the use of ethanol. Experimental work on methanol poisoning in the rat indicates that fructose aggravates the toxicity, although it appears to provide some amelioration in ethanol toxicity (23).

# References

1. HIMWICH, H. E. *J.A.M.A. 163*:545, 1957; MUEHLBERGER, C. W. *ibid.167*: 1842, 1958.
2. CASIER, H. *Bull. de l'Acad. Suisse Sci. Médicales 16*:15, 1960.
3. WILLIAMS, R. J. *Biochemical Individuality, the Basis for the Genetotrophic Concept.* New York, Wiley, 1956.
4. LESTER, D., and L. A. GREENBERG. *Quart. J. Stud. Alcohol 13*:553, 1952.
5. ASMUSSEN, E., J. HALD, and V. LARSEN. *Acta Pharmacol. et Toxicol. 4*: 311, 1948.
6. SUPNIEVSKY, J. V. *J. Biol. Chem. 70*:13, 1926.
7. WORDSWORTH, V. E. *Brit. Med. J. i*:935, 1953.
8. SMALL, M. D., M. ZAMCHEK, J. J. VITALE, A. LONGARINI, and B. FISHER. *J. Lab. Clin. Med. 46*:12, 1955.
9. NEWMAN, H., and M. E. SMITH. *Proc. Soc. Exp. Biol. Med. 100*:258, 1959.
10. LERNER, A. M., L. M. DeCARLI, and C. S. DAVIDSON. *Proc. Soc. Exp. Biol. Med. 98*:841, 1958.
11. ROGERS, L. L., and R. B. PELTON. *Quart. J. Stud. Alcohol 18*:581, 1957.

12. GOODHART, R. S. *Am. J. Clin. Nutr. 5:*612, 1957.

13. SMITH, W. O., and J. F. HAMMARSTEN. *Am. J. Med. Sci. 237:*413, 1959.

14. VALLEE, B. L., W. E. C. WACKER, A. F. BARTHOLOMAY, and F. L. HOCH. *Ann. Int. Med. 50:*1077, 1959.

15. ALTSCHULE, M. D., M. VICTOR, and P. D. HOLLIDAY. *A. M. A. Arch. Int. Med. 99:*40, 1957.

16. KOELSCH, F. *Münch. Med. Wochschr. 61:*1896, 1914.

17. HALD, J., E. JACOBSEN, and V. LARSEN. *Acta Pharmacol. et Toxicol. 4:*285, 1946.

18. HALD, J., and E. JACOBSEN. *Acta Pharmacol. et Toxicol. 4:*305, 1948.

19. HUNTER, F. E., JR., and O. H. LOWRY. *Pharmacol. Revs. 8:*89, 1956.

20. FERGUSON, J. K. W. *Can. Med. Assoc. J. 74:*793, 1956.

21. BENNETT, I. L., F. H. CARY, G. L. MITCHELL, and M. N. COOPER. *Medicine 32:*431, 1953.

22. RÖE, O. *Pharmacol. Revs. 7:*399, 1955.

23. STUHLFAUTH, K., H. NEUMAIER, and G. BOMMES. *Arch. exp. Path. u. Pharmakol. 214:*556, 1952.

# 14

# PORPHYRINS, HEMOGLOBIN, AND BILE PIGMENTS

The utilization of oxygen is based upon the transport of the gas, as oxyhemoglobin, from the lungs to the tissues and the participation therein of a series of respiratory catalysts, the cytochromes and cytochrome oxidase, which mediate the terminal reactions in the tissues. In these reactions oxygen is combined with the protons removed by dehydrogenation of substrates, and water is formed. This is not the only fashion in which oxygen is reduced by hydrogen in mammalian tissues, for the yellow (riboflavin-containing) enzymes catalyze the oxidation of a number of specific substrates yielding, not water, but hydrogen peroxide. In addition to the cytochromes and hemoglobin, other hematin pigments occur in the body: myoglobin (which assists in maintaining a reserve store of oxygen in the muscles), catalase (which catalyzes the breakdown of the hydrogen peroxide that has been formed), and verdoperoxidase (found in leucocytes). The extremely potent vitamin $B_{12}$ belongs to a related series of compounds.

Clinical disorders referable to the hematin pigments, their metabolic precursors, and especially their products, are numerous. Suffice it to mention at this point methemoglobinemia, sickle cell anemia, the porphyrias, and various forms of jaundice. A few are of psychiatric interest either because of the psychic manifestations occurring, say, in acute intermittent porphyria or because of toxic drug reactions. Some of the metabolites to be discussed have important pharmacological actions when they are present in the tissues in abnormally high concentration, and may affect the nervous system.

## Biosynthesis and Metabolism of Porphyrins and Hemoglobin (1, 2)

The fundamental structure in the porphyrin molecule is that of porphin. This compound consists of four pyrrole groups linked to one another by methine groups ($-CH=$). The porphyrins found in mammals all have side chains attached at the 3- and 4-positions of the pyrrole groups. These eight side chains theoretically permit a large number of arrangements and, therefore, distinct compounds, but the naturally occurring ones thus far described belong to two types only. The porphyrin in the hemoglobin molecule belongs to Type III. The other porphyrins, those of Type I, appear in the tissues under certain pathological conditions.

The three chief categories of porphyrins with which the clinician is concerned are the protoporphyrins (four methyl, two vinyl, and two propionic acid side chains), the coproporphyrins (four methyl and four propionic side chains), and the uroporphyrins (four acetic and four propionic acid side chains). It is not known if these have a common precursor or whether one is derived from the other. Some investigators, favoring the latter possibility, point to the fact that the acetic acid groups of uroporphyrin could give rise by decarboxylation to the methyls of the other two sets of porphyrins and that its propionic groups by dehydration and decarboxylation could form vinyl side chains; this argument would then present the biosynthetic sequence of uro-, copro-, and finally protoporphyrin. The last then combines with iron and globin to form hemoglobin.

Porphyrins are formed from readily available precursors (1, 2). Their metabolic origin is linked with the terminal oxidation of carbohydrates and fats in that acetate, a metabolic product common to both of these foodstuffs, is a prime building block for the porphyrins. Acetate combines with glycine to form δ-aminolevulinic acid; this compound is dehydrated and cyclized to form porphobilinogen, a pyrrole derivative with appropriate side chains. Porphobilinogen serves as the structural unit of the porphyrins, but still requires several metabolic alterations, including its linkage with three other chemically related molecules to form the tetrapyrrole structure characteristic of porphyrins.

The porphyrins eventually combine with a metal and sometimes with a specific protein, and it is in this form that they function in the tissues. Ferroprotoporphyrin is the heme group combined with globin in hemoglobin. In porphyrias originating in a defectively functioning liver, zinc porphyrins are found in the urine. Uro- and coproporphyrins do not function as prosthetic groups of biologically active proteins as do the protoporphyrins.

The catabolism of hemin and related substances has not been fully worked out yet in spite of the long interest in clinical medicine in the bile pigments. Hemoglobin, hematin, and myoglobin are found in the urine only as pathological constituents; they are partially degraded before reaching the kidney for disposition. At the end of the lifespan of the erythrocyte the hemoglobin loses its iron (much of which is re-utilized in ferritin and elsewhere) and the protoporphyrin ring breaks, forming a chain of four pyrrole units bound to the protein portion of the molecule. The biliverdinoglobin or choleglobin is broken down further in the reticuloendothelial cells (in man, predominantly in those of the spleen) with the separation of the globin component from the bilirubin, a brownish-orange pigment carried in a loose linkage with serum albumin to the liver. In the liver the bilirubin is conjugated with glucuronic acid, and is then secreted into the bile in this form. In the van den Bergh test bilirubin is an indirect-reacting pigment (3) and its glucuronide is the direct-reacting pigment (4), i.e., the one with greater solubility in water. When the conjugated pigment reaches the intestine it is acted upon by bacteria to form several new, reduced compounds including the colorless urobilinogens. Some of these are later oxidized in the intestine to urobilin and stercobilin (the latter also formed by synthesis *de novo* and perhaps by other biosynthetic routes), but the major portion of urobilinogen is reabsorbed and converted in the hepatic cells once again to bilirubin glucuronide. This is described as the enterohepatic circulation of bile pigment.

About nine tenths of the bilirubin formed is derived from hemoglobin, the remainder from the other hematoporphyrins (5).

# Porphyrias (2)

Normally the body contains much less than a milligram of free porphyrins, but in the porphyrias this amount is very much increased.

Three main types of porphyria occur clinically, in addition to the copro-porphyrinuria seen in pernicious anemia and in lead poisoning, and the porphyria resulting sometimes from the use of barbiturates or other drugs. The predominant clinical porphyrias originate either through defects in the erythropoietic system or in the liver. The former occur in infancy and childhood, and are very rare (6). They are characterized chemically by the presence of large amounts of Type I porphyrins in many tissues (with deposits in the teeth and bones), although the liver is not excessively loaded. Because the porphyrins are also deposited in the skin where they can exert their photodynamic action, light sensitivity is a prominent factor in this condition. The hepatogenous porphyrias are seen in adults. The most commonly occurring form, the acute intermittent type, is characterized by the presence of porphobilinogen in the tissues and urine. The clinical picture and course are variable, but include ab-dominal, neurological, and psychiatric components. The chronic type of this disease, porphyria cutanea tarda, appears even later in life; it displays some features of both the above conditions: increases in Types I and III porphyrins, but with variable amounts of urinary δ-aminolevulinic acid and porphobilinogen. Clinically there are abdominal symptoms and photosensitivity. The urinary excretion of Type I uroporphyrin is a finding common to all three diseases.

Acute intermittent porphyria is often precipitated by some emotional crisis (7), but the presenting symptom is frequently abdominal cramps of a very intense kind, with vomiting and constipation. Patients complain of weakness of the limbs. There may be some motor paralysis, neuritis, and even convulsions. Demyelinization and other neuronal changes have been observed (8), but the primary defect is considered to occur in the liver, and is manifested by the appearance of excessive amounts of porphobilinogen.

Various psychiatric symptoms occur especially during the active or toxic phase (9). When they appear together with the neurological and abdominal symptoms, the diagnosis is rendered easier. Actually, diagnosis is confirmed by the demonstration of porphobilinogen in the urine.

Persons with this disease may undergo spontaneous remissions, but the mortality is high. Acute porphyria is said to be inherited as a Mendelian dominant; it occurs more frequently in women than in men.

Recently some of the newer drugs have been tested for relief of symptoms in acute intermittent porphyria. A ganglionic blocking agent, tetraethylammonium chloride, has been used successfully in one case

(10). Chlorpromazine and Rauwolfia alkaloids have similarly been used to overcome the abdominal and neurological features of the attack (11). In cases where the psychiatric symptoms predominate electroshock therapy has been employed, with greater (12) or less success (13) in the acute psychosis.

## Pharmacological Actions of Porphyrins

Hematoporphyrin occurs in large amounts in the urine as a result of poisoning by sulfonal, barbiturates, lead, and some other substances. It lends a deep wine-red color to the urine. Hematoporphyrin resembles protoporphyrin chemically except that the two vinyl side chains are hydrated. Because of its photodynamic action it causes light-sensitivity. Small amounts cause only erythema, with some edema, upon minimal exposure to light, but larger doses cause elevation of blood pressure, increase in the pulse rate and respiratory rate, and severe erythema. Ultimately coma, followed by death, supervenes (14).

Hematoporphyrin also causes increased physical activity in animals injected with it. This was at one time made the basis of a therapeutic use for it, as the drug Photodyn, in depressive states. Huhnerfeld introduced the compound in a trial on 13 patients with psychotic depression (15). Eleven of the group were improved by the drug. Hematoporphyrin then found extensive use, for a short period, including confirmation of the original results (16). However, its action is basically a toxic one, for at post-mortem extensive degenerative changes are found in the spinal cord, peripheral nerves, and sympathetic ganglia.

For an extensive review of porphyrinurias caused by various pharmacological and toxic agents the article by Dobriner and Rhoads (17) should be consulted.

## Ferroprotoporphyrins and Hemoglobin

The protoporphyrins combine with iron to form a series of important prosthetic groups acting in oxygen-binding or oxygen-transferring capacities. The prosthetic groups function while attached to specific proteins, thus constituting hemoglobin, myoglobin, peroxidase, catalase, the several cytochrome pigments, and cytochrome oxidase. Certain compounds, notably cyanide, hydrogen sulfide, and carbon monoxide, can react with the combined iron and thereby interfere with the functions of the hematins. The combination of hemoglobin with these poisons is fortunately reversible, but if resuscitation measures are delayed, then permanent and irreversible brain damage may occur from the tissue anoxia. Oxidation of the divalent iron of hemoglobin to the ferric form results in the formation of methemoglobin, a brownish pigment which no longer binds oxygen.

As has become clear in the last few years, there are diseases arising from an abnormality of hemoglobin structure. Although these are not directly pertinent to psychiatry, the general concept of molecular diseases introduced by Linus Pauling (18) as a result of the discovery of abnormal hemoglobins is of considerable concern. In 1949 Pauling and his colleagues (19) reported the first known instance of such a disease, namely, sickle cell anemia. They found that the hemoglobin in the erythrocytes of persons with this disease is actually different from the hemoglobin found in the majority of individuals (type A). The difference is in the molecular structure of the protein (globin) portion (19). Over 100 hemoglobins have been discovered since then, each differing from the others in the structure and composition of the protein (*cf.* 20). The presence of certain of these hemoglobins in the erythrocyte renders this cell less able to perform its functions, with the resultant sicklemia or thalassemia. The formation of these abnormal hemoglobins is under genetic control. Hemoglobin F, the type found in fetal erythrocytes, appears to be an exception.

## Jaundice; Kernicterus

Hyperbilirubinemia is not uncommon in the newborn infant but it usually passes off after a longer or shorter period without inflicting any harm upon the baby. If the icterus is severe or if it persists for a longer period there is a serious threat to the health of the infant because of the toxic action of bilirubin upon the brain. Consequently in neonatal jaundice, whether of hemolytic (blood-group incompatibilities, isoimmunization) or nonhemolytic origin, brain damage is a potential hazard, liable to result in the rapid démise of the infant or to leave permanent neurological and mental defects upon those who survive the neonatal period.

Because the incidence of serious complications is relatively low, the neonatal hyperbilirubinemia other than that resulting from frank hemolytic disease has commonly been regarded as part of a physiological process signifying the changeover from the elevated hemoglobin levels of the fetal blood to the lower ones found in the infant. For this reason the physiological type has been classified as hemolytic in origin also. Although the rate of breakdown of erythrocytes is greater during the first

10 days of life (21) it is not immoderately high, and current concepts lend weight to the nonhemolytic character of much of the neonatal jaundice seen.

Billing, Cole, and Lathe (22) have collected data demonstrating that the degree of jaundice in infants (excluding that of hemolytic origin) is related to the birth weight in such a way that babies of subnormal weight (including, therefore, premature infants and small babies born at term) have a higher concentration of bilirubin in the plasma, attain elevated concentrations of the pigment earlier, and maintain these high levels for a longer period than do the larger babies. Practically all the plasma bilirubin reacts indirectly in the van den Bergh test (22) This is a rather unusual situation and suggests that the liver in these small infants is limited in its ability to detoxify bilirubin (22, 23). The hypothesis that the liver is able to excrete the direct pigment, but not the indirect one, into the bile (24) could then explain the neonatal hyperbilirubinemia. Its proof has awaited the elucidation of the chemical nature of the two types of bilirubin, as described above. These substances have now been crystallized from plasma (25).

With the pigments characterized it was logical to seek some defect in the mechanism of glucuronidation of bilirubin as the basis of the hyperbilirubinemia of the newborn. Biochemical analysis has shown that Reactions 11-33 to 11-35 are involved in this glucuronidation. Both mono- and diglucuronides of bilirubin are formed. A small proportion of the bilirubin (less than 20 percent) is conjugated with sulfuric acid. A deficiency of any one of the enzymes catalyzing these reactions could result in the detoxication of bilirubin at an abnormally low rate. Examination of Reactions 11-34 and 11-35 in extracts of liver from newborn infants dying of nonhemolytic jaundice has actually substantiated the hypothesis of an enzyme defect. Even if such extracts are fortified with added uridine diphosphate glucuronic acid they cannot carry out the conjugation of bilirubin (26). This is true also of extracts of liver of a congenitally hyperbilirubinemic strain of rats (24, 26). Fetal and neonatal guinea pig livers are also relatively inactive in the formation of direct-reacting pigment. (27). Because the glucuronidation of o-amino-phenol proceeds normally under the same conditions, Lathe and Walker consider that the enzymic defect is not in the formation of uridine diphosphate glucuronic acid but rather in the specific enzyme transferring the glucuronic acid group to bilirubin (26). Brown has observed reduced activity of the enzyme catalyzing Reaction 11-34 in neonatal guinea pig liver (27).

The nature of the brain pigment has been investigated by several investigators. Vogel (28) deduced it to be mesobilirubin, a reduction product of bilirubin, but Lathe and his colleagues have shown by chromatographic and other techniques (3, 4) that it is bilirubin.

In spite of the well-known association of hyperbilirubinemia with brain jaundice in infants, little is known of the pathogenesis of the cerebral damage. The pigment itself has been implicated by some as the toxic agent. This is a distinct possibility, for cerebral jaundice and neurological changes have been observed following the injection of very large amounts of bilirubin, sufficient to raise the plasma level to a concentration comparable to that seen in neonatal jaundice (3, 29). Such levels are capable of significantly inhibiting the respiration of brain slices *in vitro* (3); in addition they cause the release of some respiratory cofactors from liver mitochondria, and result in the dissociation of phosphorylation from oxidation (30), with the consequent disruption of energy-conserving mechanisms in these particles. The toxic action of bilirubin is more readily expressed in the young than in the adult, a fact which may be accounted for by postulating a relatively greater permeability of the brain cells of the former to the pigment. Lack of myelinization in the neonatal brain may contribute in some way to this increased permeability. Küster and Krings (29) suggest that cerebral edema facilitates the penetration of pigments. Gerrard (31) has discussed the various theories of kernicteric development.

Najjar [quoted in (5)] has suggested that the structural similarity of bilirubin to the important and ubiquitous cytochrome respiratory pigment may endow it with antimetabolite properties, *e.g.*, interference with cellular respiration.

The sequelae of kernicterus in those who survive infancy have been described on many occasions (*cf.* 20, 32). Soon after birth the jaundice is detected; initially the child may show opisthotonos with muscular twitchings, but these phenomena then disappear. Some time later the results of the cerebral damage are seen in various forms such as spasticity of the limbs in some, or atony in others, as well as in cerebellar disturbances (*e.g.*, ataxia), and athetotic and choreiform movements. Combinations of these neurological changes are also seen clinically. Deafness is a frequent defect, and mental deficiency is common. Worssam (33) has reported on an unusual case of an adult whose early history indicated the probability of kernicterus; he was of normal intelligence, had a normal encephalogram and CSF, but complained of some deafness. Examination indicated extensive calcification in the region of the basal ganglia and the dentate nucleus. The patient had suffered for many years from brief episodes of "dissociation from his surroundings." His presenting complaint was that on two such occasions he had lost consciousness.

Judging from correlations of clinical and laboratory data, the infant is most susceptible to brain damage when the plasma bilirubin reaches a level of 15 to 20 mg./100 ml. (23, 34) or even higher (5). To prevent the development of kernicterus exchange transfusion with recently drawn blood has been employed with success (23, 34, 35).

Crigler and Najjar have described hyperbilirubinemia with kernicterus (36). The prognosis is grave, but some patients with this type of jaundice have survived infancy, at least for a few years (37), and have been free of neurological symptoms. In the light of the enzyme studies described above it is possible that this disorder represents a congenital deficiency of the system conjugating glucuronic acid with bilirubin.

# References

1. RIMINGTON, C. *Brit. Med. J. ii*:189, 1956.
2. STICH, W. *Klin. Wochschr. 37*:681, 1959.
3. LATHE, G. H. *In The Chemical Pathology of Animal Pigments, ed.* WILLIAMS, R. T. *Biochemical Society Symposium No. 12,* New York, Cambridge University Press, 1954; COLE, P. G., G. H. LATHE, and B. H. BILLING. *Biochem. J. 57*:514, 1954.
4. BILLING, B. H., P. G. COLE, and G. H. LATHE. *Biochem. J. 65*:774, 1957.
5. BLACK-SCHAFFER, B., S. KAMBE, M. FURUTA, and W. C. MOLONEY. *A. M. A. J. Dis. Child. 87*:737, 1954.
6. RIMINGTON, C. *Proc. Roy. Soc. Med. 52*:963, 1959.
7. LUBY, E. D., J. G. WARE, R. SENF, and C. E. FROHMAN. *Psychosom. Med. 21*:34, 1959.
8. GOLDBERG, A. *In The Chemical Pathology of Animal Pigments, ed.* WILLIAMS, R. T. *Biochemical Society Symposium No. 12,* New York, Cambridge University Press, 1954.
9. WALDENSTRÖM, J. *Acta Med. Scand.: Suppl. 82,* 1937.
10. DURST, J. B., and M. A. KREMBS. *J.A.M.A. 160*:165, 1956.
11. MELBY, J. C., J. P. STREET, and C. J. WATSON. *J. Am. Med. Assoc. 162*: 174, 1956.
12. FREEMAN, J. G., and L. C. KOLB. *Proc. Staff Meet. Mayo Clinic 26*:401, 1951.
13. LEVY, S., and H. A. PERRY. *Arch. Neurol. Psychiat. 61*:699, 1949.
14. MASON, V. R., C. B. COURVILLE, and E. ZISKIND. *Medicine 12*:355, 1933.
15. HUHNERFELD, J. *Am. J. Psychiat. 92*:1323, 1936.
16. ANGUS, L. R. *Am. J. Psychiat. 92*:877, 1936; STEINBERG, D. L. *ibid*:901.
17. DOBRINER, K., and C. P. RHOADS. *Physiol. Rev. 20*:416, 1940.
18. PAULING, L. *Am. J. Psychiat. 113*:492, 1957.

19. PAULING, L., H. ITANO, S. J. SINGER, and I. C. WELLS. *Science* 110:543, 1949.
20. ZUELZER, W. W. *Federation Proc. 16*:769, 1957.
21. MOLLISON, P. L. *Lancet i*:513, 1948.
22. BILLING, B. H., P. G. COLE, and G. H. LATHE. *Brit. Med. J. ii*:1263, 1954.
23. HSIA, D. Y. Y., F. H. ALLEN, JR., L. K. DIAMOND, and S. S. GELLIS. *J. Pediat. 42*:277, 1953.
24. MALLOY, H. T., and L. LOWENSTEIN. *Canad. Med. Assoc. J. 42*:122, 1940.
25. NAJJAR, V. A. *Pediatrics 10*:1, 1952.
26. LATHE, G. H., and M. WALKER. *Biochem. J. 70*:705, 1958.
27. BROWN, A. K. *A.M.A.J. Dis. Child. 94*:510, 1957.
28. VOGEL, F. S. *Am. J. Path. 29*:582, 1953.
29. KÜSTER, F., and H. KRINGS. *Lancet i*:979, 1950.
30. ZETTERSTRÖM, R., and L. ERNSTER. *Nature 178*:1335, 1956.
31. GERRARD, J. W. *Brain 75*:526, 1952.
32. LANDE, L. *J. Pediatr. 32*:693, 1948; EVANS, P. R., and P. E. POLANI. *Quart. 'J. Med. 19*:129, 1950.
33. WORSSAM, A. R. H. *Brit. Med. J. ii*:683, 1957.
34. LATHE, G. H. *Brit. Med. J. i*:192, 1955.
35. MOLLISON, P. L., and M. CUTBUSH. *Lancet ii*:522, 1948.
36. CRIGLER, J. F., and V. A. NAJJAR. *Pediatrics 10*:169, 1952; JERVIS, G. A. *A. M. A. Arch. Neurol. Psychiat. 81*:55, 1959.
37. CHILDS, B., and V. A. NAJJAR. *Pediatrics 18*:369, 1956; ROSENTHAL, I. M., H. J. ZIMMERMANN, and N. HARDY. *ibid.*: 378.

# 15

# THE FUNCTION OF VITAMINS
# IN METABOLISM

The catalysts of intermediary metabolic reactions are the enzymes, of which there are many thousands. They consist of proteins whose chemical structure, functional groups, and molecular topography endow them with the specificity they exhibit toward substrates, as well as with their ability to catalyze the chemical alterations of these substrates. Some enzymes require additional substances to permit the catalysis to occur. These cofactors may be inorganic ions or organic substances; the latter are known as coenzymes. They include (*a*) compounds that are readily available to the body by reason of their endogenous origin, *e.g.*, adenylic acid and its di- and triphosphates, and the cytidine and uridine nucleotides; and (*b*) others that must be supplied either whole or in part from an exogenous source, because of the body's lack of specific enzymes capable of synthesizing them. This last category defines the vitamins: they are organic substances required in the diet in small amounts and can make only a negligible caloric contribution; they function in the body as cellular catalysts in conjunction with enzymes. This function is assumed after the vitamin has been converted into a specific conjugate, frequently by phosphorylation. A given coenzyme may function with many different enzymes.

In earlier chapters examples of coenzyme action have been given in relation to the metabolism of carbohydrates, lipides, and nitrogenous substances. The role of coenzymes in hydrogen transport is also of great importance and merits a brief description here. A considerable portion of cellular respiration depends upon the activity of the dehydrogenases, most of which require one of the nicotinamide-containing nucleotides (pyridine nucleotide, PN) as proton acceptor. Because the supply of PN in the tissues is limited, maintenance of this respiratory activity requires the regular cyclic reoxidation of the reduced coenzyme to the original state. In this process the reduced PN (PNH) contributes its hydrogen to a flavoprotein (FP) or cytochrome (Cy) reductase (Reactions 15-1 and 15-2). The dihydroflavoprotein (FPH$_2$) is re-

$$PNH + H^+ + FP \rightleftarrows PN^+ + FPH_2 \tag{15-1}$$

$$FPH_2 + 2Cy(Fe^{+++}) \rightleftarrows FP + 2Cy(Fe^{++}) + 2H^+ \tag{15-2}$$

oxidized through the operation of the cytochrome system, which consists of several hemin pigments and the enzyme cytochrome oxidase, a (ferri)hematoporphyrinoprotein (*cf.* Reaction 15-3). The net result

$$2Cy(Fe^{++}) + 2H^+ + \tfrac{1}{2}O_2 \rightleftarrows 2Cy(Fe^{+++}) + H_2O \tag{15-3}$$

$$PNH + H^+ + \tfrac{1}{2}O_2 \rightleftarrows PN^+ + H_2O \tag{15-4}$$

of these successive reductions and oxidations is the formation of water (Reaction 15-4). Thus, nicotinic acid and riboflavin, functional constituents of the pyridine nucleotides and the flavoproteins, respectively, play key roles in the oxidation of hydrogen *in vivo*.

A list of vitamins required by man, along with the coenzyme forms, is given in Table 15-1. A criterion for inclusion in this table is demonstration of a requirement for the vitamin in the prophylaxis or cure of nutritional deficiency disease, as observed clinically or induced experimentally in man. Other substances, which are vitamins for lower mammals but which have not yet been shown to be required in the diet of humans, include *para*-aminobenzoic acid, inositol, choline, and vitamin E. Lipoic acid, a bacterial vitamin, undoubtedly plays a role in mammalian metabolism.

One of the great problems in the study of the vitamin deficiency disease is the detailed derivation of the pathological changes from the failure of the vitamin to catalyze specific biochemical reactions in the affected tissue. In no case has this derivation been developed

TABLE 15-1. VITAMIN REQUIREMENTS AND FUNCTIONS

| Vitamin | Estimated Daily Requirement (mg.) | Coenzyme Forms | Examples of Metabolic Functions |
|---|---|---|---|
| Thiamine (vitamin B₁) | 1–2 | Diphosphothiamine (DPT, cocarboxylase) | Decarboxylation of pyruvic and other $\alpha$-keto acids; transketolation |
| Riboflavin (vitamin B₂) | 1.5–2 | Riboflavin monophosphate (FMN) and flavin adenine dinucleotide (FAD) | Oxidative deamination of amino acids and of diamines |
| Nicotinic acid | 10–20 | Di- and triphosphopyridine nucleotides (DPN and TPN; coenzyme I and coenzyme II) | Dehydrogenation reactions in the metabolism of carbohydrates and glutamic acid; aromatic oxidations (TPN) |
| Pyridoxine (vitamin B₆) | 2 | Pyridoxal phosphate | Transamination; amino acid decarboxylations; various amino acid transformations |
| Pantothenic acid | 3–10 | Coenzyme A | Pyruvate oxidation; fatty acid metabolism; lipide biosyntheses |
| Biotin | ? | Carboxybiotin-ADP anhydride | Transcarboxylation of organic acids; required for metabolism of leucine |
| Inositol | ? | Not known | In inositol phospholipides |
| Folic acid | ? | Tetrahydrofolic acid | Glycine:serine interconversion |
| Cyanocobalamin (vitamin B₁₂) | 0.005 | Adenylcobamide coenzyme | Conversion of glutamic to $\beta$-methylaspartic acid (in bacteria) |

TABLE 15-1 (*Continued*)

| Vitamin | Estimated Daily Requirement (mg.) | Coenzyme Forms | Examples of Metabolic Functions |
|---------|-----------------------------------|----------------|---------------------------------|
| Ascorbic acid (vitamin C) | 10–150 | Monodehydroascorbic acid? | Certain electron-transport systems |
| Vitamin A | 1.5 | Retinene (vitamin A aldehyde) | Transformation of light energy into chemical energy in retina |
| Vitamin D | 0.010 | Not known | Deposition of inorganic salts |
| Vitamin E | ? | Not known | Cellular oxidations |
| Vitamin K | 0.001 | Not known | Blood coagulation; cell oxidations (?) |

extensively. However, it is evident from the nature of the many reactions in which vitamins play essential roles as coenzymes that a vitamin deficiency will lead to a disruption or even cessation of some intermediary process in the tissues. The excess of unutilized substrate will accumulate in the tissues, or will be excreted in inordinate amounts in the urine. In some cases it may undergo metabolism by an accessory pathway of metabolism, which operates normally at a very limited rate, although capable of turning over larger amounts of the substrate. In this way, the biochemical lesion resulting from deprivation compounds itself, and reverberating effects are detectable in many parts of the body.

Withdrawal of a particular vitamin from the diet does not result in its uniform loss from all parts of the body in a synchronous fashion. Enzymes capable of degrading the coenzymatic form of the vitamin occur in different concentrations in different tissues, so that the loss of coenzyme occurs at disparate rates in different sites. Moreover, some enzymes bind the coenzyme with greater degree of cohesiveness and therefore release it at a slower rate under conditions, such as avitaminosis, which favor dissociation. These fundamental processes are partial determinants of the ultimate clinical syndrome flowing from vitamin deprivation, for upon them depends the concentration of coenzyme in a given tissue at a particular time during the deficiency. An important consideration is the abruptness of development of the deficiency state, its chronic or acute character depending upon whether the diet is slightly, marginally, or completely deficient. Nutritional conditioning factors such as the qualitative composition and quantity of the diet, concurrent deficiency of other essential nutrients, and interactions between nutrients also affect the clinical state in various ways. For example, the thiamine requirement increases as the amount of carbohydrate in the diet increases, and a thiamine level which suffices to protect against beriberi on a given diet may not be sufficient to prevent the precipitation of symptoms when the calorie content (provided as carbohydrate) is suddenly increased. Other examples of interaction stem from the fact that the synthesis of a coenzyme from a vitamin may itself depend upon the presence of some other vitamin. Thus, experimental evidence is accumulating that pantothenic acid and pyridoxine have a mutual sparing action.

The most detailed knowledge in the sphere of vitamin action is found in respect to the B vitamins. Thiamine, riboflavin, nicotinic acid, pantothenic acid, pyridoxine, folic acid, and choline have had fundamental roles depicted for them. Knowledge about biotin, ascorbic acid, and cobalamin concerns their influence over a number of metabolic processes, and specific sites of action are coming to be pinpointed. In regard to the fat-soluble vitamins, the action of vitamin A in the retina has been worked out, but not so for other tissues. Recently new light is penetrating to the actions of vitamins E and K in electron transport. One of the vitamin E-active substances found in foods is $\alpha$-tocopherol. In its oxidized form it closely resembles vitamin $K_1$, for both are fully substituted *para*-benzoquinones with very similar isoprenoid side chains. In turn, this type of structure is found in a new family of catalysts, known as ubiquinone or coenzyme Q, functioning in some intermediary step of electron transport, as in the succinoxidase complex. This is a most encouraging sign inasmuch as knowledge of the function of these vitamins in enzymatic mechanisms has long trailed behind their action in nutritional-pathological studies. Now, the discrepancy is to be eliminated.

Like other organs, brain and nerve may undergo metabolic and histological alterations as a consequence of dietary vitamin deficiency. The dominant position of carbohydrate as a cerebral fuel assigns a fundamental role to many of the vitamins that are concerned with the reactions of sugars and sugar derivatives, but of no less importance are those concerned with glutamic acid metabolism and with the formation of biogenic amines from amino acids. The formation of cerebral lipides, moreover, demands the action of many of these vitamins. Hence, from the viewpoint of the intermediary metabolism of brain and nerve the adequacy of vitamin status is of great importance. As will be shown in the following sections, experimental and clinical studies provide practical evidence that defective function at the enzymatic level may seriously affect physiological function.

# 16

# THIAMINE

## Chemistry and Function

Thiamine (vitamin $B_1$, aneurine) consists of a pyrimidine derivative linked to a thiazole nucleus, and it may be split into these parts by hydrolytic enzymes. The specific vitamin action of thiamine is mediated through its pyrophosphate derivative, diphosphothiamine (cocarboxylase, DPT). This coenzyme is required for the oxidative decarboxylation of pyruvic acid to form acetylcoenzyme A (Reaction 11-11) and of $\alpha$-ketoglutaric acid to succinylcoenzyme. A (Reaction 11-21), as well as in the transketolation reactions of the keto sugars (cf. Reaction 11-28). The most prominent biochemical change resulting from a deficiency of thiamine in the diet is the accumulation of pyruvic acid. The pyruvic acid level of the blood and CSF rises; some of this excess is excreted in the urine and a portion is reduced to lactic acid, so that the blood lactic acid content also increases. Methylglyoxal (pyruvic aldehyde) is found in the urine, and disappears therefrom when the avitaminosis is terminated. The origin of this compound is not certain; it may be formed by reduction of pyruvic acid or rearrangement of lactic acid (with dehydration). An enzyme (glyoxalase) catalyzing the conversion of methylglyoxal to lactic acid is found in reduced amounts in the liver of thiamine-deprived animals.

The requirement of thiamine in the diet varies considerably from individual to individual, as well as with the physiological state. The requirement is frequently stated as a function of the amount of calories derived from the carbohydrate portion of the diet, *i.e.*, it is considered to be proportional to the amount of that class of nutrients whose metabolism the vitamin catalyzes. However, other types of nutrient affect the thiamine requirement. For example, substitution of some of the carbohydrate calories by fat spares thiamine. Alcohol also conserves the thiamine supplies of the organism to some extent.

# Thiamine Deficiency

Clinical thiamine deficiency occurs in man in several forms. The differences depend upon the degree of vitamin deprivation and various conditioning factors (1). Because of the major role of carbohydrate in cerebral and peripheral nerve metabolism, removal of thiamine in whole or in part from the diet represents a serious interference with this metabolism, and nervous and mental symptoms ensue.

### BERIBERI

Thiamine deficiency disease is best known in the various forms of beriberi; it appears in individuals subsisting on diets low in protein and fat and high in carbohydrate, as supplied by highly milled cereals such as polished rice. Depending upon the predominant clinical feature, the disease is known as wet beriberi (*i.e.*, with edema) or as the dry form. It occurs in the Orient as a fulminating disease (*kakke, taon*) in infants breast-fed by thiamine-deficient mothers. Wernicke's encephalopathy is still another form that the deficiency may take under other conditions.

The principal features of beriberi are cardiovascular dysfunction, edema, and multiple neuritis. The disease in adults commences with anorexia, fatiguability, muscle pains, and increased irritability. Later, paralysis and atrophy of some muscles may be seen. In dry beriberi there is a peripheral neuritis; in the wet type of the disease cardiac symptoms predominate: there is right heart enlargement, increased venous pressure, along with peripheral vasodilation for which the increased level of organic acids in the blood (pyruvic, lactic) may be responsible.

The acute form of thiamine deficiency was originally described by Wernicke in 1881 in three fatal cases. He believed that an inflammatory process was at work and he described the condition as "acute superior hemorrhagic polio-encephalitis." Eventually, Wernicke's encephalopathy came to be associated with alcoholism, but many cases of the disease have now been seen in which an alcohol-containing regimen has been excluded. The cardinal etiological feature is considered to be the acute deficiency of thiamine. The literature on this subject has been reviewed by Cruickshank (2) in 1950.

The role of avitaminosis-$B_1$ became clearer through experience in the Changi prisoner-of-war camp in Singapore in 1942. At this time troops were transferred from British army rations to an inadequate diet (consisting mainly of polished rice) which favored the development of vitamin deficiency (3). Soon after the change of diet, cases were found with the characteristic triad of Wernicke's disease, viz., ataxia, ophthalmoplegia, and clouding of consciousness. The condition frequently began with diarrhea (as a result of dysentery), anorexia, and vomiting. Nystagmus was an early sign in many cases. The mental changes appeared later, although about one fifth of the cases showed a sudden onset of these before other signs were noted. Untreated cases progressed to semicoma (2, 3). De Wardener and Lennox state that in their series (3) emotional changes, such as apprehension, apathy, and excitement, were observed in two thirds of the patients; there was loss of memory for recent events in 61 percent, disorientation in 46 percent, confabulation and hallucinations in 25 percent. The specific role of thiamine deficiency was demonstrated by the relief of symptoms following parenteral injection of the vitamin (2, 3, 4). The reversal of symptoms occurred in the same order as they developed: vomiting ended, appetite returned, the diplopia disappeared, and the patients began to experience a sense of well-being. Memory for recent events returned a little later, but the other mental changes took much longer to reverse. Denny-Brown (5) has described the development of nervous and mental changes in the order of acuteness of thiamine deprivation; Wernicke's encephalopathy heads the list (4, 5; see also 6).

## EXPERIMENTAL THIAMINE DEFICIENCY

The study of the clinical and pathological effects of thiamine deficiency in experimental animals has encountered a wide species variation. In swine maintained on a deficiency diet there was no nerve degeneration (7) and in the rat it has only recently been demonstrated that degenerative changes do occur, although in but a very small proportion of the peripheral fibers (8). This may be correlated with the fact that the thiamine content of nerve tissue is sustained for long periods on a deficient diet, in contrast to many other tissues (9). Furthermore, as much as 80 percent of the cerebral thiamine must be lost before neurological symptoms are detected (10). The loss of thiamine from the brain can be accelerated experimentally, by feeding the antimetabolite pyrithiamine (11). Deficiency in the monkey results in brain changes resembling those seen in Wernicke's encephalopathy, to the extent that there are symmetrical lesions restricted to the gray matter in the periaqueductal and periventricular areas. However, the lesions in the corpus striatum and the cerebral vascular changes seen in man are infrequent in the monkey. The peripheral nerves and spinal cord are unaffected by these deficiency conditions (12). Chronic deficiency in dogs receiving about 2 $\mu$g. of thiamine per kilogram body weight daily causes the progressive development of spasticity of the hind legs and ataxia; pathologically the peripheral nerves and the posterior columns of the spinal cord show extensive myelin degeneration (13). In the acutely deficient opisthotonic pigeon such changes seldom occur, but they may be noted when the deficiency has been allowed to develop chronically and the prominent symptom is weakness of the leg muscles (14). In beriberi histopathological examination reveals that Wallerian degeneration sets in at the most distal parts of the peripheral neurones, the longer ones being affected first, and the motor more than the sensory ones (5).

Through experimentation in man it has been found that the severity of clinical symptoms is related to the degree of thiamine deprivation. In a study of adults on a diet supplying less thiamine than occurs in beriberigenic diets, Williams and his collaborators (15) noted that the subjects became distressed after several weeks and exhibited weakness, vertigo, dyspnea, precordial distress on exertion, muscle pains, insomnia, anorexia, vomiting, and weight loss. Cardiovascular symptoms appeared, among them hypotension, bradycardia at rest, and tachycardia upon exertion. In a few subjects there was apathy, difficulty in thought and memory, photophobia, and eye fatigue. The injection of thiamine after 88 days of deficiency led to rapid subjective improvement with the disappearance of symptoms. A similar picture was seen by Elson et al. (16) in one subject on a diet deficient in many of the B vitamins. At the fifth week the subject became depressed, nervous, and irritable. She suffered some memory loss, and had difficulty in concentration. These mental symptoms responded to the administration of thiamine, but did not clear up entirely until yeast was supplied as a source of other vitamins. In the Elgin experiment, which lasted for three years (17), adults placed on a thiamine- and riboflavin-deficient diet exhibited a gradual reduction of activity and interest, increased irritability and lessened sociability. The effects of thiamine deficiency were reflected in the greatly elevated blood lactic and pyruvic acids after exercise or after administration of glucose. In a further study, Wiliams et al. (18) employed a diet supplying about 0.6 mg. of thiamine per day, without restriction of calories. It was considered that this would induce a more moderate and prolonged deficiency state. The subjects on this diet showed emotional instability as exemplified by their irritability and moodiness and uncooperative behavior. They were fearful, agitated, and mentally depressed. The symptoms were less severe than observed in the acute condition induced in the first group.

Because of the marked changes in personality and affect seen in the course of development of thiamine avitaminosis other investigators have devoted attention to this problem. Brozek and Keys (19) placed volunteers on diets acutely deficient in thiamine, riboflavin, and niacin. This regimen led to changes such as apathy, anorexia, reduction in physical and mental activity, and disturbance of the feeling of well-being. The changes were reversed by thiamine therapy. Later, there were psychomotor, metabolic, neurologic, and cardiovascular changes. On the Minnesota Multiphasic Personality Inventory the subjects departed significantly from normal, a deviation that was entirely cured with thiamine. Essentially the same results were obtained by Henderson et al. in a similar study (20).

## POLYNEUROPATHIES

The polyneuritis of thiamine deficiency naturally aroused interest in its possible analogy with the polyneuritis seen in alcoholism. This form had first been described by J. C. Lettson in 1779, and for a century and a half thereafter, the symptoms were attributed to a toxic effect of alcohol upon nerve. Then, with the newer knowledge of the B vitamins at hand Shattuck (21) introduced a speculative generalization that served as the basis for a great deal of clinical research on the vitamins in ensuing years. He questioned whether "the polyneuritis seen in certain ill-nourished persons having tuberculosis, cancer, syphilis, diabetes, or alcoholism, or appearing in marasmic children (may not) be caused chiefly by failure to take or to assimilate food containing sufficient quantity of vitamin B? And may not some of these cases be properly regarded as beriberi?" Because of the value of thiamine in relieving the neuritis of beriberi there have been many attempts, following Shattuck's suggestion, to implicate a deficiency of the vitamin in other neuropathies, and to extend its therapeutic action to these. Little success has attended these trials, for neither the acute nor chronic polyneuritis responds rapidly or dramatically to thiamine or, for that matter, vitamin B complex (22). Bicknell and Prescott have summarized the results of trials with thiamine by stating (23) that despite widespread trials in neurological disorders thiamine is of demonstrated value only in those conditions associated with a deficiency of this vitamin. The therapeutic action of thiamine—and this holds for other vitamins and for the essential trace minerals as well—can be exerted only when there is a relative or absolute deficiency of that particular nutrient in the tissues. Although the therapeutic trial may serve as a rapid and direct method of attacking the problem, the ultimate justification for this comes from demonstration of lack of the vitamin in the diet and tissues. This is all the more important where a clinical entity as inclusive as polyneuritis is under consideration, for it appears under many different types of circumstance (24, 25), some of which have already been mentioned.

In those cases of polyneuritis in which a chemical factor is known to be operating, the role of thiamine can be assessed on the basis of the underlying process. Thiamine deficiency itself accounts for relatively few cases of polyneuritis outside the beriberi regions where polished rice constitutes a dietary staple, but when the deficiency occurs it results in a reduced concentration of diphosphothiamine in the tissues. This affects the oxidation of pyruvic acid by deficiency of the coenzyme. The apoenzyme of pyruvic oxidase is affected in other neuritides. For example, arsenical neuritis is associated with inhibition of pyruvic oxidase through the ability of the chemical agent to bind the essential sulfhydryl groups of the enzyme. Mercurials possess the same action, as do the sanguinarine alkaloids, the active agents of argemone oil. A number of organic phosphorus compounds causing peripheral neuritis, notably tri-*o*-cresyl phosphate (the causative agent in ginger paralysis), act as inhibitors of pseudocholinesterase, but have no known action on any enzyme system involving the thiamine coenzyme. As for alcoholic neuritis, a toxic action of distilled alcoholic beverages has been ruled out by the finding that on an ample diet, fortified with concentrated sources of the B vitamins, patients from whom alcohol is withheld exhibit the same rate of recovery as those who are permitted to continue on their whisky ration (26).

## THIAMINASE DISEASE

Thiamine is readily split by two types of enzyme. One simply hydrolyzes the vitamin into its pyrimidine and thiazole portions. The other is a transferring enzyme, shifting the pyrimidine-5-methylene group from its linkage with the thiazole to another base; this enzyme resembles the transmethylases in its action. Thiaminases are found normally in some of the species making up the intestinal flora, but in certain individuals there is an elevated level of the enzyme as judged from fecal examination. The problem has been extensively studied in Japan where it has been found that about one sixth of beriberi sufferers have this thiaminase disease. Hayashi (27) has reported incidence of the condition as high as 3 to 7 percent in certain districts. The disease is manifested in the low concentration of thiamine in the blood of these patients and in the greater degrees of intestinal destruction of orally administered vitamin than in normal individuals. In subjects with thiaminase disease the symptoms of beriberi appear earlier than usual on a thiamine-deficient diet.

Thiamine may also be destroyed before ingestion by an enzyme in the food itself: this is the case in Chastek's paralysis, seen in foxes and other animals fed on a diet containing large amounts of uncooked fish. The condition is characterized by anorexia, weakness, ataxia, spastic paraplegia, and hyperesthesia. Certain shellfish also possess very active thiaminases. In grazing animals consuming thiaminase-containing bracken, the symptoms of acute thiamine deficiency are sometimes seen (staggers in horses).

## CHEMISTRY OF THIAMINE DEFICIENCY STATES

The deficiency of thiamine in the tissues is followed by a reduction in the concentration of DPT. The first chemical consequence of this is the decrease in the rate of oxidation of pyruvic acid, with the result that this compound and its reduction product, lactic acid, accumulate in the blood, urine, and CSF (28, 29). Sometimes the increase is seen in blood lactic only, without the abnormal rise in the pyruvic acid. The reduced ability of the tissues to metabolize sugar is also reflected in the diabetic-like glucose tolerance curve: the blood sugar level rises to a normal peak but the concentration is still elevated after four hours (30). In normal subjects small amounts of pyruvic acid can be detected in the blood after glucose loading, but in thiamine-deficient persons the rise is much more marked (25, 31). It is also to be expected that the lack of DPT, the coenzyme of transketolase, would show up by accumulation of a metabolite of the monophosphate shunt (Chapter 11), perhaps a pentose, but this has not been reported. Further work on the significance in thiamine deficiency of this pathway is of importance because it operates in the brain, among other tissues.

Evidence for still another pathway of carbohydrate metabolism has come from studies on thiamine-deficiency states. This is the methylglyoxal path, which was proposed in the older biochemical literature as a main route, but has actually received little attention altogether. Methylglyoxal is formed by the action of extracts of yeast, skeletal muscle, liver, or pancreas upon hexose diphosphate. The mechanism of this conversion is unknown. Oridinarily, methylglyoxal does not accumulate because a very active catalyst in the tissues, glyoxalase, converts it to lactic acid. Glyoxalase actually consists of two distinct enzymes, one of which requires reduced glutathione as its coenzyme. Hence, methylglyoxal could be expected to accumulate (if it is a natural substrate for glyoxalase) in any condition where one or another of the enzymes is absent, or where glutathione has been removed. In thiamine deficiency glyoxalase concentration of the liver decreases (32, 33); whether both of the enzymes do so or only one is not known, but the decreased activity is not due to loss of the coenzyme (33). Methylglyoxal has been detected among the bisulfite-binding substances in the body fluids in beriberi (28) and in experimental thiamine deficiency in the dog (34) and rat (33). It has also been found in the urine and CSF of infants suffering from Säuglingstoxikose (acute toxic dyspepsia). A feature of this disease is oliguria. The administration of thiamine intravenously for therapeutic purposes causes an immediate diuresis with an increased output of methylglyoxal on the first day of treatment, and thereafter a gradual reduction in the methylglyoxaluria to zero in 3 to 4 days (34).

In seeking an agent to explain the dynamics of the pathophysiology of beriberi many have attempted to implicate pyruvic acid. Whether this compound is capable on chronic administration of bringing about the neurologic and cardiac changes seen clinically is not known. The compound can aggravate some of the features of an already present thiamine deficiency; in avitaminotic lambs convulsions can be brought on at a certain stage by the injection of pyruvate. In man it is quite possible that the elevated blood and, presumably, tissue concentration of pyruvic and lactic acids may be responsible for the muscular cramps (35), but actually little is known about the chronic toxicity of these compounds. Methylglyoxal has also been considered as the toxic agent in beriberi, as first proposed in 1931 by Vogt-Møller (36) but this has not been proved. Methylglyoxal is gluconeogenic when given in small doses, but administration of larger amounts, particularly by the parenteral route, causes nervousness, quickened respiration, piloerection, convulsions, and death (37). Liang has proposed glyoxylic acid as the toxic agent. He considers it to accumulate, following its physiological formation from glycine, through defective oxidative decarboxylation in the thiamine-deficient organism (38).

Ferrari has shown that the glutamic acid content of the brain decreases somewhat in experimental thiamine deficiency (39).

## Mental Effects of Thiamine

The striking changes in personality and behavior seen in the deficiency experiments conducted in Minnesota (15, 18, 19), Elgin (17), and elsewhere have raised the question as to whether positive benefits may be gained by supplementing the apparently normal diet with extra thiamine. Harrell (40) carried out an extensive experiment among 120 institutionalized children, divided into supplemented and placebo groups. The subjects were periodically assigned numerous tasks designed to measure skill, intelligence, and other qualities. According to Harrell the supplement of 2 mg. of thiamine per day gave the test group of children obvious advantages in a two-year experimental period. Others have not been able to confirm this. Robertson and his colleagues (41) studied uniovular twins eating their usual meals at home, but with one of the pair receiving a supplement of thiamine. After ten weeks the supplemented twins had made superior gains in height and weight; measures of manual dexterity, memory, and eyesight yielded no significant differences because of the extra vitamin. Scores obtained after a further like period showed that there was then no significant differences between the two groups. This result is a clear argument in favor of the long-term experiment in answering questions of this type. Rudolf (42) tested thiamine in mental defectives for 5 to 6 months, and found that the vitamin did not influence intelligence. His subjects included children as well as adults.

## Toxicity of Thiamine

Large repeated doses of thiamine have been known occasionally to cause toxic reactions. These usually occur with parenteral but not oral administration. Rudolf considered that oral supplements of thiamine resulted in increased excitability to the point of violence in 5 percent of his group of mental defectives (42). These results may have their analogue in animal experiments, inasmuch as the pyrimidine portion of the vitamin, in sufficient dosage, causes severe convulsions and death in the rat (43). This compound, 2-methyl-4-amino-5-hydroxy-methylpyrimidine, has been named toxopyrimidine by Japanese biochemists because it facilitates the appearance of deficiency symptoms in the rat and mouse fed pyridoxine-deficient diets. The injected animals "run round as a ball," and convulse. Pyridoxine abolishes these effects (44).

The thiazole portion of the thiamine molecule is chemically 4-methyl-5-$\beta$-hydroxyethyl-5-thiazole. Certain chloro analogues of this compound have sedative and anticonvulsant properties, and one of them, known as S.C.T.Z., has undergone clinical trials in agitated, hyperactive patients.

# References

1. HOFFMAN, M. M., and T. SOURKES. *In Practice of Medicine, ed.* MEAKINS, J. C. 6th ed. St. Louis, C. V. Mosby, 1956.
2. CRUICKSHANK, E. K. *Quart. J. Med. 19:*327, 1950.
3. DE WARDENER, H. E., and B. LENNOX. *Lancet i:*11, 1947.
4. PHILLIPS, G. B., M. VICTOR, R. D. ADAMS, and C. S. DAVIDSON. *J. Clin. Invest. 31:*859, 1952.
5. DENNY-BROWN, D. *Federation Proc. 17:*Suppl. 2, 35, 1958.
6. DAVIS, R. A., and A. WOLF. *Pediatrics 21:*409, 1958.
7. WINTROBE, M. M., M. H. MILLER, R. H. FOLLIS, JR., and H. J. STEIN. *Trans. Assoc. Am. Phys. 57:*55, 1942.
8. NORTH, J. D. K., and H. M. SINCLAIR. *A. M. A. Arch. Path. 62:*341, 1956.
9. VON MURALT, A. *Vitamins and Hormones 5:*93, 1947.
10. DREYFUS, P. M. *Federation Proc. 18:*218, 1959.
11. KOEDAM, J. C. *Biochim. et Biophys. Acta 29:*333, 1958.
12. RINEHART, J. F., M. FRIEDMAN, and L. D. GREENBERG. *Arch. Path. 48:*129, 1949.
13. STREET, H. R., H. M. ZIMMERMAN, G. R. COWGILL, H. E. HOFF, and J. C. FOX, JR. *Yale J. Biol. Med. 13:*293, 1940–41.
14. SWANK, R. L. *J. Exp. Med. 71:*683, 1940.
15. WILLIAMS, R. D., H. L. MASON, R. M. WILDER, and B. F. SMITH. *Arch. Int. Med. 66:*785, 1940.
16. ELSOM, K. O., F. H. LEWY, and G. W. HEUBLEIN. *Am. J. Med. Sci. 200:* 757, 1940.
17. HORWITT, M. K., E. LIEBERT, O. KREISLER, and P. WITTMAN. *Science 104:* 407, 1946; KREISLER, O., E. LIEBERT, and M. K. HORWITT. *Am. J. Psychiat. 105:*107, 1948.

18. WILLIAMS, R. D., and H. L. MASON. *Proc. Staff Meet. Mayo Clinic 16:* 433, 1941; WILLIAMS, R. D., H. L. MASON, B. F. SMITH, and R. M. WILDER. *Arch. Int. Med. 69:*721, 1942.

19. KEYS, A., A. HENSCHEL, H. L. TAYLOR, O. MICKELSEN, and J. BROZEK. *Am. J. Physiol. 144:*5, 1945; BROZEK, J., H. GUETZKOW, and A. KEYS. *Psychosom. Med. 8:*98, 1946.

20. HENDERSON, C. R., N. C. WHEELER, H. C. JOHNSON, R. C. COGSWELL, G. H. BERRYMAN, A. C. IVY, T. E. FRIEDEMANN, and J. B. YOUMANS. *Am. J. Med. Sci. 213:*488, 1947.

21. SHATTUCK, G. C. *Am. J. Trop. Med. 8:*539, 1928.

22. WALSHE, F. M. R. *Lancet ii:*382, 1945.

23. BICKNELL, F., and F. PRESCOTT. *The Vitamins in Medicine,* 3d ed. New York, Grune and Stratton, 1953.

24. WECHSLER, I. S. *Arch. Neurol. Psychiat. 29:*813, 1933.

25. JOINER, C. L., B. MCARDLE, and R. H. S. THOMPSON. *Brain 73:*431, 1950.

26. STRAUSS, M. B. *Am. J. Med. Sci. 189:*378, 1935.

27. HAYASHI, R. *Nutrition Rev. 15:*65, 1957.

28. PLATT, B. S., and G. D. LU. *Quart. J. Med. 5:*355, 1936.

29. WORTIS, H., E. BUEDING, M. H. STEIN, and N. JOLLIFFE. *Arch. Neurol. Psychiat. 47:*215, 1942.

30. ELSOM, K. O., F. D. W. LUKENS, E. H. MONTGOMERY, and L. JONAS. *J. Clin. Invest. 19:*153, 1940.

31. VICTOR, M., M. D. ALTSCHULE, P. D. HOLLIDAY, R. M. GONCZ, and A. COUNTY. *A. M. A. Arch. Int. Med. 99:*28, 1957.

32. FINDLAY, G. M. *Biochem. J. 15:*104, 1921.

33. SALEM, H. M. *Biochem. J. 57:*227, 1954.

34. GEIGER, A., and A. ROSENBERG. *Klin. Wochschr. 12:*1258, 1933.

35. HANDLER, P. *Federation Proc. 17:*Supplement No. 2, 31, 1958.

36. VOGT-MØLLER, P. *Biochem. J. 25:*418, 1931.

37. SJOLLEME, B., and L. SEEKLES. Biochem. Z. *176:*431, 1926; FISCHLER, F. Z. *physiol. chem. 165:*68, 1927; STÖHR. R. *ibid. 206:*15, 1932.

38. LIANG, C. G. *Nature 188:*660, 1960; *Biochem. J. 82:*429, 1962.

39. FERRARI, V. *Acta vitaminol. 11:*53, 1957.

40. HARRELL, R. F. *J. Nutrition 31:*283, 1946.

41. ROBERTSON, E. C., C. M. TATHAM, N. F. WALKER, and M. R. WEAVER. *J. Nutrition 34:*691, 1947.

42. RUDOLF, J. DEM. *J. Ment. Sci. 95:*910, 1949.

43. ABDERHALDEN, E., and R. ABDERHALDEN. *Arch. ges. Physiol. 240:*746, 1938.

44. MAKINO, K., T. KINOSHITA, T. SASAKI, and T. SHIOI. *Nature 173:*34, 1954; ABDERHALDEN, R. Z. *Vitamin. Hormon. u. Fermentforsch. 6:*295, 1954.

# 17

# RIBOFLAVIN

## Chemistry and Function

Riboflavin (vitamin $B_2$) is a yellow pigment belonging to the iso-alloxazine group. Its solutions fluoresce with a green color, a property used in the determination of the vitamin. It participates in many oxidative reactions within the cells, its active forms being the phosphorylated derivatives riboflavin-5'-phosphate (FMN, flavin mononucleotide) and flavin adenine nucleotide (FMN linked to adenylic acid through their respective phosphoryl groups). The combination of coenzyme with a specific protein apoenzyme characterizes members of the class of enzymes known as flavoproteins. Some of these also possess an inorganic ion (*e.g.,* copper, molybdenum, iron), functioning in the process catalyzed by the flavoenzyme (1).

Some yellow enzymes act as intermediaries between the primary dehydrogenases (the enzymes associated with pyridine nucleotides) and the cytochrome pigments, the terminal carriers of hydrogen; in these reactions, the hydrogen removed from the substrate is oxidized to water (*cf.* Reactions 15-1 to 15-4). Other flavoproteins can dehydrogenate certain substrates directly and combine the hydrogen they remove with oxygen to yield hydrogen peroxide. Examples of substrates of such yellow enzymes are: many of the amino acids ($\rightarrow$ the corresponding keto acid); succinic acid ($\rightarrow$ fumaric acid); hypoxanthine ($\rightarrow$ xanthine

→ uric acid) ; acetaldehyde (→ acetic acid) ; and 5-hydroxyindolylacet-aldehyde (→ 5-hydroxyindoleacetic acid).

Liver, kidney, and heart are rich in riboflavin. Brain contains moderate amounts of it, the concentration varying in different regions. The extrapyramidal system is comparatively high (as it is in iron) ; the cortex, medulla oblongata, and spinal cord contain less; and cerebro-spinal fluid none. Pichler (2) has remarked upon the strong correlation between the oxygen consumption of various parts of the brain and their riboflavin content.

## Experimental Riboflavin Deficiency in Animals

Both chronic and acute deficiencies have been produced exper-imentally. In the dog the clinical entity known as yellow liver (from the appearance of the organ at examination *post-mortem*) was early identified as a chronic form of riboflavin deficiency. In the course of the disease the animals develop a dermatitis with a dry, flaky exfoliation, bradycardia with ECG changes, and anemia. After some months, attacks of coma occur which respond to administration of riboflavin. Neu-rological changes are seen in defective reflexes, although the gait remains normal. On experimental diets from which riboflavin has been excluded the deficiency symptoms appear more quickly: there is weakness and ataxia, with falling, but without loss of consciousness. Both heart and respiration are slowed, and death soon follows (3). Riboflavin-deficient swine assume an uneconomical appearance and fail to gain weight; opacities appear in the lens; and the gait becomes abnormal. In the monkey the deficiency results in anemia, dermatitis, and loss of muscular strength. Psychologically, the animal becomes apathetic on the riboflavin-deficient regimen.

Examination of the nervous system of these animals *post-mortem* reveals degenerative changes, especially when the condition has been chronic. In the dog and pig there is myelin degeneration of peripheral nerves and of fibers in the posterior columns of the spinal cord. The latter changes are also seen in the mouse.

There is some evidence that the riboflavin-deficient rat suffers a diminished responsiveness of the anterior pituitary-adrenal cortical system (4).

## Deficiency in Man

The earliest changes seen in humans given riboflavin-deficient diets to consume are the lesions on the vermilion part of the lips (cheilosis), along with transverse fissuring at the corners of the mouth. Further developments are seborrheic dermatitis, lesions of the scrotal skin, and conjunctivitis. Changes in the eye are indicated by the reduced ability to perceive flicker (5).

Clinically, riboflavin deficiency is often associated with a deficiency of other vitamins, but there are some conditions in which the deficiency of this vitamin predominates. Symptoms of ariboflavinosis include a mild erythema, cheilosis, angular stomatitis, glossitis, and conjunctivitis. Seborrheic lesions around the nasolabial folds are found. Less frequently vascularisation of the cornea occurs. Mental and physical fatigue may be seen (6, 7). According to Stannus (6), structural changes in the capillary endothelium resulting from the vitamin deficiency lead to inadequate nutrition and oxygenation of the tissues, and he has adduced much of the syndrome, which he terms preferentially hyporiboflavinosis, by assuming this as the primary pathological feature. In addition to the well-described dermatological lesions, muscular weakness, incoordination, ataxia, paresthesia, and reduced auditory and visual perception have been reported as sequelae of riboflavin deficiency. These changes, all in the sensory component, are in agreement with the experimental findings in animals.

There are many reports in the literature attributing other changes to riboflavin deficiency. As more information about the role of vitamins in clinical disorders has been obtained, particularly during and immediately after the Second World War, it has become clear that some of these pathological changes result from deficiency of other vitamins, such as nicotinic acid, pantothenic acid, or pyridoxine. The confusion of effects has understandably arisen from the frequent association of riboflavin with these and other members of the vitamin B group in foods and, conversely, their joint absence from the diets in a multiple deficiency (6, 8). The use of diets of known and controlled composition in investigating clinical deficiency states is clearly mandatory for expansion of useful knowledge in human vitaminology.

# References

1. MAHLER, H. R. *Proc. 3d International Congress of Biochemistry, ed.* LIÉBECQ, C. New York, Academic Press, 1956; NICHOLAS, D. J. D. *Nature* *179*:800, 1957.
2. LEEMAN, H., and E. PICHLER. *Klin. Wochschr. 20*:37, 1941; PICHLER, E. *Proc. 6th International Congress of Neurology,* Brussels, Excerpta Medica Foundation, 1957.

3. SEBRELL, W. H., and R. H. ONSTOTT. *U.S. Public Health Reports* 53:83, 1938.

4. SLATER, G. S. *Endocrinol.* 65:731, 1959.

5. SEBRELL, W. H., and R. E. BUTLER. *U.S. Public Health Reports* 53:2282, 1938; HORWITT, M. K., O. W. HILLS, C. C. HARVEY, E. LIEBERT, and D. L. STEINBERG. *J. Nutrition* 39:357, 1949.

6. STANNUS, H. S. *Brit. Med. J.* ii:103, 140, 1944.

7. SYDENSTRICKER, V. P., L. E. GEESLIN, C. M. TEMPLETON, and J. W. WEAVER. *J.A.M.A.* 113:1697, 1939.

8. SPILLANE, J. D. *Nutritional Disorders of the Nervous System.* Edinburgh, E. and S. Livingstone, Ltd., 1947.

# 18

# NICOTINIC ACID

## Biosynthesis, Requirements, and Functions

The formation of nicotinic acid (niacin) and nicotinamide (niacin-amide) from the amino acid tryptophan has been touched upon briefly in Chapter 6. This biosynthesis occurs in the tissues of the animal organism, including man (1). A small proportion (1 to 3 percent) of the dietary tryptophan that gets as far in metabolism as the stage of 3-hydroxyanthranilic acid is converted into nicotinic acid (2, 3). Smaller amounts of tryptophan are excreted as picolinic and quinolinic acids.

The recommended daily allowance of nicotinic acid for adults is 10 to 20 mg. per day. This is not considered a minimal requirement, but rather the intake necessary for optimal health. Horwitt and his associates (3) have estimated that the prevention of deficiency symptoms on a pellagragenic diet requires more than 8.8 mg. of nicotinic acid (or its metabolic equivalent as dietary tryptophan) for the first 2000 calories of the diet, with proportionately more for higher caloric intakes.

Nicotinic acid functions in the cell in the form of two pyridine nucleotide coenzymes. These are nicotinamide-adenine dinucleotide (NAD, coenzyme I, cozymase, diphosphopyridine nucleotide, DPN) and nicotinamide-adenine dinucleotide phosphate (NADP, coenzyme II, triphosphopyridine nucleotide, TPN). NAD is composed of several chemical moieties connected as follows:

Nicotinamide—ribose—phosphoric acid⏋
Adenine—ribose—phosphoric acid⏌

NADP bears an additional phosphoric acid residue. The two coenzymes participate in the transfer of hydrogen from substrates, during the course of biological oxidations, to other carriers. This ultimately leads to the formation of water (*cf.* Reactions 15-1 to 15-4). The enzymic catalysts utilize one or the other of the two coenzymes, more or less specifically, but other enzymes have been found which catalyze the exchange of hydrogen from one of the reduced coenzymes to the oxidized form of the other (transhydrogenation), making the action of the coenzymes that much more versatile. The pyridine nucleotides are present in normal concentration in the blood of schizophrenic patients (4).

The main excretory forms of nicotinic acid are $N^1$-methylnicotinamide and its 2-oxo-and 4-oxo- derivatives. The amount of $N^1$-methylnicotinamide in the urine has been used as an index of availability of nicotinic acid and its precursors in the diet.

# Relation of Tryptophan and Nicotinic Acid to Pellagra (5)

Pellagra is a nutritional disease associated with multiple dietary deficiencies. It is a chronic condition, pursuing a somewhat cyclical course, with exacerbations in the spring. In the past it has had a marked geographic distribution (southern United States, the Iberian Peninsula, parts of Italy, some areas of eastern and southeastern Europe, and Egypt), but because of improved nutrition and of preventive dietary measures the endemic character of the disease is changing to a more sporadic one.

Pellagra affects primarily three organ systems: the skin, the digestive tract, and the nervous system. The cutaneous lesions are bilateral and symmetrical; they begin as an erythema, demarcated from the healthy areas, and progress to a reddish brown skin which is scaly and rough. Exposure of the affected parts to sunlight causes them to become worse, and perhaps subject to secondary infections. There is a glossitis and stomatitis; the tongue and oral mucous membranes assume a scarlet red color, becoming inflamed and ulcerated. At one time it was thought that there is a disturbance of porphyrin metabolism in pellagra, a view supported by the photosensitivity and the symptomatology. This relationship has now been disproved (6). The most serious symptom of the gastrointestinal component of clinical pellagra is a severe diarrhea.

Nervous symptoms of the disease include a peripheral neuritis, increased irritability, insomnia, and depression. With prolonged deficiency other mental symptoms appear and may develop into an organic psychosis. About 25 to 30 percent of untreated cases show mental symptoms and perhaps a quarter again of these develop serious psychiatric disorder. The early symptoms are, in addition to those mentioned, headaches, neurasthenia, anxiety accompanied by depression in some cases, and by excitement, delirium, and hallucinations in others. A toxic confusional state, like Korsakow's syndrome, may appear. Jolliffe has described an encephalopathic syndrome in elderly patients showing neurological changes (sucking reflexes, cogwheel rigidity, oculomotor disturbance, polyneuritis) as well as psychiatric alterations (clouding of consciousness, stupor, delirium, depression) (7). He considers it to be much more specifically due to nicotinic acid deficiency than pellagra is, and to develop more quickly on a deficiency diet. Spillane agrees with this view, and states that the nicotinic acid acts by meeting a cellular deficiency (8). Cleckley et al. have also described the use of nicotinic acid in this type of encephalopathy (9).

The therapeutic action of nicotinic acid has also been attributed to improved cerebral nutrition stemming from a reputed vasodilatory action. Despite a report that the acidic form of the vitamin dilates the cerebral blood vessels (10), a careful physiological study has shown that it has little effect upon the cerebral circulation (11).

The amount of $N^1$-methylnicotinamide excreted in the urine is diminished in pellagrins, and when given a test load of the vitamin they appear to retain a larger percentage of it than normals do (12). They have an increased excretion of indican and hippuric acid, and ethereal sulfates; the indicanuria may decline with clinical improvement. Indoleacetic and indoleaceturic acids have been mentioned as urinary constituents of note in pellagra. The feces contain unusually large amounts of indole and skatole (13).

Many theories have been proposed to explain the origin of pellagra but the nutritional hypothesis has been the most prominent and generally accepted one for a hundred years. In his *Traité de la Pellagra et des Pseudo-pellagres* (1866) Théophile Roussel stated: "Without dietetic measures *all remedies fail* . . . . When drugs and good food are simultaneously employed it is to the latter that the curative action belongs, the former exercises simply an adjuvant action and is without proved efficacy except against the secondary changes or accidental complications." Investigators of the United States Public Health Service became convinced, as had others, that pellagra appeared in populations lacking milk, meat, and eggs in their diet and subsisting on a diet consisting mainly of corn, wheat, and vegetables or animal fat, with relatively few green vegetables (13, 14). Extensive nutritional researches were carried out in many quarters in the attempt to pinpoint the specific factor absent in the diet of pellagrins, and these seemed to be crowned with success when nicotinic acid, which was shown in 1938 to cure clinical and experimental blacktongue in dogs (15), gave some dramatic therapeutic results in clinical trials in pellagra. At least two types of clinical observation temper the view that nicotinic acid deficiency is the sole cause of pellagra. In the first place pellagrins exhibit signs of deficiency of other nutrients such as iron, protein, and some of the B vitamins. This is not to be unexpected, considering the restricted nature of the diet. Secondly, the treatment of pellagrins with nicotinic acid alone frequently has led to the disappearance of some of the symptoms, but at the same time has precipitated others for which various members of the B complex, e.g., riboflavin, are curative. Thus, when one of the deficiencies is satisfied by nicotinic acid the balance of cellular metabolism is shifted in such a way as to yield a different clinical counterpart which can be dissipated only by supplying the additional necessary vitamins.

The presence of a toxic factor in the pellagragenic diet has also been accorded some consideration. Although the hypothesis that moldy corn is responsible for the disease was discarded many years ago, evidence for an antivitamin in maize has been found more recently, and this indicates that there may be a dietary factor contributing in a positive way to pellagra (16). It has further been shown that the niacin in corn is chemically bound to other constituents in such a way as to reduce its availability nutritionally. However, pellagra also occurs in populations which do not consume maize (6), and the role of nutritional conditioning factors there is even less understood.

The success with nicotinic acid at first obscured the older views that protein (14) or lack of certain essential amino acids (17) is involved in pellagra, but the poor correlation between nicotinic acid content of the diet and occurrence of pellagra represented a puzzle that was solved by the finding that tryptophan is converted in the animal body to nicotinic acid. In the integrated picture of the etiology of pellagra this means that persons on diets marginal in nicotinic acid may not show any symptoms of the disease as long as the tryptophan content is sufficient. Indeed, the relatively high tryptophan content of the diet of rice-consuming people is considered an important factor protecting them from pellagra. This relationship also operates in the inverse direction: in malignant carcinoid, where a considerable fraction of the ingested tryptophan is diverted into the 5-hydroxylative pathway (p. 89) insufficient is converted to nicotinic acid, and the patient may show some symptoms of pellagra. A similar finding has been made in Hartnup disease (p. 90).

The multiple nature of the deficiency in pellagra has a further significance for the pathophysiology of the disease. Thiamine, riboflavin, and pyridoxine play roles in the dissimilative pathway leading from tryptophan to nicotinic acid (18), so that when these vitamins are deficient it can be expected that less nicotinic acid will be formed endogenously.

Gopalan and Srikantia, observing an increased excretion of $N^1$-methylnicotinamide in subjects given L-leucine orally, tested this amino acid in pellagrins. It caused a deterioration in the mental condition which could be reversed by withdrawing the test compound and substituting the vitamin. *Iso*-leucine did not have these effects (19).

# References

1. PERLZWEIG, W. A., F. ROSEN, N. LEVITAS, and J. ROBINSON. *J. Biol. Chem. 167*:511, 1947; SARETT, H. P., and G. A. GOLDSMITH. *J. Biol. Chem. 167:* 293, 1947; *177:*461, 1949.
2. GOLDSMITH, G. A., O. N. MILLER, and W. G. UNGLAUB. *Federation Proc. 15*:553, 1956.
3. HORWITT, M. K., C. C. HARVEY, W. S. ROTHWELL, J. L. CUTLER, and D. HAFFRON. *J. Nutrition 60:*Supplement 1, 1956; HORWITT, M. K. *J. Am. Diet. Assoc. 34:*914, 1958.
4. SCHOU, M. *Biochim. et Biophys. Acta 4:*422, 1950.
5. GREGORY, I. *J. Ment. Sci. 101:*85, 1955.
6. BICKNELL, F., and F. PRESCOTT. *The Vitamins in Medicine,* 3d ed. New York, Grune and Stratton, 1953.
7. JOLLIFFE, N., K. M. BOWMAN, L. A. ROSENBLUM, and H. D. FEIN. *J.A.M.A. 114:*307, 1940.
8. SPILLANE, J. D. *Nutritional Disorders of the Nervous System.* Edinburgh, E. and S. Livingstone, Ltd., 1947.
9. CLECKLEY, A. M., V. P. SYDENSTRICKER, and L. E. GEESLIN. *J.A.M.A. 112:*2107, 1939.

10. ARING, C. D., H. W. RYDER, E. ROSEMAN, M. ROSENBAUM, and E. B. FERRIS. *Arch. Neurol. Psychiat. 46:*649, 1941.
11. LOMAN, J., M. RINKEL, and A. MYERSON. *Am. J. Med. Sci. 202:*211, 1941; SCHEINBERG, P. *Circulation 1:*1148, 1950.
12. HOFFMAN, M. M., and T. L. SOURKES. *In Practice of Medicine, ed.* MEAKINS, J. C. 6th ed. St. Louis, C. V. Mosby, 1956.
13. VOEGTLIN, C. *Harvey Lectures 15:*87, 1919–20.
14. GOLDBERGER, J., C. H. WARING, and D. G. WILLETS. *U.S. Public Health Reports 30:*3117, 1915.
15. ELVEHJEM, C. A., R. J. MADDEN, F. M. STRONG, and D. W. WOOLLEY. *J. Biol. Chem. 123:*137, 1938.
16. KODICEK, E., K. J. CARPENTER, and L. J. HARRIS. *Lancet ii:*491, 1946; WOOLLEY, D. W. *J. Biol. Chem. 163:*773, 1946.
17. VOEGTLIN, C. *J.A.M.A. 63:*1094, 1914.
18. PORTER, C., I. C. CLARK, and R. SILBER. *Arch. Biochem. 18:*339, 1948; DALGLIESH, C. E. *Biochem. J. 61:*328, 1955.
19. GOPALAN, C., and S. G. SRIKANTIA. *Lancet i:*954, 1960.

# 19

# PYRIDOXINE (VITAMIN B₆)

Vitamin $B_6$ is a group term for three compounds all of which possess equal and specific vitamin activity for a number of species, including man, and which differ from one another only in a single functional group. Chemically, pyridoxol is 2-methyl-3-hydroxy-4,5-dihydroxymethylpyridine.* It can be oxidized in the tissues into the corresponding aldehyde, pyridoxal, and the latter can be converted by transamination into pyridoxamine. Pyridoxal participates in many enzymic reactions in its phosphorylated form, as the 3′-phosphate; this ester is present in plasma at a concentration of about 10 μg. per liter. In the course of metabolism pyridoxine is oxidized to the 4-carboxylic acid (pyridoxic acid) in which form it no longer possesses biological activity. One to 2 mg. of the vitamin are considered sufficient to make up the daily losses incurred in metabolism.

## Deficiency Symptoms

Many species of experimental animal have been shown to develop deficiency symptoms when they are fed diets lacking pyridoxine. At first the changes are minimal, although in young animals a slightly slower growth can be detected. Later on there are dermatological

* Formerly called pyridoxine, a word now used generically for the $B_6$ vitamins without specification.

225

changes on the exposed parts (paws and snout), with edema (rat); cessation of growth; elevated systolic blood pressure; appearance of a peculiar gait; degenerative changes in the peripheral nerves and posterior roots (pig); lowered threshold to electroshock (rat); microcytic anemia (pig, monkey); enlargement of the adrenal gland with marked changes in the microscopic appearance of the cortex; and eventually convulsions. All these symptoms respond to pyridoxine administration. Vascular alterations have also been seen which are reminiscent of arteriosclerotic changes. In fact, Schroeder (1) considers atherosclerosis to be a conditioned deficiency of this vitamin.

Metabolic changes have been detected in vitamin $B_6$-deficient animals, which indicate the important role of this vitamin in protein and fat metabolism. A very early change is observed in tryptophan metabolism. Pyridoxine is required as a coenzyme in the catabolism of this amino acid at the stage of 3-hydroxykynurenine, where it plays a role in the scission of the side chain to yield 3-hydroxyanthranilic acid (action of kynureninase). Alternatively, 3-hydroxykynurenine may be converted to the corresponding keto acid under the influence of another pyridoxal phosphate-linked enzyme, transaminase. This keto acid cyclizes spontaneously to form xanthurenic acid. Under conditions of vitamin deficiency kynureninase apparently loses its coenzyme more readily than does the transaminase, with the result that the balance of tryptophan breakdown is upset and abnormally large amounts of xanthurenic acid, representing a metabolic *cul-de-sac,* are excreted in the urine.

## Function of Pyridoxine in Intermediary Metabolism

The catalogue of reactions in which pyridoxal phosphate participates is very impressive, covering as it does general reaction types (*e.g.,* transamination, decarboxylation of L-amino acids, oxidation of histamine, and diamines) as well as reactions which are specific for given amino acids (2). These reactions all have to do with amino acid metabolism, in fact, with reactions in which the amino group is the site of contact with the coenzyme. Transamination involves the transfer of the amino group of an amino acid to the α-keto acid (*cf.* Reactions 4-4 to 4-6), and represents a method of biosynthesis of new amino acids from carbohydrate precursors. Glutamic and aspartic acids are especially prominent in serving as amino donors in this reaction (Chapter 4).

Decarboxylation serves in the formation of the biogenic amines from their amino acid precursors (see Table 9-1, p. 106).

The diminished amount of pyridoxine in the tissues of deficient animals is reflected in the decreased activity of enzymes that require pyridoxal phosphate. Such enzymic alterations have been found for transaminase, cysteine desulfhydrase, glutamic decarboxylase, dopa decarboxylase, and 5-hydroxytryptophan decarboxylase. It seems likely that the last two enzymes are identical (*cf.* Chapter 23).

A specific pyridoxal phosphate-linked reaction of great importance in cerebral metabolism is the decarboxylation of glutamic acid, to form γ-aminobutyric acid (pp. 49, 52). The nature of the biological activity of this compound recalls results obtained by Davenport and Davenport in regard to brain excitability in rats (3). These authors found that the electroshock threshold, measured under standardized conditions, was lowered in pyridoxine deficiency and could be restored to normal by administering the vitamin to the animals. The threshold could be raised in mildly deficient rats by adding 2 percent L-glutamic acid to their diet. Severely deficient animals did not react in this way unless pyridoxine was also given to them. In that case they were found to have a higher electroshock threshold than those severely deficient rats given eventually only the vitamin and not the glutamic acid. These results show that the glutamic acid was not effective at the two levels of deficiency unless some pyridoxine is present. In the present context a deficiency of this vitamin might be expected to reduce the amount of coenzyme available for transamination of glutamic acid or for its decarboxylation. It is conceivable that additional dietary glutamic acid serves to form γ-aminobutyric acid by decarboxylation in the mildly deficient rats (*i.e.*, in the group still retaining effective concentrations of pyridoxal phosphate in the tissues), thus providing extra anticonvulsant substance in the brain. On the other hand, the severely deficient animals do not have sufficient pyridoxine in their tissues to ensure effective decarboxylation of glutamic acid to its inhibitory derivative. The supplementation of the diet of these rats with some pyridoxine gives those receiving the extra glutamic acid a temporary advantage over their controls receiving the vitamin alone (3).

Pyridoxine also functions in fat metabolism. For example, unsaturated fats such as lard and linseed oil exert a sparing action on the vitamin requirements. Further, the dermatological changes encountered in the vitamin deficiency can be overcome by use of essential fatty acids. Although pyridoxine is needed for the interconversion of essential fatty acids, the enzymatic basis of this relationship has not been explained. The vitamin is furthermore required for the transport of amino acids into the cell interior (4), for the absorption of vitamin $B_{12}$ from the intestine (5), and for the formation of hepatic coenzyme A (6).

## Role of Pyridoxine in Human Disease

Until recently evidence was lacking for a human requirement for pyridoxine in spite of its demonstrated essentiality for other mammalian species. Now, evidence has come from several lines of work, signifying that elimination of the vitamin from the diet or interference with its functions by the use of antivitamins such as deoxypyridoxine results in serious clinical sequelae. The aim of these experiments has been to seek clinical analogies for the dermatological, hematological, and neurological changes in deficient animals and, if possible, to identify pyridoxine deficiency symptoms with clinical entities of unknown etiology.

Thus far it has been possible to induce deficiency symptoms only under somewhat limited circumstances. Snyderman, Holt, Carretero, and Jacobs (7) withheld the vitamin from the diet of two congenitally defective infants, both of whom soon stopped gaining weight. After 11 weeks on the purified diet one of them had severe tonic and clonic convulsions, which responded quickly to pyridoxine injection. The other eventually developed a hypochromic microcytic anemia but underwent hematological remission after receiving pyridoxine. Several authors (8) have observed convulsions in infants fed milk formulas that proved to be deficient in pyridoxine. The babies displayed abdominal distress and hyperirritability at first, and as the deficiency advanced they had seizures which become progressively more severe. One patient in status epilepticus recovered almost immediately after intramuscular injection of 100 mg. of pyridoxine. Hawkins and Barsky (9) followed the course of an adult consuming a purified diet from which pyridoxine had been omitted. They noted an increase in the lymphocytes and a decrease in neutrophils; the white cells returned to normal shortly after introducing the missing vitamin into the diet. Pyridoxine deficiency anemia in man has been discussed by Verloop and Rademaker (10) and by Gehrmann (11). Chemslock and McCully observed the results of diets low in pyridoxine (12). They noted a decline in the blood pyridoxine to zero in all subjects, and a decrease in the lymphocyte count and disturbed tryptophan metabolism in five of the eight subjects.

Vilter and his colleagues (13) attempted to obviate the difficulties in depleting subjects of vitamin B$_6$ by placing volunteer patients on a regimen containing the antimetabolite deoxypyridoxine. Some subjects received the regular hospital diet, and others a diet poor in members of the vitamin B complex. A higher proportion of the latter developed symptoms of the deficiency. The most common sign of deficiency was seborrheic dermatitis. Cheilosis, stomatitis, conjunctivitis, and glossitis with reddening of the tongue and of the oral mucous membrane were also observed. Some of these features resembled changes in nicotinic acid and riboflavin deficiency, but in this case they responded only to pyridoxine. Among the blood changes noted was a decrease in the lymphocytes. Manifestations referable to the nervous system included a lethargic state and confusion in some of the patients; paresthesias and hyperesthesias; hyporeflexia; and the burning foot syndrome. All these disappeared after vitamin B$_6$ was administered orally or parenterally. The biochemical components included a rise in blood urea nitrogen and an increased output of xanthurenic acid. The latter increase preceded clinical signs of deficiency and signalized a defective metabolism of tryptophan. There was also evidence for a defective conversion of nicotinamide to its coenzyme form.

These results with pyridoxine-deficient diets and with deoxypyridoxine in human nutrition are reinforced by the results of therapeutic trials conducted initially on an entirely empirical basis. For example, some patients with a syndrome characterized by "extreme nervousness, insomnia, irritability, abdominal pain, weakness and difficulty in walking" (14) obtain relief with pyridoxine but not with thiamine, riboflavin, or nicotinic acid. Furthermore, pyridoxine has served to control convulsions in a rare condition of unexplained origin in infants whose vitamin B$_6$ intake is normal as judged by the excretion of xanthurenic acid after a tryptophan-load test (15). It has corrected a refractory hypochromic anemia in an adult whose diet contained as much as 3 mg. of pyridoxine per day (16). This patient also suffered from malaise, nocturia, and pedal edema, but had no glossal, neurological, or dermal changes. Tryptophan metabolism was abnormal (as judged by measurements of several urinary metabolites); the serum iron concentration was more than doubled. These features returned to normal after instituting pyridoxine treatment.

There has been little success with the vitamin in epilepsy and petit mal (17, 18) or anemias (18) in children, but pyridoxine has been of some therapeutic value in treating the nausea and vomiting of pregnancy, as well as the nausea following radiation therapy.

230 BIOCHEMISTRY OF MENTAL DISEASE

The specific mode of action of pyridoxine in these therapeutic applications has not been worked out. The vitamin participates in so many reactions that the ultimate metabolic imbalance caused by its insufficiency in the tissues, the basis upon which the clinical dysfunction is expressed, may be extremely complex. These factors have been analyzed by Tower (19).

Pyridoxine has been tested therapeutically in phenylketonuria; the results were negative (20).

## Substances with Antipyridoxine Activity

Under this heading there are grouped several compounds varying widely in structure but having in common antipyridoxine activity such as displacement of the vitamin from its locus of action, binding of the vitamin by chemical reaction, or some other action which results in detectable change in the treated animals or human and which can be reversed by pyridoxine.

### DEOXYPYRIDOXINE

Deoxypyridoxine is the synthetic reduction product of pyridoxol, having the structure 2,4-dimethyl-3-hydroxy-5-hydroxymethylpyridine. It is phosphorylated in the tissues in just the same way as pyridoxal and it is, in fact, in this form that it interferes with the function of vitamin $B_6$ in many, but not all (21), pyridoxal phosphate-linked enzymes: it displaces the coenzyme from the active sites on various enzymes but, unlike the natural coenzyme, it is not capable of participating any further in the reaction. As a result the action of such enzymes may be blocked. Notwithstanding this type of activity at the enzymic level, the syndrome appearing in experimental animals is not entirely identical with the symptoms of deficiency of pyridoxine alone (22). Thus, the vitamin is an antagonist for deoxypyridoxine, but the reverse may not be true (23). By extension, one might argue that the effects of deoxypyridoxine consumption in man may not represent the same clinical picture that would appear on a pyridoxine-low diet.

### HYDRAZINE DERIVATIVES

Hydrazine ($H_2N \cdot NH_2$) and its mono-substituted derivatives are carbonyl reagents, and are used in chemistry to bind aldehydes and ketones. Because of its aldehyde function, pyridoxal may also be trapped (*in vivo* as well as *in vitro*) by these derivatives. The acute administration of hydrazine itself results in hypoglycemia; this may be correlated with the increased respiratory quotient in animals injected with it. Prolonged contact with this substance results in liver damage.

The substituted hydrazines entered therapeutics in 1952–53 through the discovery of their antitubercular activity. Two compounds were outstanding in this respect: isoniazid (INH, isonicotinylhydrazine) and iproniazid (IPN, $N^1$-isonicotinyl-$N^2$-isopropylhydrazide). The action of INH in the rat does not seem to be directed simply against vitamin $B_6$. Xanthurenic excretion is actually decreased by INH in animals fed a pyridoxine-deficient ration (24), although an increase would be predicted. Animals receiving INH without pyridoxine suffer decreased growth rate, peripheral nerve degeneration, convulsions, and decreased survival time. Moreover, the administration of the vitamin maintains normal growth on pyridoxine-deficient diets and prevents the appearance of convulsions and nerve changes. INH-induced seizures have been carefully studied by Pfeiffer and his colleagues (25).

Toxic effects of INH have also been detected in man during the course of therapy of tuberculosis. The daily dose used in this disease is of the order of 5 mg. per kilogram of body weight, and this maintains a blood level of about 0.2 mg. percent. In most patients this proves to be quite satisfactory, but about 5 percent experience toxic reactions. The Committee on Therapy of the American Trudeau Society described these reactions in 1953 as follows:

> The nervous system was most frequently involved, the commonest reactions being twiching of the muscles, restlessness of the extremities, and hyperreflexia . . . . Other minor neurological reactions were nervousness, apprehension, insomnia, and headache. The more serious reactions affecting the nervous system were vertigo, syncope, convulsions, peripheral neuritis, major psychosis, and difficulty in micturition . . . . Convulsions were particularly prone to occur in patients with a history of convulsive disorder . . . . The psychoses were more common in patients with an unstable personality and those with organic brain disease . . . . Allergic reactions were next most common (26).

The peripheral neuropathy can be prevented by the administration of pyridoxine (27). Morales and Lincoln found no evidence of pyridoxine deficiency in children taking 5 to 20 mg. of INH per kilogram per day for as long as 27 months. They concluded that this dose is safe as judged by hematology and body weight, and by the absence of convulsions, or of difficulty in converting a test load of tryptophan to $N^1$-methylnicotinamide (28). On the other hand, acute poisoning with INH in children entails marked central nervous system symptoms: tonic and clonic convulsions, respiratory depression, and cyanosis.

Among the metabolic effects of INH are an increase in the excretion of pyridoxine in the urine and an inhibition of histaminase. As for the metabolism of INH itself, Hughes and his colleagues (29) have counted at least four different routes: excretion of the unchanged compound; cleavage to isonicotinic acid or a closely related compound; acetylation to $N^1$-isonicotinyl-$N^2$-acetylhydrazide, the major pathway; and degradation to an unknown compound. The occurrence of peripheral neuropathy in INH treatment is closely associated with decreased acetylation and the presence of the unknown metabolite in the urine.

The central actions of IPN are more pronounced and occur more frequently than in the case of INH (30, 31), so that the use of this drug in the treatment of tuberculosis has been abandoned. Many of the symptoms concern the central and autonomic nervous systems, including euphoria, nervousness, muscle twitching, hyperreflexia, vertigo, peripheral neuropathy, constipation, and headache (30). Psychoses of the manic and paranoid types appear in 10 percent of patients (32). Further symptoms have been observed upon withdrawal of the drug: headache, insomnia, vertigo, frightening dreams, depression, and irritability, among others. These may last up to six weeks (30). Withdrawal effects are not as common in patients who have been treated with isoniazid.

The euphorigenic action of IPN has given the drug therapeutic application in the treatment of depressive states (33). The likelihood that its marked inhibitory action of monoamine oxidase (Chapter 9) is correlated with its central excitatory action has led to a search for other inhibitors of this enzyme as a pragmatic means of detecting some new and useful central agents (34).

SEMICARBAZIDE $(H_2N \cdot NH \cdot CONH_2)$

In intravenous doses of about 40 mg. per kilogram semicarbazide exerts a convulsant action in monkey and in man (35). There is a latent period of several hours before the seizure begins. It closely resembles the seizures of grand mal epilepsy or those following metrazol or electroshock. Preconvulsive effects include ataxia and mental confusion, among others.

## TOXOPYRIMIDINE

The pyrimidine moiety of thiamine, 2-methyl-4-amino-5-hydroxy-methylpyrimidine has been recognized as a convulsant drug (Chapter 16). It facilitates the appearance of deficiency symptoms in rats and mice fed diets from which pyridoxine has been omitted. It also causes a diminution in cerebral γ-aminobutyric acid (36). The injected animals become hyperactive and then go into convulsions. The effects of this compound are antagonized by pyridoxine (36, 37).

## L-PENICILLAMINE

Administration of large doses of this compound causes running fits and convulsions in rats (38). The D-isomer, prepared from penicillin, does not do this; it has found a therapeutic use in the treatment of hepatolenticular degeneration (Chapter 21, p. 263). L-Penicillamine increases markedly the excretion of xanthurenic acid (after a test load of tryptophan) and of vitamin B$_6$-active material in the urine; there is a correspondingly decreased activity of pyridoxal phosphate enzymes in the tissues of animals given the material (39). The effect depends upon chemical combination between pyridoxal phosphate and the L-penicillamine (40).

# References

1. SCHROEDER, H. A. *J. Chronic Dis.* 2:28, 1955.
2. BRAUNSTEIN, A. E. *In The Enzymes, ed.* BOYER, P. D., H. LARDY, and K. MYRBÄCK. 2d ed., Vol. 2. New York, Academic Press, 1960.
3. DAVENPORT, V. D., and H. W. DAVENPORT. *J. Nutrition* 36:263, 1948.
4. CHRISTENSEN, H. N. *In Amino Acid Metabolism.* ed. by McELROY, W. D., and B. GLASS. Baltimore, Johns Hopkins Press, 1955.
5. HSU, J. M., and B. F. CHOW. *Arch. Biochem. Biophys.* 72:322, 1957.
6. WILLIAMS, M. A., and B. HATA. *Arch. Biochem. Biophys.* 80:367, 1959.
7. SNYDERMAN, S. E., L. E. HOLT, JR., R. CARRETERO, and K. JACOBS. *J. Clin. Nutrition* 1:200, 1953.
8. MOLONEY, C. J., and A. H. PARMELEE. *J.A.M.A.* 154:405, 1954; COURSIN, D. B. *ibid.*:406.
9. HAWKINS, W. W., and J. BARSKY. *Science* 108:284, 1948.
10. VERLOOP, M. C., and W. RADEMAKER. *Brit. J. Haematol.* 6:66, 1960.
11. GEHRMANN, G. *German Med. Monthly* 4:336, 1959.
12. CHEMSLOCK, K. E., and M. T. McCULLY. *J. Nutrition* 70:507, 1960.
13. VILTER, R. W., J. F. MUELLER, H. S. GLAZER, T. JARROLD, J. ABRAHAM, C. THOMPSON, and V. R. HAWKINS. *J. Lab. Clin. Med.* 42:335, 1953.
14. SPIES, T. D., W. B. BEAN, and W. F. ASHE. *J.A.M.A.* 112:2414, 1939.

15. HUNT, A. D., J. STOKES, JR., W. W. McCRORY, and H. H. STROUD. *Pediatrics* 13:140, 1954; HUNT, A. D. *Am. J. Clin. Nutr.* 5:561, 1957; BESSEY, O. A., D. J. D. ADAM, and A. E. HANSEN. *Pediatrics* 20:33, 1957; HENNEQUET, A., G. LYON, P. DEBRIS, and J. C. LEBALLE. *Ann. Pediatr.* 192:197, 1959.

16. HARRIS, J. W., J. M. PRICE, R. M. WHITTINGTON, R. WEISMAN, JR., and D. L. HORRIGAN. *J. Clin. Invest.* 35:709, 1956.

17. VILTER, R. W. *J.A.M.A.* 159:1210, 1955.

18. RABE, E. F., and M. PLONKO. *A. M. A. J. Dis. Child.* 92:382, 1956.

19. TOWER, D. B. *In Neurochemistry, ed.* KOREY, S., and J. NURNBERGER, New York, Hoeber, 1956.

20. McGEER, E. G., and B. TISCHLER. *Can. J. Biochem. Physiol.* 37:485, 1959.

21. DIETRICH, L. S., and E. BORRIES. *Arch. Biochem. Biophys.* 64:512, 1956.

22. STOERK, H. C. *Ann. N.Y. Acad. Sci.* 52:1302, 1950.

23. UMBREIT, W. W. *Am. J. Clin. Nutrition* 3:291, 1955.

24. ROSEN, F. *Proc. Soc. Exptl. Biol. Med.* 88:243, 1955.

25. REILLY, R. H., K. F. KILLAM, E. H. JENNEY, W. H. MARSHALL, T. TAUSSIG, N. S. APTER, and C. C. PFEIFFER. *J.A.M.A.* 152:1317, 1953; PFEIFFER, C. C., E. H. JENNEY, and W. H. MARSHALL. *EEG Clin. Neurophysiol.* 8:307, 1956.

26. EBERT, R. H. *Am. Rev. Tuberculosis* 68:302, 1953.

27. ROSS, R. R. *J.A.M.A.* 168:273, 1958.

28. MORALES, S. M., and E. M. LINCOLN. *Am. Rev. Tuberculosis* 75:594, 1957.

29. HUGHES, H. B., J. P. BIEHL, A. P. JONES, and L. H. SCHMIDT. *Am. Rev. Tuberculosis* 70:266, 1954.

30. ROBITZEK, E. H., and I. J. SELIKOFF. *Am. Rev. Tuberculosis* 65:402, 1952; SELIKOFF, I. J., E. H. ROBITZEK, and G. G. ORNSTEIN. *ibid.* 67:212, 1953.

31. CRANE, G. E. *Am. J. Psychiat.* 112:494, 1956.

32. O'CONNOR, J. B., K. S. HOWLETT, and R. R. WAGNER. *Am. Rev. Tuberculosis* 68:270, 1953.

33. ZELLER, E. A. (ed.). "Amine Oxidase Inhibitors," *Ann. N.Y. Acad. Sci.* 80: (Art. 3) 551–1045, 1959.

34. ZBINDEN, G., L. O. RANDALL, and R. A. MOE. *Dis. Nerv. System* 21: Section 2, 89, 1960.

35. LOWELL, D. J., J. K. ROSS-DUGGAN, and S. PIAZZA. *J. Pharmacol. Exp. Ther.* 106:404, 1952; STEPHENS, R. R., N. CHRISTOFF, R. LEVINE, H. ZARTMAN, D. DIMOCK, E. MAYRAND, and C. C. PFEIFFER, *ibid.:*418.

36. RINDI, G., and G. FERRARI. *Nature* 183:608, 1959.

37. MAKINO, K., T. KINOSHITA, T. SASAKI, and T. SHIOI. *Nature* 173:34, 1954; SHINTANI, S. *Pharm. Bull.* (Japan) 3:236, 1955, *seen in Chem. Abstr. 50:* 4393g, 1956; TORIGOE, K., and T. KINOSHITA. *J. Vitaminol.* 2:239, 1956, *seen in Chem. Abstr. 51:*5227d, 1957.

38. WILLSON, J. E., and V. DU VIGNEAUD. *J. Biol. Chem.* 184:63, 1950.

39. KUCHINSKAS, E. J., and V. DU VIGNEAUD. *Arch. Biochem. Biophys.* 66:1, 1957.

40. KUCHINSKAS, E. J. *Arch. Biochem. Biophys.* 80:150, 1959.

# 20

# VITAMIN B$_{12}$

## Chemistry and Metabolism

The history of research on the physiopathology of pernicious anemia has provided vitamin B$_{12}$ with many synonyms: antipernicious anemia factor, extrinsic factor, animal protein factor, and others. But with the intricacies of its structure solved, the chemical and pharmacopoeial name, cyanocobalamin, is preferentially used. At the European Symposium on Vitamin B$_{12}$ and Intrinsic Factor held in 1956 at Hamburg, the name 5,6-dimethyl-$\alpha$-benzimidazole cyanocobamide was proposed to describe the structural features of the vitamin elucidated in 1955. The vitamin is a complex red compound, constructed around a ring system made up of 4 pyrrole nuclei linked together by 3 bridges of carbon atoms. This arrangement constitutes a macro corrin ring. Hydrolysis of the vitamin by simple procedures yields other products: 5,6-dimethylbenzimidazole ribotide, aminopropanol, cobalt, and cyanide. Solutions of the vitamin are stable to heat. Several compounds occurring naturally are very similar to vitamin B$_{12}$ chemically and are, in fact, interconvertible.

The dietary sources of cyanocobalamin are foods of animal origin, but ultimately the vitamin has its origin in the synthetic activities of soil and gut microorganisms. It is not found in plant foods. Previously the erythropoietic substance had to be assayed by giving it to pernicious anemic patients in relapse and using the reticulocyte response as the measured parameter. Microbiological assays are now employed to measure the vitamin in foods, tissues, and body fluids.

Vitamin $B_{12}$ is one of the most potent chemical agents known, 1 to 2 $\mu$g. per day sufficing for the maintenance of health in the adult human. Many diets contain the vitamin in manifold excess of this, perhaps ten times as much as required. Normally, the ingested vitamin combines with a substance (intrinsic factor) found in the gastric juice and extractable from it and from the pyloric mucosa; they form a complex which is eminently absorbable through the intestinal mucosa, thus introducing the vitamin into the blood stream and thence the tissues. In the absence or deficiency of intrinsic factor (pernicious anemia, gastrectomy, gastric carcinoma) massive doses of the vitamin, measured in milligram quantities, may serve to get sufficient of it absorbed to induce a reticulocyte response, but then the cost is very high and absorption is unpredictable. The precise function of the intrinsic factor is unknown (1) but it appears to affect the permeability of the intestinal wall either by itself or in combination with cyanocobalamin, thereby favoring readier absorption of the vitamin. Chemically, the intrinsic factor has the properties of a protein.

Most of the absorbed vitamin is stored in the liver, where the concentration averages somewhat less than 1.0 $\mu$g./gm. of liver. Much of the store is lost from cirrhotic livers. In untreated cases of pernicious anemia there is less than 0.2 $\mu$g./gm. liver (2).

Serum levels of the vitamin normally extend through a rather wide range, from about 200 $\mu\mu$g./ml. to 550 $\mu\mu$g./ml., or even greater. Most of the vitamin in serum is in a bound form. The concentration is markedly elevated in hepatic cirrhosis and in acute viral hepatitis (reflecting the decline in the liver stores), but it is normal in obstructive jaundice (3, 4). Low values are found in the serum of chronic alcoholics (5). The lowest concentrations occur in the serum of patients with pernicious anemia in relapse; in these cases none of the serum vitamin is present in the free form. In macrocytic anemias other than the Addisonian type, i.e., those due to folic acid deficiency, the serum vitamin $B_{12}$ concentration is slightly lower than normal (3).

Whereas orally administered vitamin $B_{12}$ is absorbed at a variable rate and, furthermore, requires intrinsic factor, injected vitamin is readily available to the organism and is quickly distributed.

Heinrich and Lahann (6), Ungley (7), and Smith (8) have presented valuable reviews of the physiological aspects of vitamin $B_{12}$ metabolism.

# Functions of Vitamin B$_{12}$

As already mentioned, the vitamin was initially studied in higher species as a factor required for normal growth and healthy development. It has now been demonstrated that in hypovitaminosis-B$_{12}$ many aspects of organic metabolism are disrupted. This protean function in intermediary metabolism has not yet been explained, but extensive laboratory studies have provided several clues.

At one time it was thought that cyanocobalamin plays a role in transmethylation, but this is no longer considered one of its sites of action. Rather, the evidence points to its activity in catalyzing the synthesis of methyl groups *de novo* (9) as a supplement to those already present in a transferable form in the diet (in methionine and choline, for example). Inasmuch as the methyl group is formed from the formyl radical (—HC$=$O) reduction mechanisms are called into play, and it may be in these processes that vitamin B$_{12}$ serves. It has also been shown that the vitamin is concerned with maintenance of sulfhydryl groups in their reduced state. Specifically, this has been demonstrated for homocysteine, which is transmethylated to form methionine (10), and for coenzyme A, which serves in acylation processes (11). This role of vitamin B$_{12}$ may extend to maintenance of the normal complement of glutathione in the erythrocytes (12), or even to affecting the state of essential sulfhydryl groups on certain enzymes (13). The ratio of oxidized to reduced pyridine nucleotides in rat liver is increased in vitamin B$_{12}$ deficiency (14), paralleling the increased ratio of disulfide to sulfhydryl groups in certain test organisms. Thus, cyanocobalamin appears to control the intracellular reduction-oxidation potential. Smith (8) has postulated that cyanocobalamin is part of the prosthetic group of one or more reducing enzymes.

Another intermediary function which can be assigned to vitamin B$_{12}$ is in the biosynthesis of nucleic acid, for the liver of the deficient rat contains less of this component than is found in normal controls (15). Clinical studies show that the relationship of the vitamin to nucleic acid formation is not a simple one. In untreated megaloblastic anemia the bone marrow is biochemically characterized by abnormally high concentrations of RNA (ribonucleic acid) and DNA (deoxyribonucleic acid). The increased level of RNA accounts for the marked cytoplasmic basophilia in the megaloblasts. Treatment with liver extract or cyanocobalamin effects a reduction in RNA toward normal values.

On the other hand, when the full therapeutic effects have been exerted, the level of DNA in the bone marrow, *i.e.*, the amount per cell, is still high (16). How the vitamin exerts its effects upon the biosynthesis of these polymeric compounds or their constituent fragments is not certain but a useful suggestion comes from bacterial nutrition studies. It has been shown that it is possible to satisfy the growth requirement of a microorganism for folic acid by supplying large amounts of the pyrimidine thymine (5-methyluracil) in the nutrient medium. The requirement for vitamin $B_{12}$ in a parallel situation can be satisfied by the nucleoside of thymine, *viz.*, thymidine. It is, therefore, conceivable that these two vitamins function coenzymatically at successive stages in nucleotide biosynthesis: in the formation of the pyrimidine or purine (thymine being the paradigm), and in its condensation with ribose or deoxyribose. Whitby considers that normal nucleic acid metabolism is a prerequisite for erythropoiesis (17).

Recent reports indicate still other functions for cyanocobalamin. For example, subjects with low serum vitamin vitamin $B_{12}$ levels are unable to metabolize a test load of tyrosine effectively, so that the transamination product of this amino acid, *p*-hydroxyphenylpyruvic acid is readily detected in large amounts in the serum and urine (18). Perhaps cyanocobalamin helps to conserve *p*-hydroxyphenylpyruvic oxidase in an active form in the same way as ascorbic acid does.

An effect of vitamin $B_{12}$ on protein synthesis in vitro has been demonstrated recently. The method has been to employ enzymes from two portions of the liver cell (microsomes and a fraction of the cytoplasm) which, together, can effect the incorporation of alanine into protein linkage. This process is appreciably less active if the enzymes are obtained from hypovitaminotic rats, but it is reported to return to normal when vitamin $B_{12}$ is added *in vitro* (19).

Coenzyme forms of vitamin $B_{12}$, containing benzimidazole or 5,6-dimethylbenzimidazole and having adenine in place of the cyano group, have been isolated from bacteria (20). These coenzymes possess a catalytic function in the conversion of glutamic acid to $\beta$-methylaspartic acid.

## Vitamin $B_{12}$ Deficiency

Abnormal symptoms appear in animals some time after they are placed on a diet free of vitamin $B_{12}$ and its biologically active congeners, or a diet extremely low in them. Symptoms have also been observed in humans subsisting on certain types of restricted diets. In the rat the development of the deficiency symptoms is accelerated by the addition of thyroid powder to the diet in order to provoke a mild hyperthyroidism; the tissue stores of the vitamin are then lost at a faster rate. The outstanding effect of the deficiency is cessation of growth. Anemia and neurological defects have not been noted in this species. The progeny of vitamin B$_{12}$-deficient rats have a high incidence of congenital malformations and a high neonatal mortality. The pig also exhibits the growth defect, and in addition develops a normocytic anemia (21). The vitamin B$_{12}$-deficient rat and sheep have an abnormality in protoporphyrin metabolism.

In man deficiency symptoms have been observed in persons consuming vegetarian diets. The dietetic exclusion of animal products, that is, the foods which are "protective" with respect to cyanocobalamin, does not always result in a deficiency syndrome, however. "Vegans" on diets of as high a standard as that recommended by the National Research Council (U.S.A.) may show no signs of deficiency upon medical examination (22, 23). When symptoms do appear, the first reported are generally complaints of sore tongue; later on there are paresthesias and other neurological symptoms (23, 24), up to and including subacute combined degeneration of the cord (25). Poker back is so characteristic that it has been renamed vegan back by Wokes, Badenoch, and Sinclair (23). The blood cell and bone marrow pictures resemble those seen in pernicious anemia, but they tend to appear later than the neurological changes (25). The concentration of vitamin B$_{12}$ in the serum is far below normal. The symptoms in vegans have been traced entirely to the chronic deficiency of vitamin B$_{12}$.

## Pernicious Anemia

Characterization of pernicious anemia as a deficiency disease was made thirty years ago by West (26). He considered that because of abnormal gastric digestive processes there was a primary failure to free the antipernicious anemia (erythropoietic) factor from its bound form in the ingested meats. The picture is now known to be different. In this disease the cyanocobalamin content of the diet is adequate but the primary deficiency of intrinsic factor formation in the stomach renders the vitamin unavailable for absorption. The clinical picture shows variability from subject to subject but the symptoms resemble those noted in vegans and they respond specifically to parenteral cyanocobalamin therapy. The main symptoms relate to the megaloblastic anemia, changes in the epithelial surfaces, particularly of the mouth and stomach, and neurological and mental disorder. These groups of symptoms appear at different times, depending upon the particular case. The neurological disease has been termed subacute combined degeneration of the spinal cord, in reference to changes in the dorsal and lateral regions of the cord, but the degenerative process is more widespread than this in many cases of pernicious anemia. Thus, peripheral neuropathy (27) and degeneration of the white matter of the brain (28, 29) have been described. The cerebral changes occur later than do those in the spinal cord, but they are histologically similar.

In certain instances of pernicious anemia psychiatric symptoms predominate. They occur in 25 to 64 percent of the cases in various series (30), assume a wide variety of forms (29, 30, 31, 32, 33), and may precede the megaloblastic changes (34). Most often there is a confusional state (the "wandering of the mind" noted by Addison) with memory and thinking deficits, but paranoid trends, agitation and depression, affective disorders, and auditory and visual hallucinations have also been reported. Impaired vision associated with degeneration in the optic tract (28, 29) and changes in the sense of smell, as serious as anosmia (33), indicate the scope of the cerebral changes. Changes in mental state in pernicious anemia represent a serious danger signal to be met by vigorous therapeutic measures (32). Adams and Kubik (28) noted that the patients in whom they detected cerebral lesions had had mental symptoms, but that the converse could not always be demonstrated. It is quite possible, of course, that the mental picture emanates from minimal organic changes having their genesis in disturbed cerebral metabolism as detected by Scheinberg (35), *i.e.*, decreased utilization of glucose and oxygen, with the cerebral oxygen consumption falling by as much as one third below normal in spite of an increased cerebral blood flow. Scheinberg observed good correlations between cerebral oxygen consumption and the mental and neurological defects. Interestingly, after the disease had been controlled by treatment with vitamin $B_{12}$ the cerebral oxygen consumption rose from 2.2 to 2.8 ml. per 100 grams of tissue per minute, but did not attain normal values (3.3 ml./100 gm./min.).

Some of the biochemical features of pernicious anemia can be associated with findings in vitamin $B_{12}$ deficiency. The inability of the vegan to metabolize a tyrosine load efficiently (p. 238) is probably related to the observation made many years ago by Becher (36) that pernicious anemia patients have abnormally high levels of phenolic compounds in their blood, of the order of 0.12 to 0.34 mg. percent, most of which is in the bound form. Patients in remission were found to have lower values, closer to the normal range of 0.04 to 0.22 mg. percent (average = 0.12 mg. percent), all of which is bound. In Becher's studies high phenol values occurred also in liver cirrhosis (perhaps affecting the hepatic storage of vitamin B$_{12}$) and in carcinoma of the stomach (affecting the formation of intrinsic factor). Corresponding changes have since been described for the amounts of phenols and keto acids (p-hydroxyphenylpyruvic acid?) excreted in the urine of pernicious anemia patients, in relapse and remission. Hydroxyphenyl compounds and keto acids are elevated in pernicious anemia, but return to the normal range following treatment (37).

Thiamine deficiency occurs sometimes in association with subacute combined degeneration (38). It is detected by the elevated blood pyruvic acid concentration after glucose. Pyruvate metabolism is corrected by administering thiamine, but not vitamin B$_{12}$.

Defective tyrosine metabolism shows up in other ways in pernicious anemia: some patients develop vitiliginous patches, others have areas of bronze coloration. The hair may lose its pigment.

The equal ability of folic acid and vitamin B$_{12}$ to bring about hematological remission in pernicious anemia does not apply to the neurological symptoms: here only the latter vitamin is therapeutic. Indeed, in cases of pernicious anemia manifesting only the megaloblastic anemia at the time therapy is initiated, the use of folic acid alone corrects the blood condition but may eventually elicit combined nervous system disease. As pointed out above, the two vitamins are probably required at successive stages in nucleic acid formation: folic acid at an earlier step than cyanocobalamin. If this be assumed then the administration of only the former is sufficient to bring about the bone marrow changes resulting in erythropoiesis because it permits effective utilization of the small amounts of vitamin B$_{12}$ still remaining in the tissues. It appears, however, that when metabolic processes reduce this finite amount below a critical level the biochemical imbalance induced by the continuing and aggravated deficiency of cyanocobalamin in the tissues is thrown to the next most sensitive tissue in that individual, the nervous system.

# References

1. Castle, W. B. *New England J. Med.* 249:603, 1953; Girdwood, R. H. *Am. J. Digest. Dis.* 2:159, 1957.

2. GIRDWOOD, R. H. *Biochem. J. 52*:58, 1952; SWENDSEID, M. E., E. HVOLBOLL, G. SCHICK, and J. A. HALSTED. *Blood 12*:24, 1957.

3. LEAR, A. A., J. W. HARRIS, W. B. CASTLE, and E. M. FLEMING. *J. Lab. Clin. Med. 44*:715, 1954.

4. RACHMILEWITZ, M., J. ARONOVITCH, and N. GROSSOWICZ. *J. Lab. Clin. Med. 48*:339, 1956; RACHMILEWITZ, M., Y. STEIN, J. ARONOVITCH, and N. GROSSOWICZ. *A. M. A. Arch. Internal Med. 101*:1118, 1958.

5. GOUNELLE, H., and J. RICHARD. *Am. J. Clin. Nutr. 6*:422, 1958.

6. HEINRICH, H. C., and H. LAHANN. *Z. Vit. Hormon. u. Fermentforsch. 6*: 126, 1954.

7. UNGLEY, C. C. *Vitamins and Hormones 13*:139, 1955.

8. SMITH, E. L. *Brit. Med. Bull. 12*:52, 1956.

9. ARNSTEIN, H. R. V., and A. NEUBERGER. *Biochem. J. 55*:259, 1953.

10. DUBNOFF, J. W. *Arch. Biochem. Biophys. 37*:37, 1952.

11. BOXER, G. E., W. H. OTT, and C. E. SHONK. *Arch. Biochem. Biophys. 47*: 474, 1953; FATTERPAKER, P., U. MARFATIA, and A. SREENIVASAN, *Nature 176*:165, 1955.

12. LING, C. T., and B. F. CHOW. *J. Biol. Chem. 202*:445, 1953.

13. DUBNOFF, J. W., and E. BARTRON. *Arch. Biochem. Biophys. 61*:99, 1956.

14. NADKARNI, G. B., D. S. WAGLE, and A. SREENIVASAN. *Nature 180*:659, 1957.

15. WONG, W. T., and B. S. SCHWEIGERT. *J. Nutrition 58*:231, 1956.

16. DAVIDSON, J. N., I. LESLIE, and J. C. WHITE. *Lancet i*:1287, 1951.

17. WHITBY, L. *Brit. Med. J. i*:1401, 1955.

18. WOKES, F., and M. M. E. BARNARD. *Biochem. J. 71*:7P, 1959.

19. WAGLE, S. R., R. MEHTA, and B. C. JOHNSON. *J. Biol. Chem. 230*:137, 1958.

20. BARKER, H. A., R. D. SMYTH, H. WEISSBACH, J. I. TOOHEY, J. N. LADD, and B. E. VOLCANI. *J. Biol. Chem. 235*:480, 1960.

21. CARTWRIGHT, G. E., B. TATTING, D. KURTH, and M. M. WINTROBE. *Blood 7*:992, 1952.

22. HARDINGE, M. G., and F. J. STARE. *Am. J. Clin. Nutr. 2*:73, 83, 1954.

23. WOKES, F., J. BADENOCH, and H. M. SINCLAIR. *Am. J. Clin. Nutr. 3*:375, 1955.

24. HARRISON, R. J., C. C. BOOTH, and D. L. MOLLIN. *Lancet i*:727, 1956.

25. BADENOCH, J. *Proc. Roy. Soc. Med. 47*:426, 1954.

26. WEST, R. *Ann. Intern. Med. 3*:132, 1929.

27. FOSTER, D. B. *Arch. Neurol. Psychiat. 54*:102, 1945; GREENFIELD, J. G., and E. A. CARMICHAEL. *Brain 58*:483, 1935; WALSHE, F. M. R. *Diseases of the Nervous System.* 6th ed., Edinburgh, Livingstone, 1951.

28. ADAMS, R. D., and C. S. KUBIK. *New England J. Med. 231*:2, 1944.

29. HOLMES, J. M. *Brit. Med. J. ii*:1394, 1956.

30. HERMANN, M., H. MOST, and N. JOLLIFFE. *Arch. Neurol. Psychiat. 38*:348, 1937.

31. LURIE, L. A. *Arch. Neurol. Psychiat. 2*:67, 1919; MCALPINE, D. *Lancet ii*: 643, 1929; SMITH, A. D. M. *Brit. Med. J. ii*:1840, 1960.

32. BOWMAN, K. M. *Am. J. Psychiat. 92*:371, 1935.

33. RUNDLES, R. W. *Blood i:*209, 1946.

34. LANGDON, F. W. *J.A.M.A. 45:*1635, 1905; WARBURG, E. J., and S. JORGEN-
SEN. *Acta Med. Scand. 69:*537, 1928; *idem 70:*193, 1929; FRASER, T. N.
*Lancet ii:*458, 1960; WATTS, C. A. H. *Lancet ii:*599, 1960.

35. SCHEINBERG, P. *Blood 6:*213, 1951.

36. BECKER, E., S. LITZNER, and W. TÄGLICH. *Z. klin. Med. 104:*195, 1926.

37. SWENDSEID, M. E., I. F. BURTON, and F. H. BETHELL. *Proc. Soc. Exp. Biol.
Med. 52:*202, 1943.

38. HORNABROOK, R. W., and V. MARKS. *Lancet ii:*893, 1960.

# 21

# INORGANIC METABOLISM

Inorganic ions subserve a wide variety of functions, either alone or acting in association with enzymes, hormones, and vitamins. Sodium, potassium, and chloride are the prime ions responsible for maintaining the isotonicity (salt and water balance) of the tissues and body fluids, that important vestige of life's pelagic origin, and the influence of these ions extends to other spheres of homeostasis. Sodium is the principal extracellular cation; potassium is the chief intracellular one. Sodium passes freely through the cellular membrane, but most of it is kept on the outside by active, energy-requiring, metabolic processes. This situation is upset when an impulse passes along the nerve fiber, for then membrane changes occur which permit the diffusion mechanism to predominate. As a result, sodium enters the fiber substance readily, and potassium is extruded. Repolarization of the membrane reverses these movements and restores the ionic equilibrium of the resting state. Inorganic ions also serve in buffer systems maintaining physiological pH. Here the bicarbonate ($H_2CO_3$–$HCO_3^-$) and phosphate ($H_2PO_4^-$–$HPO_4^=$) systems are very important, but they are supplemented in the body fluids and cells by the proteins. In blood, for example, the plasma proteins, hemoglobin, and oxyhemoglobin are concerned in regulation of pH. Isotonicity and physiological hydrogen ion concentration are both important in the maintenance of normal irritability of nerve and muscle, that is, the ability of these tissues to respond in a physiological fashion to adequate stimuli. The absolute concentration of calcium and magnesium, and their ratio, play a role here, for various types of tetany are associated with a deficiency of calcium in the circulating fluids; magnesium deficiency, too, causes tetany, but then the calcium level in the serum is normal. Calcium functions in blood clotting, and in bone formation it is needed in conjunction with phosphate, magnesium, and fluoride.

Finally, there is a large number of metabolic and respiratory functions of specific inorganic ions, some of which have been discussed in earlier chapters. Certain metals are cofactors for coenzymes, aiding in the union of catalyst with the substrate. In the case of many yellow enzymes a metal (iron, copper, molybdenum, and others), a riboflavin-containing coenzyme, and the apoenzyme act together as the catalytic complex. Cobalt is a cofactor for some enzymes, *e.g.*, glycylglycyl dipeptidase; its most intriguing function is as part of the vitamin $B_{12}$ molecule. The prototype of respiratory-catalytic metals is iron; it is found in hemoglobin, the cytochromes, myoglobin, catalase, and peroxidase, among other proteins. The presence of iodine in the thyroid hormones must be mentioned here, for it is integral to the role of the thyroid in influencing the oxygen consumption of every cell (*cf.* Chapter 24). Examples of the metabolic functions of various elements are given in Table 21-1.

Estimates of the quantities of the various inorganic ions occurring in the body show that these range from the substantial proportions of calcium (2 percent of lean body weight) and phosphorus (over 1 percent) to barely detectable traces of such others as cobalt, molybdenum, and boron. Most of the calcium and phosphorus is present in the bony tissue as complex phosphate salts. The nonskeletal phosphorus, potassium, chloride, sodium, magnesium, and nonskeletal calcium may be said to constitute one group, quantitatively concerned with the maintenance of cellular functions of the most general kind. These are the bulk elements. A second group of essential elements occurs in amounts of the order of one part in $10^5$, or even less. These trace elements are functional components of the body, shown either by their requirement in the diet or by their presence as essential constituents of certain enzymes. The list includes iron, cobalt, copper, manganese, zinc, selenium, and molybdenum, and it is still growing. The concentrations of various trace elements in the body as a whole and in the blood and CSF are shown in Table 21-2.

TABLE 21-1. FUNCTIONS OF INORGANIC TRACE ELEMENTS

| Element | Daily Allowance* (mg.) | Function and Site of Action |
|---|---|---|
| Iron | 10–12 | Functions in $O_2$ transport and exchange; in respiratory pigments (hemoglobin, myoglobin, cytochromes), hematoporphyrin enzymes (catalase, peroxidase), and aconitase; in transferrin and ferritin |
| Copper | 2 | Required for utilization of iron in hemoglobin formation; in oxidizing enzymes (ceruloplasmin, acetylcoenzyme A dehydrogenase); in brain cuproteins |
| Zinc | 0.3/kg. | Required by animals for normal skin, hair growth; necessary for $CO_2$ exchange; occurs in some dehydrogenases (glutamic, alcohol, lactic); component of carbonic anhydrase, pancreatic carboxypeptidase |
| Molybdenum | $\ll 0.3$/kg. | Functions in purine metabolism as component of xanthine oxidase; in liver aldehyde dehydrogenase |
| Iodine | 0.1–0.2 | Functions in oxidative metabolism; constituent of thyroid hormones |
| Cobalt | (as part of vitamin $B_{12}$) | Metallic component of vitamin $B_{12}$; cofactor of glycylglycyldipeptidase |
| Manganese | 0.3/kg. | Required for normal bone development; cofactor of arginase, malic dehydrogenase; replaces magnesium as cofactor for some enzymes |
| Selenium | ? | Protects birds from exudative diathesis resulting from consumption of certain purified diets; toxic in excess |
| Vanadium | — | Metallic component of respiratory pigments of tunicates; accelerates oxidation of phospholipides by mammalian tissue *in vitro;* slows turnover rate of phospholipides and inhibits biosynthesis of cholesterol |

* Daily allowances have been taken from reference (1).

TABLE 21-2. CONCENTRATIONS OF INORGANIC ELEMENTS IN BLOOD AND CSF

| Element | Whole Blood | Serum or Plasma | Packed Erythrocytes | CSF |
|---|---|---|---|---|
| Sodium | | 330 mg.% 140–146 mEq./l. | 49 mg.% 21.2 mEq./l. | 330 mg.% |
| Potassium | | 16 mg.% 3–5 mEq./l. | 375 mg.% 95 mEq./l. | 12 mg.% |
| Calcium | | 10 mg.%(S) 5 mEq./l. | | 5 mg.% |
| Magnesium | 3.8 mg.% | 2.2 mg.%(S) 1.6–1.8 mEq./l. | 6.4 mg.% 5.29 mEq./l. | 3 mg.% |
| Iron | 40–50 mg.% | 120 μg.%* (60–180) | | |
| Transferrin protein | | ca. 0.26 gm.% | | |
| Copper | | 0.1 mg.%†(S) | | |
| Ceruloplasmin protein | | 20–40 mg.%(P) | | |
| Zinc | 0.9 mg.% | 80–170 μg.% | 1.44 mg.% | |
| Cobalt Vitamin B₁₂ | | 0.020–0.055 μg.% | | |
| Manganese | 20–50 μg.% | | | |
| Iodine | | 4–8 μg.% | | 0.6 μg.% |

* Transferrin-bound iron.
† Virtually all as ceruloplasmin copper.

# Bulk Ions

In spite of their relative abundance in the body, sodium, potassium, and chloride have received little attention in biochemical investigation of mental diseases. Probably this is because any major alteration in their concentration in tissues and body fluids is registered in the first instance as kidney or endocrine dysfunction. But Natelson has drawn attention to an alkalotic syndrome characterized by elevated blood pH, raised serum $CO_2$, and damage to the central nervous system, usually the hypothalamus. The condition responds to treatment with a carbonic anhydrase inhibitor, which makes more bicarbonate available for the excretion of base (2).

Several studies have been reported in the literature which detail the concentration of bulk cations in the brains of schizophrenic and nonschizophrenic persons, but no differences have been found, either for white or gray matter. The problem deserves systematic study for cationic balance is of utmost importance in cerebral metabolism and function (3); it is conceivable that an upset in the delicate control over the concentrations of sodium, potassium, and other ions in the brain and in the fluids bathing it would result in neurological or psychiatric dysfunction. For example, sodium (and water) is retained in depressive patients, but is gradually lost from the body water during recovery (4). Whether the retention is due to effects of drugs used in treatment, to electroshock therapy, or to basic factors in the disease process must still be decided. The role of electroshock therapy in altering ionic balance is still a controversial matter (4, 5). The stimulating action of potassium on cerebral metabolism in vitro (3) and the excitatory effects of this cation at synapses and after intracerebral or intraventricular injections attest to its significance in neurophysiology.

The calcium and magnesium contents of the body fluids have been studied more frequently. It is interesting that the magnesium concentration in the CSF is higher than in the serum (6). Its level and that of calcium fluctuate in the CSF quite independently of their respective serum concentrations (7). The Ca:Mg ratio tends to be upset in the CSF of psychotic patients (8) and this raises the question of how such changes may be related to the intracellular balance of these ions in psychotic states. Thus far, the claim that cerebral calcium and magnesium concentrations are abnormal in schizophrenia has not been substantiated, but further study of the metabolism of these two ions in nerve and brain is certainly warranted.

Another area which holds promise of interest in the chemical pathology of the brain is in the binding of cations by acidic lipide constituents (9). Potassium and sodium have been identified in such compounds, but probably other ions are similarly associated.

Crammer has described great and rapid fluctuations in the body weight of patients with periodic catatonia (Chapter 24), the changes often preceding mental changes (10). He considers that the shifts in weight are occasioned by rapid alterations in water and salt metabolism, and suggests that the controlling mechanisms—adrenal cortex, posterior pituitary, and hypothalamus—deserve special attention in this condition and, perhaps, in other psychoses.

## Trace Elements (11)

The concern with the trace elements in the present context is threefold: (a) to what extent are they involved in nervous function? (b) Does their concentration change at all in mental diseases? (c) Do any exhibit toxic actions resulting in neuropsychiatric syndromes? The example of copper deposition in hepatolenticular degeneration shows that in special circumstances, whose genesis is poorly understood, the element is no longer metabolized normally and instead accumulates in the tissues where its toxic action becomes evident after a very long time. Such idiopathic disorder is matched by the chronic exogenous toxicity of nonphysiological metals whose acute toxicity is low or of no concern at all. The syndrome of manganese poisoning is a case in point described below.

Trace elements may enter the body by various routes: oral, percutaneous, respiratory and, occasionally, intravenously, but the major entry for most is undoubtedly the first, i.e., in the diet. Regional differences in soil composition are sometimes reflected in the composition of the food plants. Certain metals such as aluminum and tin are the contribution of modern food technology. In addition, metals or their compounds handled in industry and in mining operations frequently enter the body and settle in the tissues; some cause toxic changes, others are relatively inert. There is naturally great interest in the mechanism whereby essential or toxic metals are absorbed and excreted. Unfortunately, too little is known about these. Presumably the metallic salt passes through the intestinal mucous membrane and thence into the blood. In some cases a specific protein is involved in the absorption of the metal, so that the concentration of this protein may actually exert some control over the amount of metal that can be absorbed from the intestine. This appears to be the case with iron, which is bound in the mucosa by apoferritin and ultimately transferred to a plasma protein, transferrin, for circulation to the tissues. An interesting but unsolved problem in iron dynamics is how information is relayed to the mucosal absorptive mechanism regarding the body's immediate requirement for iron. The amount of iron absorbed is thus governed by the amount required. More of a given dosage of iron salt will be absorbed after hemorrhage has occurred than before. Other factors are also important in the absorption of trace metals: the ionic state of the metal; the amount ingested; and the presence of other substances in the intestinal lumen. For example, phosphates and phytic acid depress the absorption of a number of metallic ions.

## Lithium (12)

Lithium is found in the human body in trace amounts. What its function is, if any, is not known. Larger concentrations can be achieved, however, by oral ingestion of lithium salts. The alkali metal then becomes distributed through the water phase of the body, with some variations in concentration between cells and circulating fluids, but not as marked as in the case of sodium and potassium. Equilibrium is only slowly attained, with the ratio of intracellular to extracellular concentrations of lithium being less than unity for liver, and greater for muscle (13). Penetration of lithium into the brain takes place more slowly than for many of the other large organs, and the concentration of the metal in the CSF is about half that in the serum. Lithium competes to some extent with sodium for retention by the body and its concentration in body fluids will rise the more sharply if sodium intake is concomitantly restricted. Elimination takes place rapidly, mainly by way of the urine.

The therapeutic benefits of lithium salt administration in psychotic excitement were first adequately described by Cade (14) in 1949. He employed lithium salts clinically after noting that they cause lethargy in guinea pigs and protect them from convulsive doses of urea. He found that in the manic phase of manic-depressive psychosis lithium citrate or carbonate reduces the irritability, restlessness, euphoria, and excitement without causing drowsiness. The element has shown no action on the depressive phase of the illness, nor in schizophrenia. The initial dose is 300 to 400 mg. of lithium per day, with reduced dosage for maintenance therapy. Schou has summarized much experience with lithium in the treatment of manic states (15), and others have concurred in his conclusions (16).

The most frequent side effect resulting from lithium intake is a fine tremor of the hands; this need not be an indication for terminating therapy. Toxic actions occurring at higher levels of lithium (about 3 to 4 mEq. per liter) are anorexia, diarrhea, vomiting, drowsiness, asthenia, mild ataxia, vertigo, and myoclonic twitching, among others. The action of lithium on the kidney results in a marked polyuria. The ion is lethal if it rises as high as 4 to 6 mEq. per liter in the body fluids, but with lower levels the symptoms of overdosage are completely reversed within a few days of drug withdrawal.

# Magnesium (17, 18)

Magnesium is an essential dietary requirement and serves in the structure of bone, where most of this element is found, and in the mechanism of action of numerous enzymes concerned with the metabolism of carbohydrates and other substances. Next to potassium it is the most abundant intracellular cation. Plant material is rich in magnesium for the metal is a constituent of chlorophyll, where it has a function analogous to that of iron in the hematoporphyrins. Magnesium absorption is related in some way to the albumin level of the plasma; for example, it is depressed in hypoalbuminemic states. But the other factors controlling its absorption and distribution are poorly understood at the present time.

The essential nature of magnesium for normal development was demonstrated by Kruse, Orent, and McCollum (19), who placed weanling rats on a diet containing only 1.8 parts per million of the metal. Within 3 to 5 days the exposed skin became red through vasodilatation and hyperemia; this state progressed for about another week, when the areas became cyanotic. The rats were very excitable and hyperacustic to the point where sound stimuli could induce a convulsive seizure. Furthermore, these animals did not grow. Since then a syndrome in lactating cattle, known as grass staggers or grass tetany, has been associated with hypomagnesemia; it appears as the result of a deficiency of magnesium in the soil, which determines the low magnesium content of the cattle fodder. The animals are nervous, have an unsteady gait, and show muscular fasciculations. Substantial amounts of magnesium may be lost from the bones, but the soft tissues are less affected. The syndrome is treated by giving the animals a supplement of a magnesium salt.

Magnesium deficiency has also been described in man. The large reservoir of this substance in the bones ordinarily offers a significant measure of protection against this eventuality, but clinical deficiency may nevertheless occur. The most frequent causes are chronic alcoholism, with its attendant malnutrition, and the extensive use of magnesium-free parenteral fluids (17). The hypomagnesemic individual has twitchings, muscular tremor, and choreoathetoid movements; he may become disoriented or delirious (20). A patient has been described who had lost about one quarter of his body content of magnesium; he was excitable and apprehensive, but free of convulsive attacks. However, convulsions have been observed in some cases when the serum magnesium has fallen to about 75 percent of the normal level.

Serum magnesium is low in some but not all epileptics, and it is within normal limits in other diseases of the nervous system (21).

In experimental magnesium deficiency there is usually a hypercalcemia which introduces renal complications (calcification). In the clinical disease, on the other hand, calcium tends to be low when magnesium is low. This does not gainsay the fact that the patient responds specifically to the magnesium therapy.

Magnesium has lately found some place in the treatment of delirium tremens (22, 23). Blood studies show that the serum magnesium tends to be low in this condition, and that the erythrocyte magnesium is significantly reduced. Arguing from the central excitation, Smith and Hammarsten (23) suggest that magnesium is also low in the cerebral cells, and that this is responsible for the altered irritability. The treatment of delirium tremens with magnesium sulfate by intramuscular injection decreases the duration of the tremor and of the visual hallucinations; it also causes, of course, an increase in serum magnesium. Because delirium tremens can develop in subjects with normal magnesium levels, Vallee and his colleagues emphasize that there is a coincidental, but not a causal, relationship between magnesium deficiency and the clinical disorder (20).

## Manganese

Manganese is found as a minor constituent of the body. It functions in some enzyme systems and is presumed to be essential for the human, although this has not been proved. It is excreted in the bile and hair, and it appears irregularly in the urine. Birds require the element for normal embryonic development, for hatchability, and for normal skeletal development. Thus, manganese deficiency in chicks results in perosis, or slipped tendon disease. This condition also occurs in choline deficiency, so that manganese may be associated with the metabolism of labile methyl groups. Indeed, in the rat manganous salts, like choline, exert some lipotropic action. Rats raised on a manganese-deficient diet grow at a subnormal rate, and also show poor bone growth. They may show ataxia. The males become sterile and the females fail to look after their young. Signs of manganese deficiency have been induced in the cockerel, rat, and dog by administering hydralazine to them, and these effects can be counteracted with salts of manganese but not of other trace metals. It has been claimed that the toxic effects of hydralazine in humans can likewise be reversed with divalent manganese (24).

The manganese ion acts as a cofactor for arginase and other enzymes (Table 21-1). It also has some effects upon lipide metabolism. For example, it protects phospholipides from the unduly high oxidation rate initiated by vanadium compounds. In addition, manganous salts accelerate the formation of cholesterol in the rat, as well as in liver preparations *in vitro*.

Manganese poisoning sometimes occurs in industry through contact with metal-containing dust. It causes neurologic and psychiatric changes that can be reversed if caught early and if the source of toxicity is removed. However, accumulated manganese is lost very slowly, its elimination continuing for many years after exposure. The disability rate is high. Rodier (25) has described the progressive stages in impairment resulting from manganese poisoning. At first the subject complains of weakness and loss of appetite; he may appear dull and apathetic. There may be ataxia, aggressiveness, incoherent speech, logorrhea, and impotence. Later on, the speech is slow and monotonous; the facial expression becomes fixed in a dazed appearance (*masque manganique*). The subject is often euphoric. If contact with the source of the metal continues the earlier features become aggravated; changes in gait appear and there is an inability to walk backward. The treatment of magnesium is symptomatic. Many drugs which can bind metals—dimercaprol, edathamil calcium, sodium thiosulfate—have been tried, but without effect.

The neurological features of magnesium have raised the question (26) as to whether Parkinsonism is a form of manganese poisoning; not only is there a resemblance of the syndromes but also some drugs used to therapeutic advantage in Parkinsonism can chelate manganese, and may actually do so in the body. In animals experimentally poisoned with manganese salts by chronic administration, diffuse lesions are found in the brain at post-mortem; degeneration of ganglion cells is particularly marked in the pallidum and corpus striatum, but it is also seen in the cerebral cortex (27). A syndrome not unlike that of manganese poisoning has been described as occurring among the Fore people of New Guinea (28); however, there is no evidence that this disease, kuru, is due to metal poisoning, and thus far it has not responded to any treatment.

# Iron (29)

The adult human body contains 4 to 5 gm. of iron, which is distributed through the tissues in various forms. Most of it is in the blood as hemoglobin, and all but a portion of the remainder is in the viscera and bone marrow in storage forms. A small percentage occurs as myoglobin in muscle and as cytochromes and catalase in all tissues. Myoglobin resembles hemoglobin structurally and functionally in its ability to bind molecular oxygen reversibly and to release it as needed for cellular oxidation processes. Cerebral tissue may contain some iron as a component of a lipide molecule.

The movement of iron from site to site, once it has been absorbed, is achieved through its binding to a serum $\beta_1$-globulin, transferrin (also known as siderophilin). The absorption of iron occurs from the intestinal mucosa after the metal has been reduced to the ferrous (divalent) form. Current views picture the ferrous ion as being bound to an adaptively formed protein, apoferritin, in the intestinal mucosa. The ferritin thus formed contains up to 23 per cent of its weight as iron. Iron now transferred to the plasma is oxidized to the ferric (trivalent) state by dissolved oxygen. Ferric iron then combines with transferrin to form an orange-colored complex. This protein accounts for only a few milligrams of iron *in toto,* but measurements with radioactive iron reveal that its iron content is turned over many times in the course of 24 hours. Normally less than half the iron-binding capacity of transferrin is utilized, but in certain pathological conditions or with the administration of sufficient iron the protein may become saturated. In this case an insoluble iron-protein, hemosiderin, is deposited in the tissues, especially in the viscera and bone marrow; it can be seen as brownish granules under the microscope. The hemosiderin contains a variable amount of iron, and there is evidence that it is an altered form of the soluble ferritin which precipitates out when iron balance becomes markedly positive.

Under conditions of equilibrium the net exchange of iron is only of the order of 1 mg. per day. The erythrocytes have a length of life of 120 days, and those that are broken down contribute daily about 20 mg. of the metal to the body's pool; this iron is then reutilized in the synthesis of other iron-containing molecules.

There is much yet to be learned about the regulatory mechanism of iron absorption. The ferritin system is an important one which, through the adaptive formation of apoferritin, perhaps in response to the stimulus of low iron content of the tissues or plasma, can variably adjust the amount of iron absorbed from the food. This control goes awry in certain conditions, notably in hemolytic anemia, pernicious anemia and, perhaps, in pyridoxine deficiency (30), and then abnormally large amounts of iron pass the intestinal barrier.

Another absorptive defect occurs in idiopathic hemochromatosis (31). The specific biochemical characteristic of this disorder is the continued absorption, presumably over very many years, of iron in excess of the body's requirement, *i.e.*, against a physiological gradient, even though the subject is on a normal diet. The direct result of this is the gradual deposition of hemosiderin as well as smaller amounts of an iron-free pigment, known as hemofuscin, in smooth muscle sites, and in the skin (bronzing). The plasma iron, normally slightly greater than 0.1 mg. percent, becomes greatly elevated and saturates the transferrin; this overloading of the transport mechanism causes excessive transfer of iron to the tissues, the excess apparently being deposited as hemosiderin granules. Some of the iron-containing compounds have been investigated in hemochromatosis for structural abnormalities, but the cytochromes of skeletal and cardiac muscle appear to be normal, as does the structure of the iron complex in ferritin. The metabolic defect is hence considered to reside in the absorptive mechanism.

Hemochromatosis is characterized clinically by brown pigmentation of the skin, cirrhosis of the liver, severe diabetes mellitus, and sexual hypoplasia, but not all these features need be present to establish the diagnosis. The disease has been observed only in adults, primarily men, with a marked incidence around the age of 50. Ultimately, death ensues from hepatic cirrhosis or from the diabetes. Moore and Dubach have suggested (29) that the damage to the liver and pancreas is caused by the iron overload in association with another (undefined) metabolic defect. On the other hand, they also consider it possible that the iron deposition alone, operating over a prolonged period, can interfere with the function of the parenchymal cells.

Another form of hemochromatosis occurs in which the characteristic changes are absent but in which excessive amounts of iron pigment are deposited in the brain, and in which neurological signs predominate. This "hemochromatosis of the central nervous system" has been characterized as "a distinct clinicopathological entity . . . quite different from the usual cases" (32). The chief neurological signs are progressive bilateral deafness and ataxia. Vomiting may be frequent, as is malaise. The skin may be slightly pigmented, and the CSF contains pigment. At post-mortem examination a small amount of visceral pigmentation may be found, but deposition of the iron compound is distinct in the midbrain, pons, and cerebellum. This pattern is quite unrelated to the normal distribution of iron in the brain; that is, hemochromatosis of the brain does not represent an overabundance of pigment in those areas ordinarily richly endowed with it. It is noteworthy that the cerebrum is unaffected and mental changes do not occur as a result of the hemochromatotic disorder.

Finally, hemochromatosis occurs in other than the idiopathic forms. Frequent blood transfusions or intravenous iron therapy will contribute extra iron, which finds its way into pigment. Excessive absorption of exogenous iron also occurs under unusual and incompletely understood dietary conditions as among the African Bantu, whose diet is based upon maize. In some way iron absorption is unduly high and the pigmentation, which results in the disease known as cytosiderosis, causes hepatic cirrhosis, but rarely diabetes (29).

# Copper (33, 33A)

Much of our knowledge of the metabolism of copper has come from studies on experimental and economic animals. Although copper deficiency has not been unequivocally demonstrated in the human it has nevertheless been concluded that this metal is a nutritional requirement for man (33). Several milligrams are supplied in most diets, more than enough to satisfy this requirement, estimated at about 2 mg. per day. There is less doubt about this matter in the case of infants, for milk is deficient in both copper and iron, and the liver stores of copper are soon used up if none is supplied in the diet. Indeed, the first indication that copper is necessary for normal development came from studies on the anemia caused by feeding mammals on milk as the sole article of the diet. In many of the species tested copper deficiency causes a microcytic, hypochromic anemia. Copper is necessary for the incorporation of iron into hemoglobin and the cytochromes; hence, in animals with milk anemia copper alone causes an increase in the volume of the erythrocyte and provokes a reticulocytosis; the hemoglobin levels are unaffected as long as iron continues to be withheld. Copper deficiency has been noted in farm animals under range conditions where the soil is deficient in this mineral. In the sheep and goat the primary symptom is anemia; in others it is a neurological disturbance, as in swayback or the falling disease of cattle and posterior paralysis in pigs. Lambs born of copper-deficient mothers fail to lay down myelin normally.

**COPPER CONTENT OF THE TISSUES**

The adult body contains about 100 to 150 mg. of copper (34). There are still many uncertainties about the disposition of this material, but it can be expected that some previously insoluble problems will yield to experiments with radioactive copper ($Cu^{64}$) salts. The discovery of the metabolic defects in hepatolenticular degeneration, including one in copper metabolism, has also directed attention to the gaps in our biochemical knowledge of this element.

The absorption and transport of copper represent some of these little understood areas and current conclusions about them are tentative. Probably at least 25 percent of ingested copper is absorbed from the intestinal tract. Ordinary balance studies (with analyses of dietary, urinary, and fecal copper) are insufficient in this work because of two factors: (a) the probable excretion of some copper through the intestinal wall and (b) the operation of an enterohepatic cycle in which substantial amounts of absorbed copper are carried to the liver through the portal circulation and are then secreted into the bile. The bile, therefore, serves as an additional excretory route. Oral administration of copper salts is not followed by a rise in the blood level, but within a few days an increase in biliary and fecal copper can be detected. Ravensteyn (35) and Gubler (33) have reviewed this subject.

Copper absorption can be assessed, apart from balance studies, by following the plasma concentration of $Cu^{64}$ after ingestion of the radioactive salt. Normally, a peak of absorption is reached in 1 to 2 hours; at this time only a minor portion of the labeled copper is bound to the plasma globulins. Later the globulin-bound fraction registers a continuous increase (up to at least 60 hours) whereas the fraction not so bound declines to a low level, and thereafter continues at this plateau (36).

In the determination of plasma copper only a small fraction of the total (about 5 percent) reacts directly with the reagent used, sodium diethyldithiocarbamate; this copper is loosely bound to the plasma albumin. The remaining portion can be estimated after treatment of the plasma with acid to release the indirect-reacting copper. The blue cuproprotein ceruloplasmin represents most of the fraction; it appears to be identical with the major copper-containing protein separated electrophoretically from normal serum, an $\alpha_2$-globulin (37).

Ceruloplasmin is probably not a transport form of copper (37), a function which has been attributed to the more labile albumin-bound copper (36).

The concentration of serum copper is altered sensitively in stressful conditions. It is well above normal levels in pregnancy, especially in the second and third trimesters (38); it is also elevated in infections, several blood dyscrasias, hemochromatosis, and cirrhosis (33). Heilmeyer claims that the organism responds to every bacterial infection or toxic influence with an increase in the copper and a reduction of the iron levels of the plasma, among other changes. According to him the reticuloendo-thelial system participates in this process. In the same way, the plasma copper is said to be elevated in schizophrenia and other psychoses, and in epilepsy [reviewed by Elste (39)]. There has been disagreement about the level of serum copper in schizophrenia, but the weight of evidence now indicates that the values lie in the normal range. Serum copper is notably reduced in Wilson's disease and in sprue. The concentration of copper in normal body fluids is shown in Table 21-3.

Copper occurs in many parts of the brain, and it is higher in the gray than in the white matter. It is present in greatest concentration in the locus ceruleus; but it is also high in the substantia nigra and the dentate nucleus (39A).

Small amounts of copper are excreted in the urine, but individual variation here is very wide. The amounts are markedly increased in hepatolenticular degeneration and in the nephrotic syndrome. Oral ingestion of inorganic copper salts is not reflected in the urinary excretion, but after the intravenous administration of sodium copper allylthiourea benzoate excessive amounts of copper appear in the urine (37, 45). Copper diuresis can be provoked by dimercaprol (42, 46), increased protein intake, cortisone (37), and penicillamine (47). Compounds that proved ineffective in this regard include edathamil, mercurial diuretics, Benemid, and thioctic acid.

About 1 to 4 mg. of copper are excreted daily in the feces and, as mentioned above, it is not certain what proportion of this represents nondigestible copper. The copper content of the bile (Table 21-3) is high and undoubtedly contributes most of the copper detected in the feces.

TABLE 21-3. COPPER CONTENT OF HUMAN BODY FLUIDS

| Body Fluid | Condition | Concentration of Copper (μg. %) | Reference |
|---|---|---|---|
| Serum: total copper | Normal | 108 | 40 |
| | Hepatolenticular degeneration (HLD) | 40–60 | 37 |
| Plasma: ceruloplasmin copper | Normal | 107 | 41 |
| | HLD | 32 | 41 |
| Urine | Normal (range) | 0–100* | 41 |
| | Normal (average) | 10.5* | 40 |
| | HLD | 207–713* | 42 |
| Cerebrospinal fluid | Normal (approx. mean) | 30 | 43 |
| | Psychoneuroses | 27 | 44 |
| Gastric juice | Normal | 10–40 | 35 |
| Bile | Normal | 5–31 | 42 |
| | HLD | 8–20 | 42 |

* Figures for urine are μg./24 hours.

**CUPROPROTEINS**

Several copper-containing proteins have been isolated from mammalian tissues, and others undoubtedly occur there. A few have had enzymatic activity ascribed to them. Dopa oxidase, which occurs in the melanocytes of the skin, functions in melanin formation. Urate oxidase (uricase) occurs in many species below the primate level. A polyphenolase oxidizing catechol and hydroquinone has been found in hog kidney. Ceruloplasmin exhibits the properties of an oxidase. Other copper proteins have been described but their functions are unknown.

Among them are erythrocuprein (isolated from red blood cells), hepatocuprein (a very pale compound from ox liver), and cerebrocuprein I [from brain (48)]. Several plant enzymes contain copper as their prosthetic group; ascorbic acid oxidase is one of these.

Ceruloplasmin is an $\alpha_2$-globulin of the plasma, having a molecular weight of 151,000. It possesses a blue color owing to the linkage of copper (0.34 percent of the molecule by weight) with the protein. It can be reduced by ascorbic acid to an autoxidizable *leuco* form. About four of the eight atoms of copper in this molecule can exchange with ionic copper (49, 50). It exists in several molecular forms, each differing somewhat in composition (51). Since 1951 it has been known to possess enzymatic properties and it is probably the principal agent responsible for the oxidase activities of plasma as studied during the past half-century (*cf.* 52). Thus, it acts as an oxidase toward ascorbic acid, epinephrine, benzidine, guaiacol, *p*-phenylenediamine, and N,N'-dimethyl-*p*-phenylenediamine. By taking advantage of this enzymatic property it is possible to obtain simple and rapid estimates of serum ceruloplasmin. It is not known whether the oxidation of ascorbic acid and of epinephrine by ceruloplasmin actually occurs *in vivo*. Human ceruloplasmin has been purified in two laboratories (53).

The concentration of ceruloplasmin in plasma has been carefully studied by Scheinberg and his colleagues. The normal level is 20 to 40 mg. percent in the serum. In patients with hepatolenticular degeneration the ceruloplasmin level is reduced below 20 mg. (41), a fact which is readily (but roughly) demonstrable by the enzymatic technique. The conflicting reports on the level of copper in the serum of schizophrenic patients have not clarified the role, if any, of ceruloplasmin in this disease. Heilmeyer (54) claimed some twenty years ago that the concentration of blood copper is abnormally high in schizophrenia and, though Munch-Petersen contested this point (55), there were a number of confirmations of Heilmeyer's report (56). The most notable was Akerfeldt's finding (57) that ceruloplasmin, as estimated by the rate of oxidation of N,N'-dimethyl-*p*-phenylenediamine, is elevated in the serum drawn from schizophrenics. Scheinberg et al. then made spectrophotometric measurements of the serum ceruloplasmin in a small series of schizophrenic and normal persons (58) and found an average of 23.7 mg. percent in the plasma of control subjects, but 27.8 percent in that of schizophrenic patients. Values in the two groups overlapped to such an extent that the authors concluded that ceruloplasmin determination is quite unsatisfactory as a diagnostic test.

Through carefully controlled investigations (59, 60) the differences observed by applying Akerfeldt's test have for the most part been ascribable to incidental factors, such as low serum ascorbic acid levels. For example, Horwitt et al. (59) also found frequent positives in schizophrenics, but they attributed this in many cases to the low ascorbic acid content of institutional diets, which in turn determines low concentrations of the vitamin in the serum. McDonald (60) has also demonstrated the relationship between ascorbic acid status and the results of the Akerfeldt test. Horwitt and his colleagues have also considered the possibility of raised ceruloplasmin levels in mental patients as a result of nonspecific stress, which is known to elevate other plasma globulins. They have concluded from their work that "serum copper levels or tests of oxidation of phenylenediamine or its derivatives are not, in their present form, definitive for evaluating mental illness." Holmberg, one of the discoverers of ceruloplasmin and of its oxidase properties, states that he is "still far from convinced that quantitative alterations in ceruloplasmin have anything to do with the development of schizophrenia (61).

### HEPATOLENTICULAR DEGENERATION (37, 45)

The neurological disorder described by Wilson in 1912, previously described as pseudosclerosis, and renamed hepatolenticular degeneration in 1921, is a familial disorder inherited in an autosomal recessive fashion. Clinically, it is characterized by progressive rigidity, intention tremor, hepatic cirrhosis of the coarse type, and recurrent hepatitis. It has sometimes been mistaken for multiple sclerosis, Parkinsonism, or hysterical reaction, because of the neurological features. The Kayser-Fleischer ring in the cornea, formed by the deposition of copper in granular form there, is a pathognomonic sign. The unusual pattern of copper metabolism in hepatolenticular degeneration comprises an elevated output of copper, the metal, in the urine, low concentrations of copper and ceruloplasmin in the serum, and a great excess of copper in the brain, especially in the basal ganglia, as well as in the liver and kidneys. Some of the cerebral copper is, moreover, present in abnormal forms (62). In addition there is a prominent aminoaciduria.

The specific biochemical lesion in the disease is not known, but several views about it have been presented in the literature. According to Uzman and his colleagues (63) copper metabolism in Wilson's disease is bound up with that of amino acids. The constant aminoaciduria and hypercupruria are associated through the ability of the amino acids to form complexes with copper. In addition to the amino acids large amounts of peptides containing aspartic and glutamic acids are excreted. This has raised the question of whether there is also a tissue deficiency of dicarboxylic acid carboxypeptidase (64). In spite of its striking character the aminoaciduria appears to be a strictly renal defect, for the plasma amino acid level is normal.

Another hypothesis about the biochemical etiology of hepatolenticular degeneration asserts that the renal disturbance is the primary lesion. Cooper et al. (65) have pointed to the large daily variations in the degree of aminoaciduria, fluctuations which do not follow changes in the amount of protein ingested and which are not related to the level of amino acids in the plasma. Four of their series of six patients exhibited other metabolic defects, three having glycosuria and one a deranged calcium:phosphorus metabolism, with osteomalacia.

Matthews (45, 66) attributes the excessive copper content of the body to overabsorption of the metal from the intestinal tract, because his experiments indicated that the copper-removing mechanism is not at fault. For example, when the serum copper level is artificially raised by intravenous administration of sodium copper allylthiourea benzoate, the die-away curve of serum copper is identical for normal persons and for patients with hepatolenticular degeneration.

A widely held view considers the primary defect to lie in the limited ability of the body to synthesize ceruloplasmin. Scheinberg has postulated (50, 67) that ceruloplasmin plays a role in the regulation of copper absorption from the intestine, and he and his associates have shown that in persons with subnormal concentration of plasma ceruloplasmin there is a constant accretion of copper. However, this cannot be the sole cause of defective metabolism because some patients with hepatolenticular degeneration have a normal concentration of ceruloplasmin (68). Whatever the absorptive mechanism at work, the copper content of the liver is excessively high in hepatolenticular degeneration and the excretion of copper by the kidneys is increased many times over (42). Although the urinary copper represents a significant proportion of the dietary intake, it is a minor quantity in the over-all copper economy of the body in the disease, for the afflicted person is still in positive copper balance.

Besides the low level of serum copper (and ceruloplasmin) there is an increase in the nonglobulin-bound copper, the fraction considered to be the main source of urinary copper. The nonglobulin fraction consists of a more labile form of copper than the globulin-bound element;

this property facilitates excretion of the copper in the urine and deposition of some of it in the tissues (36, 69).

Until a few years ago there was no treatment available for hepato-lenticular degeneration, and patients deteriorated progressively. The introduction of dimercaprol as a chelating agent to promote the excre-tion of copper led to some success, but this has not been consistent. The copper diuresis following injection of this agent persists for about 3 to 4 days, and the Kayser-Fleischer rings become visibly lighter in color, but the aminoaciduria remains constant. The most effective drug of the several agents causing cupruria has been D-penicillamine (β,β-dimethylcysteine) (47, 70). Patients who receive this compound regularly have shown progressive clinical and laboratory improvement, without toxic reactions.

The severity of the aminoaciduria can be increased by raising the protein content of the diet. This may have a beneficial effect, for then extra copper is excreted (37). The relationship between amino acid and copper excretion deserves further exploration, at least in determining which amino acids are the most efficient in provoking the excretion of copper and the form in which this element is excreted (37). Needless to say, selection of the diet from foods analyzing low in copper, and the use of distilled water and pyrex dishes in food preparation are of utmost importance.

Bickel et al. (71) have examined the possibility that parenteral administration of human ceruloplasmin will affect hepatolenticular de-generation favorably. Up to 1 gm. of the protein per day, sufficient to restore the ceruloplasmin level of plasma to normal, did not influence the disease, and the urinary copper and amino acids were not altered. Sternlieb et al. (72) have found that the administration of ceruloplasmin does not affect the absorption of copper from the gastrointestinal tract into the blood nor its subsequent excretion, and they do not, therefore, consider ceruloplasmin as a potentially useful therapeutic agent in Wilson's disease.

The administration of ceruloplasmin to normal volunteers does not appear to induce any unusual mental symptoms.

# Zinc (73)

Zinc is associated in the body with several proteins, notably carbonic anhydrase and certain dehydrogenases (lactic, L-glutamic, alcohol), and with Waldenstrom's uroporphyrin, which is excreted in acute porphyria (Chapter 14). Its serum level and urinary output fluctuate away from normal in certain diseases, but the significance of these abnormalities is not known, nor has the metal found a place yet in human therapeutics.

Ionic zinc is absorbed from the food in amounts of 10 to 15 mg. per day. It passes largely to the liver whence it is distributed to the other tissues. In a state of balance most of the zinc which is absorbed is later excreted in the feces, less than 1 mg. appearing in the urine. Much of the fecal zinc is probably derived from the secretion of the zinc-containing pancreatic enzyme, carboxypeptidase, in the course of digestion. Excessive amounts of calcium in the diet interfere with the absorption of zinc, but other details of the physiological mechanisms entailed in zinc uptake are lacking.

Zinc is an essential growth factor required in the diet of the rat. Deficient animals have an altered fur, and show some nonspecific changes in metabolism, including a shift of zinc from the bones to the soft tissues. Parakeratosis in pigs has been induced experimentally by placing the animals on a zinc-deficient diet, and it has been specifically cured by zinc therapy.

Zinc occurs as 0.33 percent of the weight of carbonic anhydrase, and it is required for the action of this enzyme. Carbonic anhydrase catalyzes the hydration of carbon dioxide, which is released from the tissues into the blood; the gas diffuses in solution into the plasma and thence to the erythrocyte which contains the enzyme. In the lungs, the reverse reaction occurs, releasing carbon dioxide, and this now diffuses into the pulmonary alveoli (Reaction 21-1). In Reaction 21-1 the

$$CO_2 + H_2O \overset{a}{\rightleftarrows} H_2CO_3 \overset{b}{\rightleftarrows} H^+ + HCO_3^- \qquad (21\text{-}1)$$

formation of $H_2CO_3$ is catalyzed by carbonic anhydrase. This enzyme is inhibited by sulfanilamide and by Diamox, with the result that the exchange of carbon dioxide takes place less rapidly than normal. With extra bicarbonate available in the body, more base is excreted in the urine. The fact that these two drugs also have anticonvulsant action has led Millichap to suggest (74) that carbonic anhydrase plays an essential role in the induction and propagation of seizures.

The administration of zinc by mouth or by injection exerts no influence upon the enzyme in the brain, but the enzyme activity can be increased in both cerebral cortex and cerebellum of the rat by subjecting the animals to reduced atmospheric pressures for prolonged periods (75). The simulated high altitudes cause, of course, an increase in the erythrocyte count. Electric shock given in the head region to guinea pigs causes a decrease in carbonic anhydrase activity in those portions of the brain lying between the electrodes (75). There are no characteristic and consistent changes in the distribution of the enzyme in the brains of schizophrenic patients away from the normal pattern (76), although the enzyme concentration in the frontal cortex of the brain of a majority of schizophrenics examined was considered to be on the low side of normal. The same tendency was observed in cases of neurosyphilis (76, 77).

Alcohol dehydrogenase functions not only in the metabolism of ethanol, but also appears to catalyze the reversible conversion of vitamin $A_1$ to retinene, the vitamin $A_1$-aldehyde (Reaction 21-2). The role

$$\text{Vitamin } A_1 + DPN^+ \rightleftarrows \text{Retinene} + DPNH + H^+ \qquad (21\text{-}2)$$

of this zinc-containing enzyme is correlated with the high levels of zinc in the retina. Vallee and his coworkers have studied the metabolism of zinc in cirrhosis of the liver in alcoholics, i.e., in conditions where the enzyme is presumably in contact with its substrate for prolonged periods (78). The concentration of zinc in the serum of such patients was well below normal, and the decrease was more or less in proportion to the severity of the liver changes. The excretion of zinc in the urine was markedly raised but could be brought back to normal levels by providing zinc supplements to raise the daily intake of the metal by 50 to 100 percent. Any greater supplementation than this caused the urinary excretion of zinc to rise once again (78).

## Bromine (79)

Bromide poisoning stems from the unwitting and excessive consumption of salts of bromine in proprietary tonics, from the use of bromides as substitutes for table salt, and from therapeutic overdosage. The therapeutic use of bromides must be accompanied by careful monitoring of the serum level to avoid the toxic effects. The bromide ion is not readily distinguished from chloride by the body and with excessive intake much bromide is retained. Excretion is predominantly in the urine, but the complete elimination is a prolonged process: bromide may be detected in the urine for weeks after its withdrawal from the diet.

Plasma bromide is 2.4 to 3 times as high as the CSF bromide after the acute administration of the salt to test the permeability of the blood-brain barrier. The ratio is much lower (around 1.5) in cases of bromism, for then the concentration in the CSF has risen seriously. Little bromide gets into the brain but that which does so is reputed to be higher in the cerebral cortex than in other parts of the brain.

Bromism is characterized by apathy, somnolence, loss of memory for recent events, tremors of the lips and hands, ataxia, slurred speech. A small percentage of patients with bromism develop a skin rash. The more severe changes observed include disorientation, paranoia, delirium, confabulation, stupor, and coma. Levin has described "bromide hallucinosis" (80). There is no threshold value of bromide in the plasma which, once attained, triggers the occurrence of these symptoms. On the other hand, the blood value at the time bromism is first recognized is quite variable, ranging from as low as 6.2 mEq. per liter to over 25 mEq. per liter. (The normal blood chloride is about 83 mEq. per liter.) In spite of this variable degree of sensitivity the severity of the symptoms for a given individual is a function of the blood level.

Specific therapy entails substituting chloride for bromide. This is done by giving adequate sodium chloride or ammonium chloride, along with fluids. Some advocate insulin to stimulate appetite (81). The resemblance of the dermatological and mental symptoms to those of pellagra led to the use of nicotinic acid at one time, but there is no evidence that this vitamin is deficient as a result of taking excess bromides, or that it has a useful role to play in therapy of this condition.

## Mercury and Lead

Mercury poisoning is now fortunately rare. It results from the handling of mercury, its salts, or solutions of mercurial salts in manufacturing operations and in scientific occupations. Chronic use of or overdosage with organomercurial compounds can also cause toxicity. The early signs are weakness, stomatitis, and erethism. Later there is a tremor and, perhaps, ataxia; these neurological changes are usually associated with cerebellar pathology. Mercury, like many other heavy metals, is capable of reacting with several functional groups of enzymes, most notably the sulfhydryl groups (of cysteine residues), but also with carbonyl and imidazolyl groups; these reactions usually result in the inactivation of the enzyme. It is not known if mercury poisoning is the result of inhibition of a single enzyme or of many, nor which ones are attacked specifically by it in the course of mercurialism. There is some evidence that pink disease, an affliction of infants, is actually a form of mercury poisoning.

Lead poisoning (81A) occurs industrially, but cases also occur in the home; a frequent domestic cause in children results from gnawing on woodwork that has been coated with a lead paint. The toxic effects of lead are manifested by a marked pallor, secondary anemia, spastic constipation, muscular incoordination, and motor paralysis. In chronic cases the lead may cause degenerative changes in the central nervous system resulting in tremor, ataxia, and mental changes (lead encephalopathy). Recently electroencephalographic changes have been noted. The erythrocytes show a basophil stippling. Lead is excreted in the urine and feces.

Byers and Lord followed the school progress of 20 children who had been treated in infancy, apparently successfully, for mild lead poisoning. In their follow-up study they found that all but one of these children exhibited a learning defect. They considered the unsatisfactory scholastic attainment in this group as a possible permanent stigma resulting from the entry of lead into the body at an early age (82).

# References

1. MONTY, K. J., and W. D. McELROY. In Food, the Yearbook of Agriculture, 1959, ed. A. STEFFERUD. Washington D.C., U.S. Department of Agriculture.
2. NATELSON, S. Clinical Chem. 4:32, 1958.
3. QUASTEL, J. H. In Proceedings IVth International Congress for Biochemistry, Vienna, 1958, Vol. 3. London, Pergamon, 1959.
4. GIBBONS, J. L. Clinical Sci. 19:133, 1960; RUSSELL, G. F. M. ibid. 327, 1960.
5. ALTSCHULE, M. D., I. ASCOLI, and K. J. TILLOTSON. Arch. Neurol. Psychiat. 62:618, 1949; EIDUSON, S., N. Q. BRILL, and E. CRUMPTON. J. Ment. Sci. 106:692, 1960.
6. COHEN, H. Quart. J. Med. 20:173, 1927.
7. HUNTER, G., and H. V. SMITH. Nature 186:161, 1960.
8. HARRIS, W. H., and E. H. SONNENBLICK. Yale J. Biol. Med. 27:297, 1955; idem, 29:117, 1956.
9. FOLCH, J., M. LEES, and G. H. SLOANE-STANLEY. In Metabolism of the Nervous System. ed. RICHTER, D. London, Pergamon, 1957.
10. CRAMMER, J. L. Lancet ii:259, 1957.
11. SCHROEDER, H. A. Advances Int. Med. 8:259, 1956; UNDERWOOD, E. J. Trace Elements in Human and Animal Nutrition. New York, Academic Press, 1956.
12. SCHOU, M. Pharmacol. Rev. 9:17, 1957.

13. Schou, M. *Acta pharmacol. 15:*115, 1958.
14. Cade, J. F. J. *Med. J. Australia 36:*349, 1949.
15. Schou, M. *Psychopharmacologia 1:*65, 1959.
16. Gershon, S., and A. Yuwiler. *J. Neuropsychiat. 1:*229, 1960; Kingstone, E. *Comprehensive Psychiat. 1:*317, 1960; Vartanian, M. E. *Zh. Neuropatol. i. Psikhiatr. 59:*586, 1959.
17. Flink, E. B. *J.A.M.A. 160:*1406, 1956.
18. Randall, R. E., E. C. Rossmeisl, and K. H. Bleifer. *Ann. Int. Med. 50:* 257, 1959.
19. Kruse, H. D., E. Orent, and E. V. McCollum. *J. Biol. Chem. 96:*519, 1932.
20. Vallee, B. L., W. E. C. Wacker, and D. D. Ulmer. *New England J. Med. 262:*155, 1960.
21. Haury, V. G. *J. Lab. Clin. Med. 27:*1361, 1942.
22. Krystal, H. *Am. J. Psychiat. 116:*137, 1959.
23. Smith, W. O., and J. F. Hammarsten. *Am. J. Med. Sci. 237:*413, 1959.
24. Comens, P. *Am. J. Med. 20:*944, 1956.
25. Rodier, J. *Brit. J. Indust. Med. 12:*21, 1955.
26. Cotzias, G. C. *Physiol. Rev. 38:*503, 1958.
27. Tolskaya, M. S., *Zh. Nevropatol. i Psikhiatr. 52:*32, 1952; Penalver, R. *Indust. Med. Surg. 24:*1, 1955.
28. Anonymous. *Brit. Med. J. ii:*1480, 1957; idem *ii:*1796, 1960.
29. Moore, C. V., and R. Dubach. *J.A.M.A. 162:*197, 1956.
30. Gubler, C. J. *Science 123:*87, 1956.
31. Sheldon, J. H. *Lancet ii:*1031, 1934; Granick, S. *In Bochemical Disorders in Human Disease,* ed. Thompson, R. H. S., and E. J. King. New York, Academic Press, 1957.
32. Neumann, M. A. *J. Neuropath. Exp. Neurol. 7:*19, 1948.
33. Gubler, C. J. *J.A.M.A. 161:*530, 1956.
33A. Scheinberg, I. H., and I. Sternlieb. *Pharmacol. Rev. 12:*355, 1960.
34. Chou, T. P., and W. H. Adolph. *Biochem. J. 29:*476, 1935.
35. van Ravensteyn, A. H. *Acta Med. Scand. 118:*163, 1944.
36. Jensen, W. N., and H. Kamin. *J. Lab. Clin. Med. 49:*200, 1957.
37. Bearn, A. G., and H. G. Kunkel *J. Clin. Invest. 33:*400, 1954.
38. Nielsen, A. L. *Acta Med. Scand. 118:*87, 1944.
39. Elste, R. *Multiple Sklerose und Schizophrenie als Syndrom bei Spurenelementmangelkrankheiten.* Stuttgart, Hippokrates-Marquardt & Cie., 1951.
39A. Warren, P. J., C. J. Earl, and R. H. S. Thompson. *Brain 83:*709, 1960.
40. Gubler, C. J., H. Brown, H. Markowitz, G. E. Cartwright, and M. M. Wintrobe. *J. Clin. Invest. 36:*1208, 1957.
41. Scheinberg, I. H., and D. Gitlin. *Science 116:*484, 1952.
42. Denny-Brown, D., and H. Porter. *New England J. Med. 245:*917, 1951.
43. Kjellin, K. *J. Neurochem. 6:*95, 1960.
44. d'Andrea, F., and M. Congiu. *Acta neurologica 7:*633, 1952.
45. Matthews, W. B., M. D. Milne, and M. Bell. *Quart. J. Med. n.s. 21:* 425, 1952.
46. Cumings, J. N. *Brain 74:*10, 1951.

47. FISTER, W. P., J. BOULDING, and R. A. BAKER. *Can. Med. Assoc. J. 78*:79, 1958.
48. PORTER, H., and J. FOLCH. *In Progress in Neurobiology,* Vol. 1, *ed.* KOREY, S. R., and J. NURNBERGER. New York, Hoeber, 1956; PORTER, H., and J. FOLCH. *J. Neurochem. 1*:260, 1957.
49. HOLMBERG, C. G., and C. B. LAURELL. *Acta Chem Scand. 2*:550, 1948.
50. SCHEINBERG, I. H., and A. G. MORELL. *J. Clin. Invest. 36*:1193, 1957.
51. MORELL, A. G., and I. H. SCHEINBERG. *Science 131*:932, 1960.
52. HOLMBERG, C. G., and C. B. LAURELL. *Scand. J. Clin. Lab. Invest. 3*:103, 1951.
53. SANDERS, B. E., O. P. MILLER, and N. M. RICHARD. *Arch. Biochem. Biophys. 84*:60, 1959; CURZON, G., and L. VALLET. *Biochem. J. 74*:279, 1960.
54. HEILMEYER, L., W. KREIDERLING, and G. STUEWE. *Kupfer und Eisen als körpereigene Wirkstoffe und ihre Bedeutung beim Krankheitsgeschehen.* Jena, Gustav Fischer, 1941.
55. MUNCH-PETERSEN, S. *Acta psychiat. et neurol. scand. 25*:423, 1950.
56. BRENNER, W., and A. BREIER. *Z. Kinderheilk. 66*:620, 1949; BISCHOFF, A. *Monatschr. f. Psychiat. und Neurol. 124*:211, 1952; OZEK, M. *Arch. Psychiat. Nervenkrankh. 195*:408, 1957.
57. AKERFELDT, S. *Science 125*:117, 1957.
58. SCHEINBERG, I. H., A. G. MORELL, R. S. HARRIS, and A. BERGER. *Science 126*:925, 1957.
59. HORWITT, M. K., B. J. MEYER, A. C. MEYER, C. C. HARVEY, and D. HAFFRON. *A. M. A. Arch. Neurol. Psychiat. 78*:275, 1957.
60. MCDONALD, R. K. *In Chemical Concepts of Psychosis, ed.* RINKEL, M., and H. C. B. DENBER. New York, McDowell, Obolensky, 1958.
61. HOLMBERG, C. G., and R. BLOMSTRAND. *Ann. Rev. Biochem. 28*:321, 1959.
62. PORTER, H., and J. FOLCH. *A. M. A. Arch. Neurol. Psychiat. 77*:8, 1957.
63. IBER, F. L., T. C. CHALMERS, and L. L. UZMAN. *Metab. Clin. and Exptl. 6*:388, 1957.
64. UZMAN, L. L., and B. HOOD. *Am. J. Med. Sci. 223*:392, 1952.
65. COOPER, A. M., R. D. ECKHARDT, W. W. FALOON, and C. S. DAVIDSON. *J. Clin. Invest. 29*:265, 1950.
66. MATTHEWS, W. B. *J. Neurol. Neurosurg. Psychiat. 17*:242, 1954.
67. SCHEINBERG, I. H., D. T. DUBIN, and R. S. HARRIS. *J. Clin. Invest. 34*:961, 1955.
68. SASS-KORTSAK, A., M. CHERNIAK, D. W. GEIGER, and R. J. SLATER. *J. Clin. Invest. 38*:1672, 1959.
69. BEARN, A. G., and H. G. KUNKEL. *J. Lab. Clin. Med. 45*:623, 1955.
70. WALSHE, J. M. *Lancet i*:188, 1960.
71. BICKEL, H., H. E. SCHULTZE, W. GRÜTER, and I. GÖLLNER. *Klin. Wochschr. 15*:961, 1956.
72. STERNLIEB, I., A. G. MORELL, and I. H. SCHEINBERG. *Lancet ii*:1177, 1958.
73. VALLEE, B. L. *J.A.M.A. 162*:1053, 1956.
74. MILLICHAP, J. G. *Proc. Soc. Exp. Biol. Med. 97*:606, 1958.
75. ASHBY, W., M. A. BUSHROD, and E. M. SCHUSTER. *Diseases Nerv. System 18*:226, 1957.

76. ASHBY, W. R. *J. Nerv. Ment. Dis. 105:*107, 1947.

77. ASHBY, W. *J. Nerv. Ment. Dis. 112:*425, 1950.

78. VALLEE, B. L., W. E. C. WACKER, A. F. BARTHOLOMAY, and F. L. HOCH. *Ann. Int. Med. 50:*1077, 1959.

79. MOORE, M., T. SOHLER, and L. ALEXANDER. *Confinia Neurol. 3:*1, 1940; SENSENBACH, W. *J.A.M.A. 125:*769, 1944.

80. LEVIN, M. *A. M. A. Arch. Gen. Psychiat. 2:*429, 1960.

81. TILLIM, S. J. *Am. J. Psychiat. 109:*196, 1952.

81A. KEHOE, R. A. *Arch. Environmental Health 2:*418, 1961.

82. BYERS, R. K., and E. E. LORD. *Am. J. Dis. Child. 66:*471, 1943.

# 22

# LIVER FUNCTION

From earliest times medicine has associated visceral functions with mood and temperament. The Hippocratic concept of the relation between the humors of the body and disease attempted to derive the psychic qualities of man from the variable quantities of these humors. The black bile of the ancients, memorialized in our word *melancholy*, was supposed to be secreted by the spleen. In more recent times, many investigators have sought a role for somatic factors in mental disease through brain-liver relationships. At the end of the last century Leyden pictured the accumulation of *toxic* biliary constituents in the blood as the manner in which the liver brought about mental disorder. This hypothesis of a hepatogenous intoxication of the central nervous system stimulated the search for a cerebrotoxic agent in bile. Leyden's cholemic concept met opposition, for other possibilities were recognized. Some considered that an endogenous toxin could have an effective action because of too sluggish elimination, because of failure of its detoxication to keep pace with the rate of production or, as we know from studies on genetic disorders of metabolism (Chapter 10), because there is a defective step in its intermediary metabolism to nontoxic products. The opposition to Leyden's theory of overproduction of toxin was led by several German clinicians, including Quincke and G. Hoppe-Seyler. They held that the *detoxifying activity* of the liver is disturbed in mental disease, with the consequence that metabolites stemming from protein and carbohydrate precursors are not detoxified quickly enough and their accumulation disturbs brain function.

These older views are of interest for two reasons. In the first place they express a direct relationship between diseases of the brain and diseases of the liver, a relationship that has been substantiated for at least a few specific clinical entities. Secondly, they represent the foundation for more complex theories with which we are concerned nowadays. This sophistication has necessarily appeared as clinical experience and the fund of scientific information have increased. For example, both concepts, overproduction of toxin and its inefficient detoxication, may be applicable in a given condition. In kernicterus there is a surfeit of bilirubin, the offending agent, as well as a deficiency of the enzyme system which glucuronidates (and detoxifies) it.

In addition to the theories of the hepatocerebral relationship which assume the primacy of liver disease there are others which propose etiology in the reverse direction as well as in parallel. F. Boenheim (1920) considered that vegetative nerve centers become diseased first, and that this disturbance of their functions later leads to disorder of the liver. A decade earlier Schultze and Knauer studied glycosuria as a function of affect. Some concepts of psychosomatic disease may fall into this category. The view that liver and brain diseases are simultaneous but independent processes is usually attributed to Bielschowsky and Henneberg, who presented the somewhat vague concept that the disorders reflect a congenital deficiency in the organs concerned. Perhaps this may claim paternity for the concept of genetically determined diseases. Buscaino's theory of the etiology of psychoses is similar, for he has proposed since the early 1920's that the etiological agent is produced endogenously, but outside the brain and liver, and that this substance affects the two organs in a deleterious fashion. As part of the theory it is assumed that the detoxifying action of the liver suffers a lapse for some reason or other, thus permitting the toxin to wreak its action on both organs alike.

Although much attention has been paid to the hepatocerebral relationship in the nineteenth century and although numerous cases of simultaneous mental and hepatic disease had gradually accumulated in the literature (see Table 22-1), it was not until well after the beginning of the present century that a pathogenetic relationship rather than a fortuitous one was established. This accomplishment belongs primarily to S. A. Kinnier Wilson, because of his classic description of associated lenticular degeneration and hepatic cirrhosis. Wilson

TABLE 22-1. HEPATOCEREBRAL RELATIONSHIPS: A CHRONOLOGY*

| | |
|---|---|
| 1875 | First description of "brain jaundice." Crystals of bilirubin detected in sections of brain (1). |
| 1892 | Klippel investigates liver function in the psychoses. Coins the term "folie hépatique" for a group of cases in which a hepatic lesion is considered primary to the psychoses. |
| 1896 | L. Levi describes a case of "coma hépatique." |
| 1899 | H. Quincke and G. Hoppe-Seyler stress disturbances in the protective functions of the liver, in contrast to the views that the liver produces toxic factors endogenously (2). |
| 1903 | G. Schmorl introduces the term "Kernicterus" for the staining of specific nuclei in brain jaundice (3). |
| 1904 | R. Beneke describes the pathology of kernicterus. |
| 1908 | P. Esch gives a clinical description of jaundice of the newborn resulting in death, with kernicterus established at post-mortem (4). |
| 1912 | Wilson's description of progressive lenticular degeneration associated with cirrhosis of the liver (5). |
| 1923 | V. M. Buscaino presents the theory that toxic amines from the chronically diseased intestine enter the circulation and, if hepatic insufficiency exists, may cause schizophrenia (6). |
| 1924 | Georgi suggests that the alterations he has observed in the plasma proteins of schizophrenics are due to disturbed liver function (7). |
| 1945 | The Schryvers describe disturbances of liver function in schizophrenics, using a variety of tests (8). |
| 1932 | R. Gjessing reports on longitudinal studies in periodic relapsing catatonia (Chapter 24). |
| 1933 | Crandall and Weil find a neurotoxic agent in the serum of dogs with experimental liver damage (9). |
| 1934 | Baruk and Camus observe catalepsy in pigeons following injection of human bile (10). |
| 1938 | Quastel and Wales report a difference in the hippuric acid excretion test between catatonic and other types of schizophrenic patients (p. 32ff.). |
| 1945 | H. H. De Jong's monograph on experimental catatonia (11). |

* For a chronology of reports on "toxic factors" in mental disease, see Reference 12.

actually gave considerable credit for the concepts he outlined to the German pathologists who had studied the brain changes occurring in neonatal jaundice. The yellow staining of the basal ganglia and the presence of bilirubin in brain had been described as early as 1875 by Orth, but it was Schmorl who in 1903 introduced the descriptive name kernicterus for the staining of the lenticular nucleus, the corpus

Luysii, Ammon's horn, the dentate nucleus, and the olivary nucleus in "brain jaundice." In this case the pathological description preceded the clinical, for not until 1908 was the picture of the events that lead up to kernicterus described (by Esch): gradually increasing jaundice over the whole body, the feces retaining normal color, tonic limb contractions beginning within the first few days of life, Cheyne-Stokes respiration, weakening heart beat, disappearance of the radial pulse, and early death. A few years later when Wilson published his extensive article (5) entitled "Progressive lenticular degeneration: a familial nervous disease associated with cirrhosis of the liver," he described some novel pathological findings. In the first place, the cirrhosis of the liver was quite unexpected because the symptoms were exclusively nervous. Secondly, the central nervous system was found *post-mortem* to be affected only in specific areas. Wilson had no explanation for the selective action of the toxin on the lenticular nucleus, apart from other areas of the brain.

Since that time other results of clinical and experimental investigations have been adduced bespeaking an influence of hepatic function over that of the brain, under certain conditions. Among these conditions are severe liver disease leading up to coma or to the encephalopathy described by several authors. There is also the example of patients with kernicterus who manage to survive infancy: in such persons the neonatal liver abnormality generally leaves stigmata of neurological and mental symptoms stemming from the localized pathological changes in the brain. Some of the genetically determined diseases with associated or predominant symptoms of mental deficiency, such as phenylketonuria, originate in hepatic dysfunction in the sense that a specific liver enzyme necessary at one stage of normal conversion of an important metabolite is lacking from the parenchymal cells. Hepatolenticular degeneration may itself fit into this category.

These examples all involve a liver abnormality. As already pointed out, some investigators maintain that an analogous situation exists in the major psychoses, with respect to a defective liver function. Although this claim has not been backed up by consistent demonstrations, the theory of the hepatic origin of mental diseases is a general one, and it has inspired many laboratory investigations in psychiatry. Such studies have taken two directions: (a) the study of liver function in the mentally ill; and (b) the search for a toxic substance in the blood, CSF, urine, or bile of psychotic patients. It is possible at the present time to point to a very large literature on hepatic physiology in psychotic states; in this literature there can be found, for example, reports on toxic factors in the body fluids of mental patients, although not one of these factors has been satisfactorily characterized. The work on liver function has also, unfortunately, not really yielded the clear-cut and definitive results that have been claimed on occasion.

The metabolic classification of hepatic disorders comprises two major classes. One includes the diseases of underexcretion, whether this be due to (a) failure of the body to excrete a specific metabolite in the normal way, or (b) failure to metabolize it to some harmless product which can be easily disposed of. The metabolite concerned may well be one which occurs physiologically and which is of no concern unless it accumulates and then is able to display its neurotoxicity. This situation pertains to kernicterus, phenylketonuria, galactosemia, and other conditions. Other hepatic disorders may arise from overproduction of some substances—perhaps normal constitutents—which then exert a toxic action on the nervous system. These two categories obviously overlap. A further type of dysfunction is the underproduction of some essential substance. As already pointed out (p. 262) the question has been raised as to whether an insufficiency of ceruloplasmin may be the cause of the increased absorption of copper in hepatolenticular degeneration. A demonstrated case in point is Hartnup disease, in which the defective absorption of tryptophan from the intestinal lumen ensures that the bacterial formation of indole will assume a major share of the body's daily supply of this amino acid. Other paths of tryptophan metabolism, in particular the route to nicotinic acid, suffer a reduced traffic because of the limited availability of the primary precursor. The decrease in endogenously formed nicotinic acid results in the appearance of symptoms of pellagra. A similar situation, though not as severe, occurs in cases of malignant carcinoid, through the diversion of excessive amounts of tryptophan into the serotonin channel.

# Some Neurotoxic Agents of Hepatic Origin, and Related Substances

The injection of bile into animals has been known for long to cause a high mortality. In sublethal doses it causes severe and protracted convulsions in rats (13) or, in the hands of other experimenters, pathological sleep or stupor (14). Bilirubin has a toxic action on the brain (Chapter 14). These facts lend support to the inviting theory that some normal constitutents of liver can, under certain circumstances, cause nervous and mental changes in man.

In 1933 Crandall and Weil performed a classical experiment delineating the liver-brain relationship (9). After inducing hepatic damage in dogs by ligating the common bile duct the serums of the animals were tested for histopathological reaction upon the separated spinal cord of rats. Serum taken on the fourth day postoperatively or later was found to exert a toxic action on nervous tissue. Histological examination revealed neuropathological changes similar to those found in human brain when there has been an associated liver disease. Thus, this work by Crandall and Weil demonstrated the potentiality of liver to release neurotoxic agents. A year later Baruk and Camus discovered the cataleptizing action of human bile (14). The injection of this bile into the muscle of pigeons caused the birds to cease spontaneous movements and to exhibit a plasticity of body position without loss of the usual reflexes. This reaction was not obtained with all biles, but did occur with fluid obtained from catatonic schizophrenics and from selected patients with chronic rheumatism, asthma, jaundice, or severe migraine (10, 15). Baruk's cataleptizing principle has not yet been identified chemically, but he describes it as being thermolabile, soluble in benzene, precipitable by heavy metals, and neutralized in its action by cholesterol. It is present in the urine greatly diluted. It is not identical with the bile salts, bile pigments, polypeptides or amino acids. Baruk was originally led to carry out these experiments because of his interest in post-icteric forms of schizophrenia and because of evidence of hepatic insufficiency in a considerable proportion of catatonic subjects (15). More recently he has produced all the principal features of the catatonic state by the injection of bile into pigeons: a more or less prolonged suspension of voluntary movement, conservation of posture, active resistance to movement, and automatic movements. Considerable interest is, of course, attached to further research designed to characterize his cataleptizing principle so that its pharmacological properties can be intensively investigated. These experiments, performed originally in 1934, are said to be the first to reproduce in animals a condition resembling the objective features of a human mental disease thus "removing problems in the study of volition from the speculative and metaphysical plane to that of experimental psychophysiology and pharmacology" (15).

The two examples cited above are drawn from the large area of experimental and clinical observation encompassed by experimental psychiatry. A multitude of articles concerned with tests of body fluids of psychotic patients can be found in the psychiatric and other journals: many purport that it is possible to distinguish such fluids from normal ones by employing suitable chemical or biological methods (12). Among the end points that have been used are: behavioral changes in man, monkey, rat, pigeon, Siamese fighting fish, and the spider; toxicity, up to and including mortality, in the mouse, *Xenopus levis,* and *Rana catesbiana;* phytotoxicity to oat (*Lupinus albus*) and other seedlings; toxicity to cells *in situ* as well as in tissue culture; metabolic changes in yeast cells, or rat organs (diaphragm, retina). Hypotheses ascribing psychopathological symptoms to the action of a toxic chemical factor in the blood or CSF have had a long history, but currently they are influenced by the newer studies on the phantastica, beginning with the discovery of the hallucinogenic action of LSD in 1943. Many of these hypotheses attribute the presence of the postulated toxin in this or that individual to genetic determinants.

Among the attempts to purify the toxic agent is the work of the group at Tulane University on taraxein. This is said to be a protein obtained by the fractionation of plasma drawn from schizophrenic patients. It is said to be in the globulin fraction and to be distinct from ceruloplasmin (16). Heath and his colleagues, who have reported this work, state that the action of taraxein is displayed in monkeys not only through electroencephalographic changes, which are used as a means of biological assay, but also as mild behavioral changes, including a reduced level of awareness resembling incipient catatonic symptoms. In man, the changes induced by rapid intravenous injection of 2 to 3 ml. of a solution of taraxein (derived from about 900 ml. of blood) causes "marked blocking with disorganization and fragmentation of thought, . . . impairment of concentration," and other changes. Simple transfusion of blood of schizophrenic patients does not cause the same changes because, it is claimed, the plasma albumin neutralizes the effect of the abnormal protein. Normal serum, when processed as for the preparation of taraxein, yields much less of the active material. Since the appearance of the original report the animal investigation with taraxein has been repeated successfully in a second laboratory (17), but the studies on man have led to contradictory claims (18).

On the basis of the toxic factor hypothesis, some investigators have attempted to dilute out the factor in the blood of schizophrenics, by performing transfusions with blood from mentally normal persons (19). The results have been negative.

# Tests of Hepatic Function

In assessing the significance of tests of hepatic function and of the results obtained with them in mental diseases, it must be kept in mind that the liver has hundreds of functions and that no single test can be expected to yield general information about the state of this organ. The liver is concerned with the formation of the α- and β-globulins, as well as some other proteins of the plasma; it possesses the mechanisms for the synthesis and storage of glycogen, the degradation of glycogen, formation of lipides, metabolism of the amino acids, and the excretion of bile pigments and certain dyes. Theoretically, a severe deficit in a single enzyme could result in alteration in liver function. Such a deficiency would give rise to an excess of unattacked substrate in the body fluids and the degradation of administered substrate to normal end products would proceed at an abnormally slow pace. Such a test then reveals information about a highly specific function. However, if several enzymatic activities are unusually low, then more complex processes will be affected and defective liver function will be reflected in the results of several tests. The number of tests which have been applied in the study of liver function is exceptionally large (20, 21) and many of them have been applied to the study of psychiatric patients, not only as a check upon physical condition but as a potential correlate of the mental state. In an exhaustive review V. M. Buscaino (6) readily lists about 35 substances whose concentration has been measured in connection with liver function in schizophrenic patients. This is apart from the various searches that have been made for abnormal compounds in the urine of these patients. The several demonstrations of reduced liver weight in schizophrenics as compared with normal individuals, even after tuberculosis and other wasting diseases have been excluded (6, 22), also warrants the investigation of the role of hepatic dysfunction in mental illness. Some authors have described major histopathological changes in the gastrointestinal tract and in liver of schizophrenics, but there is by no means complete agreement on this, nor are the changes which have been described seen in all cases of schizophrenia.

In these clinical-laboratory investigations it has been frequently demonstrated that many, but not all, schizophrenic patients have liver function altered in a pathological direction.

From the point of view of the histophysiologist the liver function tests tell about the functional state of (a) the parenchymal cells—what is measured is the concentration of plasma enzymes and other proteins, the detoxication of foreign substances, the metabolism of a "test load" of a normal metabolite, and the excretion of dyes; and (*b*) the reticuloendothelial system of the liver and other organs—these are tests of lability of the plasma proteins, particularly the globulins: flocculation and turbidity tests.

For the biochemist there are four categories of hepatic function tests varying in complexity of the biochemical function measured. These categories are as follows:

*Group I.* Tests measuring the change of concentration of an enzyme in the serum. Some of the enzymes measured are ceruloplasmin (Chapter 21), lipase, protease, procainesterase, alkaline phosphatase, serum glutamic-oxaloacetic transaminase (SGOT), serum glutamic-pyruvic transaminase (SGPT).

*Group II.* Tests measuring the activity of liver enzyme systems acting on (*a*) endogenous substrates (serum bilirubin, cholesterol ester ratio, urinary coproporphyrins) or (*b*) exogenous substrates. Tests in the latter group are designed to load the liver (perhaps other organs also, as when intestinal absorption is involved) with material which can ordinarily be metabolized readily, but whose defective metabolism becomes evident as soon as there is a significant reduction in the number of effective parenchymal cells. The tests for hippuric acid synthesis (Chapter 3), for assimilation of glycine (Chapter 3), or of *p*-hydroxyphenylpyruvic acid (Chapter 5), and for the detoxication of santonin fall under this heading.

*Group III.* Tests detecting changes in the composition of the plasma proteins other than the enzymes mentioned in Group I. The changes sought are in the albumin and globulin concentrations and their ratio, and in the prothrombin and $\gamma$-globulin concentration, among others. Information about the globulin fraction may be obtained from the electrophoretic patterns of plasma proteins or from one or another of the flocculation and turbidity tests.

*Group IV.* Tests of the ability of the liver to excrete dyes, such as bromsulphthalein.

Some of these tests are considered elsewhere in this book. Additional tests omitted from this discussion are referred to in review articles on mental disease (23).

# Plasma Protein Tests

The plasma proteins are manufactured in the liver, bone marrow, and spleen. Their concentrations may vary quite independently of one another, and these variations should be expected to give quite different types of information. Because of the dominant role of the liver in protein metabolism and specifically in the biosynthesis of the α-globulins, β-globulins, and albumin, information about its functional state may be reflected in the concentration and physical condition of the plasma proteins, even those which are synthesized elsewhere. The techniques that have been used include (a) quantitation of more or less specific protein fractions by salt or by immunological precipitation, followed by micro-Kjeldahl determination; (b) resolution of the protein components of the serum by paper electrophoresis; and (c) production of flocculation or turbidity with saline or other reagents whose concentrations have been sensitively adjusted. These tests are, of course, widely used in clinical laboratories. No direct relation of the substances measured by them to mental disease has been found. The technique of paper electrophoresis has in the last few years become available for convenient use in the clinical laboratory; its application is still expanding. Through this method one can obtain precise data on the amounts of serum albumin and of various globulin fractions, using a fraction of a milliliter.

The search for an association between hepatic dysfunction, as indicated by blood proteins, and mental disorders has relied almost exclusively upon the flocculation and turbidity tests. Usually these tests have been developed on a highly empirical basis, and their chemistry has been appreciated only later on. The mechanism of the flocculation precipitation (turbidity) in these tests is manifold: precipitation of γ-globulins by dilution, precipitation by salts of heavy metals or by alcohol, gel formation, rupture of linkages in serum lipoproteins by a phenolic reagent (21). These reactions depend, in turn, upon the actual structures of the proteins, the shape of their molecule, the functional groups available for reaction, presence of prosthetic or similar groups (e.g., a lipide moiety), the state of hydration of the molecules forming the colloidal micelles, and the electrical charge on these particles, the presence of stabilizing groups in the serum, and so on. Positive tests are often attributed to the increased lability of the proteins. The determination of the electrophoretic pattern of the serum proteins side by side with these tests has lately aided in interpreting the latter. In general, serum lability increases with an increase in the amount of globulins or with a decrease in the albumin level. The changes resulting in the labilization usually signify some degree of hepatocellular dysfunction or damage, so that the tests tend to be markedly positive in hepatic jaundice, for example, but not so in obstructive jaundice. In spite of this distinction it should be realized that the lability tests as read in the laboratory are the resultant of all the quantitative and qualitative changes that have occurred in the serum, in particular those affecting the proteins, so that the degree of turbidity or the amount of flocculant precipitate is not proportional to any one particular substance.

The first to draw attention to the possibility that changes in the plasma proteins may yield information useful in the study of mental disease was Georgi, in 1924 (24). Using sodium chloride solution and alcohol as reagents he found that changes in colloid stabilization occur in the acute stages of schizophrenia and that the proteins return to their normal physicochemical state if there is remission from the attack or if the illness proceeds to the chronic condition. Since then, many of the flocculation tests have been tested in mentally ill patients, with varying results and, frequently (but not consistently), with a substantial number of positives among the schizophrenic group. This has been the case with the Takata-Ara test and modifications of it, the Wunderly-Wuhrmann cadmium sulfate tests, the cephalin-cholesterol flocculation test, thymol turbidity test, erythrocyte sedimentation test, and others (6). One can understand that given individuals do not react positively to all of a battery of these tests if they are positive in any one of them, for each test indicates somewhat different changes and many of the changes are in opposed directions. It requires further investigation to determine why there is not greater uniformity of response among schizophrenics of a particular diagnostic subgroup in the given test. Buscaino (6) has reviewed much of this work and considers the positive character to many of the test results as support for his concept of the role of hepatic dysfunction in the etiology of schizophrenia.

As an example of the results obtained with these tests, the experience with the cephalin-cholesterol flocculation test is instructive. The original application of Hanger's method (25) to the study of mental patients, carried out by De Jong and St. John (26), indicated striking differences between control subjects (7 percent positive), catatonic schizophrenics (47 percent positive), and noncatatonic schizophrenics (30 percent positive). Later investigators, using either the cephalin-cholesterol flocculation test or the related thymol turbidity test of Maclagan (27), were not able to confirm the high proportion of positives among catatonics (28). In fact, in his further studies with the Hanger test De Jong himself reported that he now rarely found a positive among the schizophrenic patients (29). The reason for this lies in the fact that the cephalin-cholesterol flocculation test is light-sensitive, and errors of interpretation have been made by attributing to parenchymal damage what is simply a photo-catalyzed positive reaction.

# References

1. ORTH, J. *Arch. f. Path. Anat. Physiol. 63:*447, 1875.
2. QUINCKE, H., and G. HOPPE-SEYLER. *Die Krankheiten der Leber,* Vienna, A. Hoelder, 1899.
3. SCHMORL, G. *Verhandl. d. deutsch. path. Ges. 6:*109, 1903.
4. ESCH, P. *Zentralbl. f. Gynäkol. 32:*969, 1908.
5. WILSON, S. A. K. *Brain 34:*295, 1912.
6. BUSCAINO, V. M. *Proceedings First International Congress on Neuropathology,* Rome, 1952, Vol. 1. Turin, Rosenberg and Sellier, 1952.
7. GEORGI, F., and G. MALL. *In Pathophysiological Aspects of Psychoses, ed.* GEORGI, F., and G. MALL. Basle, S. Karger A. G., 1958.
8. SCHRYVER, D., and S. SCHRYVER-HERTZBERGER. *Z. f. Ges. Neurol. Psychiat. 93:*472, 1924.
9. CRANDALL, L. A., and A. WEIL. *Arch. Neurol. Psychiat. 29:*1066, 1933.
10. BARUK, H., and L. CAMUS. *Presse Méd. 57:*1065, 1949.
11. DE JONG, H. H. *Experimental Catatonia, a General Reaction-Form of the Central Nervous System, and Its Implications for Human Pathology.* Baltimore, Williams & Wilkins Co., 1945.
12. MCGEER, E. G., and P. L. MCGEER. *J. Ment. Sci. 105:*1, 1959; TURNER, W. J. *An Annotated Bibliography on the Reported Singularities and Toxicities of Schizophrenic Fluids;* duplicated and distributed by the Technical Information Unit. Bethesda, Maryland, Psychopharmacology Service Center, 1959.
13. FROLICH, A., and I. A. MIRSKY. *Proc. Soc. Exp. Biol. Med. 50:*25, 1942.
14. BARUK, H., and L. CAMUS. *Compt. Rend. Soc. Biol. 116:*27, 1934.
15. BARUK, H. *Compt. Rend. des Séances Premier Congrès Mondial de Psychiatrie,* Paris, 1950. Paris, Hermann et Cie., 1952.
16. HEATH, R. G., S. MARTENS, B. E. LEACH, M. COHEN, and C. ANGEL. *Am. J. Psychiat. 114:*14, 1957; HEATH, R. G., B. E. LEACH, L. W. BYERS, S. MARTENS, and C. A. FEIGLY. *ibid. 114:*683, 1958.
17. MELANDER, B., and S. MARTENS. *Dis. Nerv. System 19:*478, 1958.
18. ROBINS, E., K. SMITH, and I. P. LOWE. *Transactions Fourth Conf. Neuropharmacology,* Josiah Macy, Jr., Foundation, 1957; HEATH, R. G., S. B. COHEN, F. SILVA, B. LEACH, and M. COHEN. *Dis. Nerv. System 20:*206, 1959.
19. GOLDBLATT, H., and A. KRAPIWKIN. *Psychiat.-Neurol. Wochschr. 34:*638, 1932; FREEDMAN, A. M., and D. GINSBERG. *J. Nerv. Ment. Dis. 126:*294, 1958.

20. SMITH, H. W., and J. J. NORDLAND. *Am. J. Digest. Diseases 2:*559, 1957.
21. DISCOMBE, G. *Lancet i:*1004, 1959.
22. MOORE, M., and W. G. LENNOX. *Am. J. Psychiat. 92:*1439, 1936.
23. BUSCAINO, G. A. *Acta neurologica (Naples) 8:*475, 1953; HUSZAK, I. *Arch. f. Psychiat. 197:*32, 1958.
24. GEORGI, F. *Arch. f. Psychiat. 71:*55, 1924.
25. HANGER, F. M. *J. Clin. Invest. 18:*261, 1939.
26. DEJONG, H., and J. H. ST. JOHN. *J. Nerv. Ment. Dis. 101:*572, 1945.
27. MACLAGAN, N. F. *Brit. J. Exp. Path. 25:*234, 1944.
28. ZIMMERMAN, F. H., M. GALLAVAN, and M. T. EATON, JR. *Am. J. Psychiat. 105:*225, 1948; SHATTUCK, F. M. *Proc. Roy. Soc. Med. 43:*623, 1950; OLTMAN, J. E., and S. FRIEDMAN. *Arch. Neurol. Psychiat. 64:*60, 1950; SMITH, S. *J. Nerv. Ment. Dis. 120:*245, 1954.
29. DE JONG, H. H. *J. Clin. Exp. Psychopath. 17:*388, 1956.

# 23

# NEUROENDOCRINE
# RELATIONSHIPS

*The emphasis has now changed from regarding the endo-
crines as prime movers in the shaping of personality and behavior to that of the endocrines themselves being regulated, in part
at least, by the central nervous system, the importance of the
central nervous system in physiology and psychology having
been rediscovered.—D. J. Ingle (1).*

## The Agencies of Homeostasis

It is to Claude Bernard that we owe the concepts of the organism's
internal environment and its constancy despite all the forces impinging
upon the body and tending to disturb it. Many years after Bernard,
Cannon coined the term homeostasis to describe succinctly "the stable
state of the fluid matrix" (2). Our present appreciation of homeostasis
recognizes this stability as an apparent one: the shadow of the continuous, smaller and larger metabolic and physiological adjustments
underlying the maintenance of normality. This dynamic steady state
is maintained through three interconnected agencies—the central nervous
system, the autonomic nervous system, and the endocrine glands (3).
The latter two were for a long time considered to be essentially
autonomous in their operation, a view which was fortified in the case

of the endocrine glands by two circumstances. In the first place, the isolation of the hormones was soon followed by the demonstration of their very great potency, and the clear successes with them in therapeutics detracted from the study of the nervous control over their secretion. The second factor contributing to this situation was the discovery of the tropic hormones in the anterior pituitary gland which, with their respective target hormones, appeared to constitute a self-regulatory system.

Although it is true that the endocrine system possesses a measure of autonomy, this is variable as between the various glands, and moreover, is limited by the higher control exerted by the central nervous system. Difficulties are encountered when concepts of endocrine autonomy are introduced into problems of human behavior, personality, and psychology, for clinical observation has shown that, unlike tissue pathology, the mental changes in endocrine disorders do not bear any simple order of relationship to the direction or the intensity of hormonal dysfunction (4). The psychic changes vary in severity and may accompany the states of both hormonal deficiency and excess. Moreover, they are nonspecific and vary distinctly in different individuals.

Recognition of the nervous control of endocrine secretion stems from many types of anatomical and physiological studies, and from clinical observation (5, 6, 7). Laboratory investigations have elucidated the more direct controls, e.g., of the adrenal medulla through the splanchnic nerves, and of both portions of the hypophysis by hypothalamic centers. In the case of the neurohypophysis, its hormones are believed to be synthesized in the supraoptic and paraventricular nuclei and then to pass down into the neural lobe of the pituitary gland, where they are stored. The discovery of the hypophysial-portal circulation has indicated an additional pathway for humoral transmission from the brain to the pituitary gland. Other neuroendocrine relationships, such as the increased output of pituitary hormones in emotional states or the hormonal dysfunctions associated with certain types of hypothalamic lesions, have been revealed through studies in the clinic. Thus, neurophysiological processes, which make up the substratum of mental activity, have available the endocrine glands in the chief supportive role for the maintenance of the organism's responsiveness and steady state (8). It is for this reason that the study of neurohumoral activity represents one of the closest approaches that the biochemist can make to the mental disease process itself.

One of the great concepts in the sphere of neuroendocrine relationships was that of W. B. Cannon, who described the integrated
functioning of the sympathoadrenal system in states of emergency
and introduced a thalamic theory of emotion (cf. 9). For twenty
years studies of this system relied solely upon the techniques of
physiology, but in the past decade convenient chemical methods have
introduced a new dimension of considerable significance, with the
chemical identification of sympathins and their measurement in the
body fluids under a large variety of conditions. In fact, some of these
techniques have been developed specifically in the study of the pathophysiology of the sympathoadrenal system in relation to mental disease.
This relatively new technical achievement makes it possible to re-
examine the concepts of autonomic imbalance that have at various
times been invoked to explain the pathogenesis of mental disorder
(10). Unfortunately, the rate of progress in chemical studies of the
contrapuntal parasympathetic system has not been as rapid, and the
determination of acetylcholine in serum or tissues still entails use of
biological preparations.

The diencephalic-vegetative responses are characterized by the
rapidity of their sequence, and represent the immediate responses of
the nervous and endocrine system to conditions upsetting homeostasis.
These are the factors taken into account in Cannon's hypothesis.
The slower and delayed responses of the organism to continuing
emergencies, that is, to persistent stressful situations, were only somewhat later found to have their functional basis located in the adenohy-
pophysial-adrenal cortical axis, and were therefore not encompassed
in this view. These slower changes effected by adrenal cortical hormones
enable the organism to avoid succumbing to many types of noxious
influences of a nonspecific type. The association of a characteristic
set of responses to stress with the functioning of the anterior pituitary
and adrenal cortical glands has been elaborately investigated experimentally by Selye. He has labeled the stereotyped pattern of responses
the general adaptation syndrome, and defines it as the stress syndrome.
Stress itself is "a state manifested by a specific syndrome which
consists of all the non-specifically induced changes in a biological
system" (11, 12). Selye's picture of biologic events following the application of a stressor is as follows: locally, there are changes (local
adaptation syndrome) which cause the release of some mediator substance. This "first mediator of stress," a postulated humoral substance,
passes to distant organs, e.g., to the hypothalamic-pituitary system, to

"transmit the message of stress" (12). As one of the consequences of this the adrenal cortex is stimulated to activity by the ACTH which has been secreted. This introduces a hormonal imbalance, which may result in the manifestation of disease. On the experimental side, pathological changes which are supposed to be analogous to those occurring in natural disease can be produced by the administration of adrenal cortical steroids, but large amounts of these are required. Indeed, frequently even excessive amounts of steroid are effective only when the animals have been sensitized by unilateral nephrectomy and are maintained on a high-salt diet.

The theory of the general adaptation syndrome has been developed upon the basis of many experimental data, and has even been extended to human disease (13), including mental illnesses (14). However, the biological results have been shown to be capable of other interpretations, and the correct picture of events will probably have to await clarification of the biochemical mode of action of adrenal cortical hormones at the subcellular metabolic level. In an article written shortly after the 11-oxygenated corticosteroids (glucocorticoids) had been introduced into therapeutics, and just before specific chemical methods for the measurement of adrenal steroids in the body fluids came into general use, Sayers has pointed to difficulties in the way of attributing pathological changes to hypercorticalism, for the physiological requirement above which the secretion is counted as excessive is not an unvarying one (15). The organism's needs for the hormones fluctuate from time to time. Moreover, the particular functional state of the tissue cells partly determines the action of the corticosteroids. Sayers assigns to the adrenal cortex a passive role in the restoration of homeostasis following emergency situations, whereby this gland potentiates the action of the regulatory systems of the body. A similar view of the cortical function has been expressed by D. J. Ingle (16, 17). In contrast to the conclusion that increased cortical secretion on a background of hormonal imbalance accompanying stress may cause disease, he suggests that the hyperfunction of the adrenal cortex during stress is part of the homeostatic responses. "The cortical hormones play a supporting role in the manifestation of certain diseases but are only rarely the primary causative agents" (17). In fact, the full set of responses to stress is seen in adrenalectomized animals receiving a steady dosage of cortical hormone, so that the increased cortical secretion in intact animals is not necessary to the phenomenon. It thus appears that the thesis that nonspecific stress can bring about disease in man still requires a firmer basis in experiments with normal animals (or sensitized ones, for that matter) consuming a normal diet (17). A biological view of stress when applied to human illness necessarily neglects factors that are at least equally important to the hormonal and may overshadow them. Social experience and psychological characteristics are major determinants in the whole process and intercede in the biological processes *via* the higher nervous activities. These are, accordingly, accounted for in Wolff's definition of stress as "the interaction between external environment and organism, with the past experience of the organism as a major factor" (18). Many examples of this in relation to the pituitary-adrenal axis have been summarized by Mason (19): the influence of the environment, including change to new surroundings and situations, the effect of disturbance of the usual sleeping-waking time cycle, the effect of psychological stress, and others. The intimate connection between cerebral physiology and endocrine responses in higher animals is expressed as follows:

> . . . The pituitary-adrenal cortical system is remarkably sensitive to the psychological influences in both man and monkey. . . . ACTH release occurs, not in association with a specific emotional state, but rather with a wide variety of emotional disturbances which may have the relatively undifferentiated element of distress or arousal (19).

The influence of the higher nervous centers upon the endocrines is exerted indirectly, by pathways channeled through the hypothalamus (20, 21). Nuclei in this region regulate not only the autonomic activity associated with emergency situations and other vegetative changes, all of which taken together represent the physical component of emotion accompanying the acute stress, but also influence the hypophysis through nervous and humoral connections which function in the delayed and slowly acting responses to continued stress. In this way the hypothalamic-endocrine system functions as coordinator of all those responses in which the integrated action of the autonomic nervous system and the endocrines is displayed (6, 7, 22).

The degree of dependence of endocrine function upon the central nervous system is different for different hormones. In some cases the nervous connection is required for glandular activity, and is exemplified by the failure of the gland to secrete its hormone. This is the case with respect to the neurohypophysis (vasopressin and oxytocin) and the adenohypophysis (gonadotropins and growth hormone). In others, hormone secretion continues even when the nervous connections to the gland have been severed. Thus, the anterior pituitary gland may be able to release small amounts of the thyrotropic hormone in these circumstances, but the hypothalamus nevertheless affects this process both under normal conditions and in duress (23). In the case of the adrenal medulla, also, there is greatly reduced secretion from it following section of the splanchnic nerves, and the rate of repletion of the catecholamine store following the administration of reserpine is lower for the denervated adrenal (24). The mechanism of nervous control over the anterior pituitary tropic and growth hormones is still largely unknown but, in the case of ACTH, at least one chemical mediator has been found which precedes it. This is the corticotropin-releasing factor, found in large amounts in the neurohypophysis. It appears to be a polypeptide, and is effective *in vivo* and *in vitro* (25, 26). This type of more remote or mediated effect extending downward from the central nervous system has been postulated also for the release of gonadotropins, and certainly it operates in the case of the sex glands and the adrenal cortex.

The neural control of the glands of internal secretion has thus been revealed by analysis of the mechanism of release of their hormones. It has been demonstrated also in another way, that is, by the formation of conditioned reflexes with an endocrine response (19, 27). The inverse influence of the endocrine secretions on cerebral function is in some cases simply regulatory, in which the secreted hormones, such as those of the sex glands and adrenal cortex, exert a feedback control over the hypothalamus and anterior pituitary gland (20, 26). But the influence of the hormones may be much more widespread than this indicates, for many of them affect thought and behavior (3, 4, 28). How they accomplish this is a problem awaiting a detailed solution (29). Some aspects of the relation of hormones to mentation are discussed in ensuing chapters.

# Neurohormones and Other Pharmacologically Active Substances in the Nervous System

Many substances with pharmacological activity have been detected in the brain, and there has naturally been great interest in learning what functions they perform in the nervous system. The substances concerned are various amines, including choline, acetylcholine, 5-hydroxytryptamine, norepinephrine, and dopamine; some peptides, potassium, adenylic acid; and others. The hormonal functions of norepinephrine, vasopressin, and oxytocin are well known, and account for their citation here. This is doubly justified in the case of the latter two compounds because of the evidence for their synthesis in neurosecretory cells, *viz.*, those of the supraoptic and paraventricular nuclei, and for norepinephrine because of its formation in nervous tissue. According to the Scharrers (30) neuro-secretory cells are "true nerve cells producing and releasing substances in aggregates large enough to be visible in supravital preparations at the usual magnifications of the light microscope . . . . " Such cells possess the characteristics of both nerve and gland cells. It is not known what type of cell manufactures 5-hydroxytryptamine and substance P in the brain, but they are mentioned here because of the probability of their having specific (but as yet unexplained) functions in nervous tissue. The same argument applies in the case of cerebral acetylcholine and dopamine.

The role of these substances in brain function has been sought primarily in two experimental directions. The first of these consists in measuring their concentration in discrete anatomical portions of the nervous system. One presumes that compounds which are more or less evenly distributed throughout the brain, spinal cord, and peripheral nerves must subserve some general metabolic function in that tissue. This applies in the cases of adenylic acid and potassium ions, for example. On the other hand, it can be expected that those agents which display an uneven pattern of distribution in the various regions of the brain have some special relation to the physiological function of the parts in which they occur most prominently. Data on the composition of nervous tissue with respect to a few of these substances are given in Table 23-1.

The second type of study is oriented toward the neurophysiological actions of these substances. Such tests employ systems of various degrees of complexity so that the effect measured may represent an action, for example, on simple neuronal or synaptic transmission, on the reticular formation in the midbrain, or on conditioned responses, to mention a few that have been studied.

These methods have, of course, been supplemented by biochemical, pharmacological, and electroencephalographic techniques in investigating the active substances in neural tissue: their potentiation or antagonism by centrally acting drugs, their activity and role in cerebral metabolism, and their effects on cortical-electrical activity and overt behavior. All the compounds mentioned except the neurohypophysial hormones occur in other locations as well, and this has meant that the neurophysiologist can draw upon already established data regarding the pharmacodynamic actions of these substances.

This very active field of research has yielded much information about the physiology and chemistry of the brain; yet, the complexity of the processes has detracted from a successful synthesis of this information into a perfectly clear picture of the role of the pharmacologically active substances in the brain. In the case of the two polypeptides, vasopressin and oxytocin, not only is their composition known, but also their site of synthesis in the hypothalamus and their endocrine functions. The situation about substance P is not so clear. This peptide occurs in many regions of the nervous system, but it is especially high in concentration in the hypothalamus, midbrain, caudate nucleus, the cuneate and gracile nuclei, the dorsal roots, and the gray matter of the spinal cord; the largest concentration is found in the area postrema (32, 40). The two current hypotheses dealing with this compound, its function as a transmitter liberated by somatic afferents, or as a transmitter released by inhibitory neurones, respectively, have already been discussed in Chapter 2 (p. 22).

The amines, 5-hydroxytryptamine, norepinephrine, and dopamine are also irregularly distributed in the brain and spinal cord. High concentrations of the first two are found in the thalamus, hypothalamus, midbrain, and area postrema. In general, they are prominently present in the portions of the brain representing the central connections of the sympathetic nervous system (32, 34). The values for 5-hydroxytryptamine given by Bogdanski et al. (31) for dog and cat brain are substantially higher than those reported earlier by Amin et al. (32) for dog. This discrepancy is due, at least in part, to differences in the procedures used by the respective groups to extract the amine from the brain. Costa and Aprison have measured the 5-hydroxytryptamine content of human brain (33). Dopamine is also found in the same regions as norepinephrine, but, unlike that compound, it occurs in unusually high concentrations in some of the basal ganglia: the corpus striatum, the globus pallidus, and the red nucleus, *i.e.*, in the subcortical nuclei which constitute a part of the extrapyramidal system (35, 41). Dopamine is well known for its role as the immediate precursor of norepinephrine in biosynthesis. Its peculiar distribution indicates, however, that it has another function in the brain, independent of that of norepinephrine, perhaps as a transmitter substance at certain synapses within these nuclei. Its concentration (along with that of norepinephrine) is unusually low in the basal ganglia of persons having Parkinson's disease (42); and in the urine of patients with this condition the dopamine output is significantly below normal (43). The pineal gland is relatively rich in dopamine (35).

Data on some enzymes which are active in the biosynthesis and further metabolism of 5-hydroxytryptamine and the catecholamines are

TABLE 23-1. SOME PHARMACOLOGICALLY ACTIVE SUBSTANCES
AND ENZYMES IN THE BRAIN
(All values are per gram of tissue)

| Unit | 5-Hydroxytryptamine µg. | | | Norepinephrine µg. | | Dopamine µg. |
|---|---|---|---|---|---|---|
| Species | dog | man | | dog | man | man |
| Reference | 31 | 32 | 33 | 34 | 35 | 35 |
| Cerebral gray | 0.27 | 0.03 | | 0.04–0.18 | 0–0.06 | 0.02–0.17 |
| Cerebral white | — | 0 | | 0.05 | — | — |
| Corpus callosum | 0 | 0 | 0.05–0.35 | 0.08 | 0 | 0.05 |
| Putamen | — | — | | — | 0.07 | 8.25 |
| Pallidum | — | — | 0.10–0.73 | — | 0.02 | 1.01 |
| Internal capsule | — | — | | — | 0.04 | 0.38 |
| Caudate nucleus | 0.72 | 0 | 0.20–0.70 | 0.06 | 0.04 | 5.74 |
| Red nucleus | — | — | | — | 0.23 | 1.17 |
| Substantia nigra | — | — | 1.11–1.96 | — | 0.07 | 0.38 |
| Olfactory bulb | 0.35 | 0.04 | | 0.05 | — | — |
| Optic nerves | 0 | 0 | | 0.02 | — | — |
| Hippocampus | 0.64 | 0.04 | | 0.04 | — | 0.04 |
| Thalamus | 0.57 | 0.02 | 0.23–2.70 | — | — | — |
| Medial thalamus | — | 0.07 | | 0.24 | 0.09 | 0.46 |
| Lateral thalamus | — | — | | — | 0.04 | 0.30 |
| Hypothalamus | 1.7 | 0.28 | 0.32–1.53 | 1.03 | 1.11 | 1.12 |
| Midbrain | 1.0 | 0.21 | | 0.37 | — | — |
| Colliculi | — | 0.13 | | 0.13 | — | — |
| Cerebellum | <0.09 | 0 | 0.01–0.09 | 0.07 | 0.01 | 0 |
| Medulla oblongata | 0.62 | 0.03 | 0.20–0.50 | 0.14 | 0.17 | 0.02 |
| Area postrema | — | 0.22 | 0.42–0.81 | 1.04 | — | — |
| Spinal gray | — | 0.08 | | 0.16 | — | — |
| Pyramidal tracts | — | 0 | | 0.06 | 0.01 | 0.17 |

TABLE 23-1 (*Continued*)

| Substance P units | Dopa Decarboxylase μmols of dopa converted per hour | 5HTP Decarboxylase mμmols of 5HTP converted per hour | Catechol O-methyl-transferase μmols metanephrine formed per 90 min. | Monoamine Oxidase mg. 5HT oxidized per hour | Choline Acetylase relative values | Acetylcholine Esterase μl.CO₂ per 10 min. |
|---|---|---|---|---|---|---|
| dog | ox | dog | monkey | dog | dog | dog |
| 32 | 36 | 31 | 37 | 31 | 38 | 39 |
| 5 | — | 0.04 | 0.58, 0.73 | 0.82 | 57–81 | 107–466 |
| — | — | — | — | — | — | 10 |
| 6 | — | 0.02 | 0.82 | 0.47 | 26 | 16 |
| — | — | — | } 0.82 | — | 35 | — |
| — | — | — | — | — | 127 | 3936 |
| 46 | 3.02 | 1.74 | 0.78 | 0.94 | 87 | — |
| — | — | — | — | — | 51 | — |
| — | — | — | — | — | — | — |
| 6 | — | 0.03 | — | 0.57 | 55 | 197 |
| 6 | — | 0.04 | 0.92 | 0.70 | 6 | 11 |
| 15 | — | 0.09 | 0.46, 0.70 | 1.18 | 108 | — |
| 13 | 2.10 | 0.22 | — | 0.94 | } 100 | — |
| 11 | — | — | — | — | | — |
| 8 | — | — | — | — | | 409 |
| 70 | 3.41 | 0.67 | 0.73 | 1.62 | — | 323 |
| 68 | — | 0.56 | 0.83 | 0.84 | — | — |
| 20 | — | — | 0.96 | — | 74 | — |
| 2 | — | <0.05 | 0.34 | 0.93 | 15 | 931–1756 |
| 25 | 2.62 | 0.18 | 0.75 | 1.12 | — | — |
| 290 | — | — | 0.94 | — | — | — |
| 68 | 2.74 | — | 0.65 | — | 128 | 611 |
| 6 | — | — | — | — | 12 | 82 |

given in Table 23-1. Decarboxylases for dopa and 5-hydroxytryptophan, which may actually be a single catalytic entity (*cf.* Chapter 19) and whose action results in the formation of these amines, are present at their highest levels in those regions where the amines themselves are especially concentrated. On the other hand, the enzymes acting upon cerebral amines, monoamine oxidase and catechol O-methyltransferase, are rather evenly distributed through the brain substance. The posterior pituitary gland has much of the latter enzyme (37).

# References

1. INGLE, D. J. *Recent Progress Hormone Res.* *15:*381, 1959.
2. CANNON, W. B. *Am. J. Med. Sci. 189:*1, 1935.
3. CLEGHORN, R. A., and B. F. GRAHAM. *Recent Progress Hormone Res. 4:* 323, 1949.
4. CLEGHORN, R. A. *In The Biology of Mental Health and Disease, ed.* KRUSE, H. D. New York, Hoeber, 1952.
5. CAWADIAS, A. P. *Proc. Roy. Soc. Med. 34:*303, 1940–41; HUME, D. M. *In Reticular Formation of the Brain, ed.* JASPER, H. H., and Others. Boston, Little, Brown and Co., 1958.
6. HARRIS, G. W. *Neural Control of the Pituitary Gland.* London, Edward Arnold Ltd., 1955.
7. ROTHBALLER, A. B. *Excerpta Medica 11:*Section III, 1957.
8. REISS, M. *J. Ment. Sci. 101:*683, 1955; BATT, J. C., W. W. KAY, M. REISS, and D. E. SANDS. *ibid. 103:*240, 1957.
9. CANNON, W. B. *Am. J. Psychol. 39:*106, 1927.
10. LANGFELDT, G. *The Endocrine Glands and Autonomic Systems in Dementia Praecox.* Bergen, J. W. Eide, 1926; FUNKENSTEIN, D. H., M. GREENBLATT, and H. C. SOLOMON. *J. Nerv. Ment. Dis. 108:*409, 1948; *idem, Am. J. Psychiat. 108:*652, 1952; FUNKENSTEIN, D. H., and L. W. MEADE. *J. Nerv. Ment. Dis. 119:*380, 1954; GELLHORN, E. *Physiological Foundations of Neurology and Psychiatry.* Minneapolis, University of Minnesota Press, 1953; FAURBYE, A. *Acta Psychiat. Neurol. Scand. 30:*665, 1955.
11. SELYE, H. *Metabolism 5:*525, 1956.
12. SELYE, H. *Perspectives in Biol. Med. 2:*403, 1959.
13. SELYE, H. *In Fifth Annual Report on Stress, ed.* SELYE, H., and G. HEUSER. New York, MD Publications, Inc., 1956.
14. SELYE, H. *Am. J. Psychiat. 113:*423, 1956.
15. SAYERS, G. *Physiol. Rev. 30:*241, 1950.
16. INGLE, D. J. *J. Endocrinol. 8:*xxiii, 1952; *idem, Acta Endocrinol. 17:*172, 1954.
17. INGLE, D. J. *In Fifth Annual Report on Stress, ed.* SELYE, H., and G. HEUSER. New York, MD Publications, Inc., 1956.
18. WOLFF, H. G. *Stress and Disease.* Springfield, Ill., Charles C Thomas, 1953; RAFFLE, P. A. B. *Lancet ii:*839, 1959.

19. MASON, J. W. *Recent Progress Hormone Res. 15:*345, 1959.
20. SAYERS, G., E. S. REDGATE, and P. C. ROYCE. *Ann. Rev. Physiol. 20:*243, 1958.
21. JØRGENSEN, C. B., and L. O. LARSEN. *Ergebn. d. Biol. 22:*1, 1960.
22. MIRSKY, I. A. *Am. J. Digest. Diseases 3:*285, 1958; CLEGHORN, R. A. *Psychosom. Med. 17:*367, 1955.
23. D'ANGELO, S. A., and R. E. TRAUM. *Ann. N.Y. Acad. Sci. 72:*239, 1958.
24. KRONEBERG, G., and H. J. SCHÜMANN. *Experientia 15:*234, 1959.
25. SAFFRAN, M. *Can. J. Biochem. Physiol. 37:*319, 1959.
26. SAFFRAN, M., and J. SAFFRAN. *Ann. Rev. Physiol. 21:*403, 1959.
27. LIBERSON, W. T. *Ann. Rev. Physiol. 19:*576, 1957.
28. IVANOV-SMOLENSKY, A. G. *Essays on the Pathophysiology of the Higher Nervous Activity.* Moscow, Foreign Languages Publishing House, 1954; HOAGLAND, H. ed. *Hormones, Brain Function, and Behavior.* New York, Academic Press, 1957; REISS, M. ed., *Psychoendocrinology.* New York, Grune and Stratton, 1958; COBB, S. *J. Nerv. Ment. Dis. 130:*97, 1960.
29. HARRIS, G. W. *In Reticular Formation of the Brain*, ed. JASPER, H. H. and Others. Boston, Little, Brown and Co., 1958.
30. SCHARRER, B., and E. SCHARRER. *Recent Progress Hormone Res. 10:*182, 1954.
31. BOGDANSKI, D. F., H. WEISSBACH, and S. UDENFRIEND. *J. Neurochem. 1:* 272, 1957.
32. AMIN, A. H., T. B. B. CRAWFORD, and J. H. GADDUM. *J. Physiol. 126:*596, 1954.
33. COSTA, E., and M. H. APRISON. *J. Nerv. Ment. Dis. 126:*289, 1958.
34. VOGT, M. *J. Physiol. 123:*451, 1954.
35. SANO, I., K. TANIGUCHI, T. GAMO, M. TAKESADA, and Y. KAKIMOTO. *Klin. Wochschr. 38:*5, 1960.
36. HOLTZ, P., and E. WESTERMANN. *Arch. Exp. Path. Pharmakol. 227:*538, 1956.
37. AXELROD, J., W. ALBERS, and C. D. CLEMENTE. *J. Neurochem. 5:*68, 1959.
38. FELDBERG, W., and M. VOGT. *J. Physiol. 107:*372, 1948.
39. BURGEN, A. S. V., and L. M. CHIPMAN. *J. Physiol. 114:*269, 1951.
40. ZETLER, G., and L. SCHLOSSER. *Naturwiss. 41:*46, 1954.
41. BERTLER, A., and E. ROSENGREN. *Experientia 15:*10, 1959.
42. EHRINGER, H., and O. HORNYKIEWICZ. *Klin. Wochschr. 38:*1236, 1960.
43. BARBEAU, A., G. F. MURPHY, and T. L. SOURKES. *Science 133:*1706, 1961.

# 24

# THYROID GLAND

The influence of the thyroid gland on mentation has been known for many years and recognition of the hypoendocrine state underlying certain forms of subnormal mental development, as in cretinism, long ago led to the use of thyroid gland preparations in its treatment. A further connection between thyroid and brain function was detailed in 1888 by the Committee of the Clinical Society of London whose report on myxedema contained the following passage (1): "Delusions and hallucinations occur in nearly half the cases, mainly where the disease is advanced. Insanity . . . takes the form of acute and chronic manias, dementia, or melancholia, with marked predominance of suspicion and self-accusation." Three years later G. R. Murray in Newcastle demonstrated the curative value of sheep thyroid extracts in this disease (2). Other connections between disturbances of thyroid function and mental processes have since become apparent and will be dealt with in this chapter. Although extensive studies have been carried out on thyroid metabolism in schizophrenia and other psychoses, it has not been possible to detect a specific endocrine dysfunction with etiological significance in these illnesses.

## Regulation of Thyroid Activity

The thyroid gland is able to absorb inorganic iodide from the blood and to concentrate it. This process is blocked by a large number of ions, especially the perchlorate and thiocyanate ions. The inorganic iodide is converted in the gland to several organic forms, with tyrosine playing the major role as the acceptor molecule for the initial binding of the iodide. Iodinated compounds that have been identified in thyroidal tissue include mono- and di-iodotyrosine; 3,3'-di-iodothyronine; 3,5,3'-tri-iodothyronine (liothyronine); 3,3',5'-tri-iodothyronine; 3,5,3',5'-tetra-iodothyronine (thyroxine); and 2-(or 4)-iodohistidine. Although tryptophan can be readily iodinated by chemical means no iodo-derivative of this amino acid has been found in nature. Of the compounds mentioned the important ones quantitatively are the two iodotyrosines and thyroxine. Thyronine itself has not been found in the gland.

The organic iodide is synthesized into iodothyroglobulin in the colloid of the gland, and it is stored there in this protein form. When conditions favor the release of hormone the iodothyroglobulin depolymerizes, and tri-iodothyronine and thyroxine are released into the effluent blood. This iodinated material is bound to plasma proteins and hence is termed protein-bound iodine, or PBI.

The thyroid gland in man possesses a variable but limited degree of autonomous control. Although hypophysectomy usually results in a marked suppression of thyroidal activity, some persists and is occasionally sufficient to guarantee the euthyroid state. Pazianos et al. (3) have described such cases, in which the PBI of the serum and the uptake of $I^{131}$ by the thyroid gland were normal and which gave normal responses to the administration of the adenohypophysial thyroid-stimulating hormone (TSH).

Ordinarily the anterior pituitary gland is affected by the level of PBI in the plasma: when the concentration of hormone decreases, the adeno-hypophysis secretes more TSH until the PBI level is raised appropriately. It is generally considered now that this self-regulatory mechanism is supplemented by influences upon the pituitary gland from higher nervous centers, which exert their action in response to environmental or internal stimuli. In this chain of stimulating-responding organs the hypothalamic centers precede the anterior pituitary gland. Some of these higher influences have been studied experimentally (4).

The action of TSH has been widely studied in experimental animals. On injection it causes small vacuoles to appear around the periphery of the colloid substance. The amount of colloid decreases, iodine is lost from the gland, and the cells hypertrophy. As the activity of the gland increases the oxygen consumption rises. At the same time there is an increased capacity to trap exogenous inorganic iodide.

## Functional and Diagnostic Tests (5)

Until the introduction of radioactive iodine into the metabolic clinic the measurement of the basal metabolic rate (BMR) was the most widely used test of activity of the thyroid gland. The determination of the plasma cholesterol, although a somewhat insensitive indicator of thyroid function, also gave useful information. For example, high cholesterol levels are associated with hypofunction and low titers with hyperfunction of the gland. The BMR is an over-all measure of the rate of oxidative (heat-producing) processes in the body and, in particular, of the action of thyroid hormone upon peripheral tissues. Usually it reflects the level of thyroid activity as judged clinically, but exceptions occur. On the other hand, there is a wide variety of clinical states in which the thyroid gland is not involved, yet in which the BMR is abnormally elevated. This occurs in certain cases of pheochromocytoma and of anemia. The BMR is also high in pregnancy and leukemia. In spite of extensive studies on the BMR by many investigators of mental illness only very limited evidence can be adduced to associate or implicate the thyroid gland in the etiology of the major psychoses.

Most of the organic iodide of the blood is bound to protein; this PBI amounts to 4 to 8 $\mu$g. percent. The determination of PBI then measures the concentration of thyroid hormone in the circulation. High values without hyperthyroidism are found in pregnancy, after radiation therapy (which causes the release of thyroidal iodine into the blood), and after the use of iodinated anti-infective drugs or contrast media. Man and Bondy have recommended the determination of butanol-extractable iodine in conditions where PBI values would be unreliable (6).

The uptake of radioactive iodine ($I^{131}$) measures the avidity of the thyroid gland for the element. A standard dose of radioiodine is administered, and the rate of its accumulation in the thyroid gland is determined. The rate is increased in cases of hyperthyroidism. A decreased urinary excretion of iodine can also be noted in these patients. On the other hand, in myxedema the rate of uptake is subnormal. The sensitivity of this method is offset by certain limitations to its specificity, sometimes making interpretation of the result difficult. For example, a low rate of uptake of a tracer dose of $I^{131}$ may be due either to a hypofunctioning gland or to a pituitary which is secreting a deficient amount of TSH. In the latter case the injection of TSH renders the iodine uptake normal.

But if there is a primary deficiency in the thyroid itself, the TSH has no effect. Increased iodine uptake is favored by radiation therapy, and the use of antithyroid drugs. The prior administration of inorganic or organic iodine (*e.g.*, contrast media) may depress the uptake of radioiodine significantly.

Reiss and his colleague have reported upon the routine measurement of the uptake of radioiodine in mental patients, and have found about 20 percent of these to yield values outside the normal limits. However, not all the patients with abnormal rates of uptake showed clinical evidence of thyroid malfunction. For nonmental patients serving as controls there was a sharp separation of values into three groups, the rates for euthyroid individuals being distinctly demarcated from those of persons displaying clinical hypo- or hyperthyreosis. In contrast to this, the series of mental patients provided a continuum of values. In most of the diagnostic group in which their patients were classified there was no relation between thyroid function and psychiatric status. However, in objective anxiety states a substantial proportion of the female patients displayed a high rate of uptake. The opposite held true for males in this category (7). In this study one of the side effects of treatment (electroshock therapy) was a normalization of the rate of uptake of radioiodine in patients who previously had accumulated the tracer dose at an abnormal rate (8). Kelsey and his colleagues observed increased uptake of $I^{131}$ in a high proportion of state hospital patients lacking signs of clinical hypothyroidism. This phenomenon was traced to the low iodine content of the diet and was corrected by the introduction of iodized salt (9).

Bowman et al. (10) determined serum PBI in 71 mental patients; the values obtained were within the normal range, but the distribution of values for the schizophrenic group fell into two divisions: those with serum PBI levels above 6.3 $\mu$g. percent included the 11 paranoid schizophrenics; the "low normals" consisted predominantly of catatonic schizophrenics and "other types" (19 subjects). This biphasic distribution was not seen among the manic-depressives and psychoneurotics. These investigators extended their study of thyroidal function by measuring BMR, radioactive iodine uptake, and plasma cholesterol. Clinically, the patients were all judged as euthyroid. On the laboratory tests, small differences showed up between some of the psychiatric groups, but the ranges of individual values were at least as large. Schizophrenic patients studied by Lingjaerde et al. (11) showed a lower rate of uptake of $I^{131}$ during an active phase of the psychosis than in an inactive one.

# Hypothyroidism

The complex sequence of reactions beginning with the ingestion of iodine and terminating in the release of thyroid hormone into the blood can be deranged or interrupted at any point, thereby resulting in clinical hypothyroidism. This state can usually be reversed by treating the patient with desiccated thyroid powder, but if the deficiency has existed for long, then the effects may not all disappear. This is especially seen in cases of cretinism where delayed treatment may result in irreversible damage to the brain during the very sensitive period of growth (12). In contrast to cretinism, the etiology of the adult form of hypothyroidism, myxedema, is unknown in most cases. The patient's history includes non-specific symptoms: lethargy, weight gain, vague leg pains, memory defect, constipation, deafness, loss of hair, dry skin, and a feeling of coldness even in a warm atmosphere. The change in facies and voice, along with the development of snoring, are more characteristic. The BMR may be normal, or even elevated, but it is generally low. The blood cholesterol is high. What is of particular interest here is that some, but not all, myxedematous patients develop psychotic symptoms. Indeed, the personality change is occasionally detected before the hormonal change has been assessed so that the psychosis may be the first indication of the developed hypothyroid state (1, 13). In some cases the anxiety or schizoid state may mask the hypothyroidism and delay correct diagnosis (14, 15). To the untreated condition Asher gave the name myxedematous madness (1), although he did not mean thereby to imply that this is a specific psychiatric entity. Indeed, in various persons it may resemble paranoia, schizophrenia, mania, or depression (1). Although treatment with thyroid usually cures the condition rapidly, in some cases the psychosis persists. It is possible that in the latter irreversible brain changes have taken place (1, 16). Mitchell et al. describe a serious hazard (coma) in using chlorpromazine in myxedematous psychosis (17).

Medvei (15) has described a patient who developed a hallucinatory psychosis with delusions some time after undergoing subtotal thyroidectomy; this patient responded to thyroid.

Jellinek and Kelly have associated a cerebellar syndrome, characterized by ataxic gait, incoordination, slow speech and low-voltage EEG, with myxedema (17A).

Hoskins (18) and his colleagues concluded from extensive metabolic and endocrinological studies on schizophrenic patients that in this disease there may be a low-grade hypothyroidism (cf. 19). The most prominent deviations noted were a low BMR, secondary anemia, and a scanty urine low in total nitrogen, and frequently there was a subnormal body temperature, low blood pressure and low pulse rate. When significant changes of this type were present, a course of thyroid therapy usually produced some degree of benefit (18). A second feature of the schizophrenic subject, as noted by Hoskins, is the unusually high tolerance that such patients sustain toward thyroid hormone. In some the signs of hyperthyroidism appear only after dose levels of 3 gm. of desiccated thyroid or 5 mg. of thyroxine per day have been attained. It is possible that these patients have a partial metabolic block in the deiodination of thyroxine to tri-iodothyronine or at some other point in its conversion to the compound immediately active at the level of cellular oxidative enzymes. Such a block would limit the amount of hormonal catalyst available to the peripheral tissues, and would result in the clinical observation of a hypometabolic state (low BMR) and relative tolerance to exogenous thyroid hormone. If such a block actually exists it would be possible to find at least one compound in the iodothyronine (or related) series which, on administration, yields the same stimulus to metabolism in these tolerant schizophrenic subjects as in nonschizophrenic patients and healthy individuals. This compound would presumably occur in the metabolic sequence of conversion of serum PBI at some point peripheral to the blocked enzyme and would resemble in its action the synthetic derivative tetra-iodothyroacetic acid, which has an immediate, stimulatory effect (20), demonstrable *in vitro*, on oxygen consumption of rat liver and kidney slices (21). A second clinical state in which such a metabolic block might be sought is periodic catatonia (see below). Several clinics (*e.g.*, 22) have tested tri-iodothyronine in schizophrenic patients, but this hormone has not proved useful.

Closely related to the problem of thyroid tolerance are the observations of Reiss and Haigh (23) on the uptake of radioactive iodine in some cases of hypothyroidism. These authors considered that the failure of certain patients to respond to an adequate supply of their own (or exogenous) hormone is the result of peripheral end-organ insensitivity. Lerman (24) considered this condition to be a theoretical possibility which, when found, would be characterized by a low BMR and an elevated serum PBI. The American Medical Association Council on Drugs has also considered the possibility of a "nonthyroidal deficiency of metabolic-regulating principle(s) at the cellular level" (25), characterized by low BMR but by normal serum PBI and normal thyroidal uptake of $I^{131}$. This syndrome has been variously termed metabolic insufficiency, non-myxedematous hypometabolism, and euthyroid hypometabolism. Its existence as a true endocrine entity has been frequently questioned (26). The patients who do exhibit the clinical features of metabolic insufficiency respond erratically to thyroid medication, and the syndrome is regarded as based upon a psychological rather than biochemical disorder (27).

# Hyperthyroidism

In hyperthyroid states the BMR and serum PBI are both elevated. The rate of uptake of radioactive iodine is also increased in Graves's disease and in toxic nodular goiter. These conditions come to the attention of the internist, but they are of some interest to the psychiatrist because of the significant role which psychological factors may play in their etiology. Thus, an emotional reaction frequently precedes the appearance of the symptoms of hyperthyroidism. Hypothalamic nuclei may have the role of intermediary between the higher nervous centers and the thyroid, but how the persistent elevation in thyroid activity is maintained has not been explained. Medvei (15) states that "in thyroid crisis, particularly when precipitated by some infection, signs of acute mania and delirium occur." Psychoses associated with hyperthyroidism were more commonly observed before the introduction of controlled thyroidectomy and other normalizing measures (28).

# Periodic Catatonia

In 1908 Kraepelin defined a subgroup within dementia praecox as periodic catatonia. The onset of this condition usually occurs during adolescence and is displayed as erratic behavior, suddenly going on to a state of catatonic excitement, or, less commonly, stupor. Eventually this clears up and a period of remission ensues during which the patient is withdrawn and apathetic, but is free from catatonia. In the absence of treatment relapse eventually follows, so that the disease pursues a cyclical course. Through prolonged and detailed biochemical, nutritional, and psychiatric studies Gjessing (30) detected phasic changes in the nitrogen balance of his patients: he showed that at times the retention of nitrogen is very marked but is reversed after some weeks, with a net loss of protein from the body. In some patients this period of excess nitrogen excretion coincides with the catatonic (reaction) phase (31, 32), and when the excretion of excess nitrogen is complete the patient enters the state of remission; as nitrogen storage reaches its peak, the excitement phase reappears. This is Gjessing's type A course of the illness. In others (type C) the period of positive nitrogen balance was found to coincide with the reactive phase (33). Cases exhibiting the disturbed phase at an intermediate point in the cycle, *i.e.*, just after the nitrogen balance becomes negative (34) have also been recognized (type B). The nonprotein nitrogen of the blood also undergoes fluctuations, in inverse relation to nitrogen storage (59). These cases fall into Gjessing's synchronous-syntonic group; in others the reaction phase and the noncatatonic interval are not so clearly defined, and the periodicity is not recognizable without close kinetic scrutiny of the patient (30). Other investigators have also met such difficulties in detecting the cycles (35).

When the fluctuations in nitrogen balance are present the excretion of stored nitrogen is frequently reflected in a rapid and large decrease in body weight, even up to nine pounds in 24 hours (30, 36, 37). Crammer (37) considers that these changes point to alterations in salt and water metabolism (p. 249).

Many of the other biochemical and physiological changes occurring in the reaction phase of periodic catatonia fit into the picture Cannon has given of the emergency reaction: there is evidence of sympathoadrenal discharge in the sudden rise in blood pressure and pulse rate, skin pallor, sweating, mydriasis, increased oxygen consumption, and high blood sugar.

Gjessing postulated, after detecting the cyclical changes in nitrogen metabolism, that at the time of phase change one or more toxic substances are formed and released into the blood to be carried to the diencephalic centers where they act as irritants. A substance of this nature might be an amine or a product of protein degradation. In order to rid the body of this source of toxic material and to keep the store of nitrogen depleted, Gjessing introduced thyroxine (in 1929) and later on desiccated thyroid, as therapeutic agents. The results were outstanding in many cases. The administration of thyroid preparations interrupted the cycle and provided relief from the physical and mental features of the disease. This remission persisted as long as therapy was continued, and ended when thyroid was no longer taken. Danzinger (8) has used desiccated thyroid and thyroxine with equal success. Mall states that thyroid must be administered at the time of maximal nitrogen storage (39). Gornall et al. (32, 40) have tested tri-iodothyronine also, with beneficial results in one patient. The therapeutic effects are not due simply to an increased rate of cellular oxidation, because dinitrophenol is not useful in periodic catatonia (41).

# References

1. ASHER, R. *Brit. Med. J. ii:*555, 1949.

2. LANGDON-BROWN, W. *Proc. Roy. Soc. Med. 39:*507, 1946.

3. PAZIANOS, A., R. BENUA, B. S. RAY, and O. H. PEARSON. *J. Clin. Endocrinol. & Metab. 20:*1051, 1960.

4. HARRIS, G. W., and J. W. WOODS. *Brit. Med. J. ii:*737, 1956; AMIRAGOVA, M. G. *Fiziol. Zhur. S. S. S. R. 43:*65, 1957.

5. KEATING, F. R., JR. *J. Clin. Endocrinol. & Metab. 17:*797, 1957; WOLFF, J., and R. C. GOLDBERG. *In Biochemical Disorders in Human Disease,* ed. THOMPSON, R. H. S., and E. J. KING. New York, Academic Press, 1957.

6. MAN, E. B., and P. K. BONDY. *J. Clin. Endocrinol. & Metab. 17:*1373, 1957.

7. REISS, M., R. E. HEMPHILL, R. MAGGS, C. P. HAIGH, and J. M. REISS. *Brit. Med. J. i:*1181, 1951; *idem, Brit. Med. J. i:*906, 1953.

8. REISS, M., R. E. HEMPHILL, R. MAGGS, C. P. HAIGH, and J. M. REISS. *Brit. Med. J. ii:*634, 1951.

9. KELSEY, F. O., A. H. GULLOCK, and F. E. KELSEY. *A. M. A. Arch. Neurol. Psychiat. 77:*543, 1957.

10. BOWMAN, K. M., E. R. MILLER, M. E. DAILEY, A. SIMON, and B. F. MAYER. *J. Nerv. Ment. Dis. 112:*404, 1950.

11. LINGJAERDE, P., O. E. SKAUG, and O. LINGJAERDE. *Acta Psychiat. et Neurol. Scand. 35:*498, 1960.

12. EAYRS, J. T. *Brit. Med. Bull. 16:*122, 1960.

13. CALVERT, R. J., E. SMITH, and L. G. ANDREWS. *Brit. Med. J. ii:*891, 1954.

14. ZONDEK, H., and G. WOLFSOHN. *Lancet ii:*438, 1944.

15. MEDVEI, V. C. *Practitioner 162:*139, 1949.

16. RULLO, F. R., and F. N. ALLAN. *J.A.M.A. 168:*890, 1958.

17. MITCHELL, J. R. A., D. H. C. SURRIDGE, and R. G. WILLISON. *Brit. Med. J. ii:*932, 1959.

17A. JELLINEK, E. H., and R. E. KELLY. *Lancet ii:*225, 1960.

18. HOSKINS, R. G. *The Biology of Schizophrenia.* New York, W. W. Norton, 1946.

19. LINGJAERDE, O. *Acta Psychiat. et Neurol. Scand. 8:*573, 1933.

20. IBBETSON, K., R. FRASER, and D. ALDIS. *Brit. Med. J. ii:*52, 1959.

21. THIBAULT, O., and R. PITT-RIVERS. *Compt. Rend. Soc. de Biol. 149:*880, 1955.

22. MEYER, B. J., A. C. MEYER, and M. K. HORWITT. *A. M. A. Arch. Gen. Psychiat. 1:*372, 1959; TOLAN, E. J., B. KOVITZ, and L. DILLON. *Am. J. Psychiat. 116:*1111, 1960.

23. REISS, M., and C. P. HAIGH. *Proc. Roy. Soc. Med. 47:*889, 1954.

24. LERMAN, J. *Missouri Medicine 50:*35, 1953.

25. KAUTZ, H. D. *J.A.M.A. 164:*972, 1957.

26. KEATING, F. R., JR. *J. Clin. Endocrinol. & Metab. 18:*531, 1958.

27. McINTOSH, H. W. *In Practice of Medicine,* ed. MEAKINS, J. C. 6th ed. St. Louis, C. V. Mosby Co., 1956; LEVIN, M. E. *J. Clin. Endocrinol. & Metab. 20:*106, 1960.

28. DUNLAP, H. F., and F. P. MOERSCH. *Am. J. Psychiat.* *91*:1215, 1934–35; JAMIESON, G. R., and J. H. WALL. *Psychiat. Quart.* *10*:464, 1936.
29. GJESSING, R. *Arch. f. Psychiat.* *200*:350, 1960.
30. GJESSING, R. *J. Ment. Sci.* *84*:608, 1938.
31. GJESSING, R. *Arch. Psychiat. Nervenkrankh.* *96*:319, 1932; *ibid.* *191*:247, 1953.
32. GORNALL, A. G., B. EGLITIS, A. MILLER, A. B. STOKES, and J. G. DEWAN. *Am. J. Psychiat.* *109*:584, 1953.
33. GJESSING, R. *Arch. Psychiat. Nervenkrankh.* *109*:525, 1939.
34. GJESSING, R. *Arch. Psychiat. Nervenkrankh.* *104*:355, 1935; *ibid.* *191*:191, 1953.
35. ALTSCHULE, M. D. *Bodily Physiology in Mental and Emotional Disorders.* New York, Grune and Stratton, 1953; MAYER-GROSS, W., E. SLATER, and M. ROTH. *Clinical Psychiatry,* London, Cassell, 1954.
36. LINDSAY, J. S. B. *J. Ment. Sci.* *94*:590, 1948.
37. CRAMMER, J. L. *Lancet* *ii*:259, 1957.
38. DANZIGER, L. *Diseases Nerv. System* *19*:373, 1958.
39. MALL, G. *Arch. Psychiat. Nervenkrankh.* *187*:381, 1952.
40. GORNALL, A. G. *In Psychoendocrinology,* ed. REISS, M. New York, Grune and Stratton, 1958.
41. GJESSING, R. *Arch. Psychiat. Nervenkrankh.* *191*:297, 1953.

# 25

# THE ADRENAL MEDULLA
# AND SYMPATHETIC
# NEUROHUMORS

## Catecholamines ( I )

The remarkable pressor properties of extracts of the adrenal gland were first noted by Oliver and Schäfer in 1895. An active principle was isolated from such extracts by Takamine in 1901 and given the name *adrenaline*. A few years later Stolz and Dakin independently synthesized the compound. For many years adrenaline (epinephrine) was considered the sole sympathomedullary hormone, although the effects of its injection were not strictly identical to those caused by stimulation of sympathetic postganglionic nerves; indeed, it simulated nervous action less than noradrenaline (arterenol, norepinephrine) does. Through the efforts of Holtz's group in Germany and of von Euler's in Sweden, norepinephrine was revealed as a physiological constituent first of the urine and later of sympathetic nerves, adrenal, brain, spleen, liver, and other tissues. Since then a third catecholamine, dopamine (3-hydroxytyramine), has been identified in urine, brain, intestine, and some other tissues. N-Isopropylnorepinephrine (isoproterenol) has been reported to occur in the adrenal medulla and elsewhere, but this has not been confirmed. The four amines mentioned have rather different pharmacological actions, qualitatively as well as quantitatively; these are summarized in Table 25-1. Their structural relationships together with those of other catecholic and related compounds, are illustrated in Table 25-2.

Epinephrine and norepinephrine occur in the blood, chiefly in the erythrocytes and platelets, but also to some extent in the plasma. Claims have been made for the presence of adrenalone, the keto analogue of epinephrine, in the blood but this has not been verified.

The urinary catecholamines which have been thus far identified are dopamine, norepinephrine, and epinephrine. Because most of the epinephrine disappears from the urine after bilateral adrenalectomy (3, 4) it is believed that its main source is the adrenal medulla. On the other hand, norepinephrine is essentially unaffected by adrenalectomy and this fact, taken together with the identification of this compound (but not epinephrine) in sympathetic postganglionic nerves and the release of norepinephrine when sympathetic nerves are stimulated (5) indicates the origin of norepinephrine primarily at the sympathetic nerve terminations in glands and smooth muscles such as the arterioles (3).

In 1939 it was suggested that the function of the enzyme dopa decarboxylase, discovered two years earlier by Holtz and his colleagues, was to be found in the biosynthesis of epinephrine in the tissues. The pathway proposed began with the oxidation of phenylalanine to tyrosine, and of the latter to dihydroxyphenylalanine (dopa). The decarboxylation of dopa results in the formation of the weakly pressor compound, dopamine, one of whose functions is to serve as the precursor of norepinephrine in biosynthesis (cf. Table 25-2). N-Methylation of norepinephrine then yields epinephrine. All these steps have been individually demonstrated to occur in systems studied in vitro, that is, through the mediation of partially isolated or crude enzyme systems, and together with data from experiments employing isotopically labeled compounds these facts are strong evidence in favor of the pathway described. However, other possibilities are not thereby excluded. For example, the demonstration that meta-tyrosine serves as a precursor of urinary dopamine (6) introduces the possibility of an alternative route of biosynthesis from phenylalanine via this isomer of tyrosine. Moreover, it is desirable to determine whether the hydroxyphenylserine series of compounds plays a role in the formation of the catecholamines (7).

Small amounts of catecholamines are excreted in the urine. Typical mean values for normal adults are (in micrograms per 24 hours): dopamine, 316, norepinephrine, 42, and epinephrine, 17. The rate may

TABLE 25-1. PHARMACOLOGICAL ACTIONS OF CATECHOLAMINES

| | Epi-nephrine | Norepineph-rine | Dopamine | Isopropyl-norepi-nephrine |
|---|---|---|---|---|
| Effects on cardio-vascular system* | | | | |
| Cardiac output | + | 0 or − | | |
| Blood pressure | | | | |
| systolic | + | + | | |
| diastolic | 0 or + | ++ | | |
| mean | + (1.0) | ++ (1.6) | (0.02) | − |
| Total peripheral resistance | − | + | | |
| Pulse rate | + | − | | |
| Effect on smooth muscle | | | | |
| Rabbit small intestine † | 1.0 | 1.0 | 0.02–0.04 | 1.0 |
| Cat small intestine † | 1.0 | − | 0.06 | − |
| Rabbit uterus (non-gravid) | 1.0 E‡ | 1.0 E | − | I |
| Rat uterus (non-gravid) | 1.0 I | 0.03–0.10 E | 0.0002–0.0005 | I 1.0–2.0 I |
| Local vasocon-striction | 1.0 | 0.5 | | vasodilator |
| Bronchodilation (guinea pig) | 1.0 | 0.016–0.06 | 0.003 | 3–8 |
| Hyperglycemic action in the fasted rabbit | 1.0 | 0.17 | − | 0.006 |
| CNS stimulation effective dose subcutaneously (mg./kg.) in rat | 0.25 | 0.25–2.0 | 80 | − |
| Subjective component in man | + | − | ? | + |

Adapted from data in Reference 2.
* + = increase; − = decrease; 0 = no effect.
† Inhibitory.
‡ E = excitatory; I = inhibitory.

vary within wide limits; for example, the excretion of norepinephrine during sleep is much reduced below the rate for the waking hours. Norepinephrine excretion increases in the change from the resting to the vertical position, reflecting the role of this hormone in circulatory adjustments secondary to changes in posture. It also increases during muscular exertion. Relatively little is known about the physiological conditions affecting the output of hydroxytyramine. By the usual pharmaco-

TABLE 25-2. PYROCATECHOL AND RELATED COMPOUNDS

$$P-\langle\!\!\!\!\!\raisebox{0pt}{\bigcirc}\!\!\!\!\!\rangle-\underset{Y}{CH}-\underset{Z}{CH}-\underset{R}{NH}$$

with M on the ring.

| | M | P | Y | Z | R |
|---|---|---|---|---|---|
| Phenylalanine | H | H | H | COOH | H |
| Phenylserine | H | H | OH | COOH | H |
| Tyrosine (*para*-tyrosine) | H | OH | H | COOH | H |
| *Meta*-tyrosine | OH | H | H | COOH | H |
| Octopamine | H | OH | OH | H | H |
| Dopa | OH | OH | H | COOH | H |
| Dops | OH | OH | OH | COOH | H |
| Dopamine | OH | OH | H | H | H |
| Norepinephrine | OH | OH | OH | H | H |
| Epinephrine | OH | OH | OH | H | $CH_3$ |
| Isoproterenol | OH | OH | OH | H | $CH\begin{smallmatrix}CH_3\\[2pt]CH_3\end{smallmatrix}$ |

dynamic tests it has little activity (Table 25-1), although it is now evident that it has biological activity of a kind other than those tested. Its high concentration in the basal ganglia (Table 23-1) indicates that it may have a function at certain types of central synapses (Chapter 23).

Although only a small fraction of the total catecholamines turned over in the body is excreted in the free form, this portion nevertheless is of considerable significance as a mirror of changes in physiological state. The conjugated forms of the catecholamines have been little studied, although the formation of both glucuronides and sulfates has been reported; neither constitutes a fraction any larger than the free portion. The major portion of the catecholamines follows other pathways: (a) methylation of the *meta*-phenolic group, yielding 3-O-methyldopamine, normetanephrine (from norepinephrine), and metanephrine (from epinephrine); (b) oxidation of the side chain to form catecholacetic (dopacetic) acid from dopamine, and 3,4-dihydroxymandelic acid, from the other two amines; (c) a combination of these two changes resulting in the formation of homovanillic acid (HVA) from dopamine, and 3-methoxy-4-hydroxymandelic acid (vanilmandelic acid, VMA) from epinephrine and norepinephrine.

## Adrenochrome and Related Compounds (8)

The discovery in 1937 of adrenochrome, obtained by the treatment of epinephrine with various oxidants, indicated another possible but as yet unproved physiological pathway for the metabolic disposition of this hormone. The oxidation resulting in adrenochrome can also be carried out with inorganic oxidants and presumably proceeds through several steps: (a) formation of the quinone of epinephrine (adrenoerythrin). (b) This reaction is readily reversible, but under ordinary conditions the side chain cyclizes, and *leucoadrenochrome* (3,5,6-trihydroxy-2,3-dihydro-N-methylindole) is formed. (c) The excess oxidant which is usually present oxidizes this hydroquinone derivative to adrenochrome, first described adequately by Green and Richter (9) and since then prepared as dark reddish-violet rodlike crystals (10). The oxidation of norepinephrine and dopamine results in analogous compounds, although that from dopamine has been less well characterized. These compounds rearrange spontaneously under alkaline conditions to form fluorescent derivatives: *adrenolutin* and *noradrenolutin* fluoresce in the visible range, but the derivative of dopamine fluoresces in the near ultraviolet. The fluorescent properties of these compounds are utilized in the chemical estimation of the corresponding catecholamines by the Ehrlen-Euler-Floding procedures and their various modifications (trihydroxyindole, or THI, methods). The reaction of an *ortho*-quinone such as adrenochrome at an elevated pH with ethylene diamine, forming a fluorescent derivative, is made use of in the Weil-Malherbe and Bone procedure for the determination of the parent amines.

There is little information available in the literature regarding the metabolism of the chromes and lutins. Adrenochrome administered to the rabbit disappears rapidly from the blood. It is converted in the liver and kidney to adrenolutin, which is then excreted in the urine (11). In a study made with radioactive-labeled epinephrine no endogenously formed adrenochrome was found (12).

Some investigators consider adrenochrome to act as a hydrogen carrier. Conceivably, it can do this in either of two ways: (a) in an adrenochrome-leucoadrenochrome system; or (b) by isomerization to adrenolutin, which can then form a new oxidation-reduction system with its oxidation product, oxoadrenochrome (N-methyl-3-keto-5,6-dihydroxyindole). Little is known of these further oxidations of adrenochrome and adrenolutin, but it may be in this region that the chemical nature of *adrenoxine* is to be found. This substance, or more correctly, material with a specified pharmacological activity, is formed by the action of tyrosinase and other plant oxidases on epinephrine (13). Inorganic oxidants do not give rise to the material. When this enzymatic oxidation is allowed to take place the resulting solution no longer causes a rise in blood pressure upon parenteral administration, but rather a fall. Its inhibitory properties in such pharmacological tests first recommended the name *adrénaline oxydée inhibitrice.* Its structure is unknown.

Many enzymes oxidize epinephrine without yielding ammonia or otherwise causing scission of the side chain. Among these are ceruloplasmin, ferritin, serum catechol oxidase, and various other enzymes referred to simply as adrenaline oxidase. Cytochrome c is also capable of oxidizing epinephrine. The presence of these catalysts in the body has lent support to the view expressed by Bacq (14) regarding the role of oxidation of the catechol nucleus in the metabolism of the catecholamines. This has also encouraged the opinion that the oxidation of epinephrine to adrenochrome occurs under physiological conditions, and some experimental results have been interpreted in this way. For example, Leach and Heath (15) have applied the well-known observation that the plasma contains a system capable of oxidizing epinephrine, by making a comparison of normal and schizophrenic blood. Measuring the rate of change in the ultraviolet absorption spectrum of epinephrine (added for the purpose of the experiment in about thousandfold greater concentration than its normal level in the plasma) they found that the two series of samples overlapped in their ability to catalyze the changes, but that the blood drawn from schizophrenic patients gave a larger mean rate. In these experiments very high concentrations of the amine were employed relative to the native antioxidants of the plasma, so that the systems normally protecting the catecholamines of the plasma are swamped. However, under physiological conditions the catecholamines are perfectly stable in plasma (16). Furthermore, the rate of disappearance of infused epinephrine and norepinephrine from the plasma is the same for schizophrenic as for normal persons (17) and adrenalectomy does not ameliorate schizophrenia (18).

The work of Leach and Heath was repeated by Hoffer and Kenyon (19), who claimed that the product of oxidation is a mixture of adrenochrome and adrenolutin. Ceruloplasmin and a second plasma enzyme adrenaline oxidase were reputed to be the catalysts of this oxidation. These studies on the oxidation of epinephrine gave results which fitted the hypothesis on etiology of mental diseases, as presented by the group of investigators in Saskatchewan. Their hypothesis holds that a disordered metabolism of epinephrine results in the accumulation of a hallucinogenic product in the body: adrenochrome, adrenolutin, or some related substance. This hypothesis was first promulgated in 1952 by Osmond and Smythies, but has since undergone changes, partly because of increasing knowledge of the metabolism of the catecholamines, partly because of the lack of any clear supporting evidence (20). Thus, the Saskatchewan group have claimed that adrenochrome and adrenolutin exert hallucinogenic actions and that the changes in thought and mood produced by these derivatives of epinephrine resemble early schizophrenia. Smythies, one of the originators of the adrenochrome theory, has reviewed the evidence for the hallucinogenic action of adrenochrome (21) and has concluded that "the experiments which [were] supposed to show that these compounds are psychotomimetic are unconvincing because, in most cases, no double-blind controls were used." He stresses the role of placebo effects and points out that others who have tested pure adrenochrome did not observe hallucinogenic effects.

It has also been stated that relatively large amounts of adrenochrome are found in the plasma (22), but this result has been demonstrated to be due to an artefact (23) in the method devised to measure adrenochrome (24).

One of the hypotheses proposed by Osmond et al. (20) held that an abnormality in the metabolism of norepinephrine leads to methylation of one of its phenolic groups, forming a mescalinelike compound, instead of methylation of the amino group as in the normal biosynthesis of epinephrine. Since then it has become known that both processes, O-methylation as well as N-methylation, occur under normal conditions, as pointed out above. Studies on the pharmacological activity of O-methylated catecholamines (25) show that these derivatives retain some of the activity of the parent compounds, but thus far it is not known if any of them has central actions of the types already known for mescaline (hallucinogenic action), epinephrine (affective changes, electrocortico-graphic changes), and norepinephrine (electrocorticographic changes). It is of interest that one of the minor products of the oxidation of dopamine *in vivo* is 2,4,5-trihydroxyphenylethylamine; mescaline is the fully O-methylated derivative of 3,4,5-trihydroxyphenylethylamine. Furthermore, in the course of its metabolism, dopamine is converted to homo-vanillic acid, 3-methoxy-4-hydroxyphenylacetic acid, and on its side, mescaline yields 3-methoxy-4,5-dihydroxyphenylacetic acid (conjugated with glutamine).

## Binding and Release of CAs in Chromaffin and Nervous Tissue

The cells of the adrenal medulla are modified postganglionic sympathetic nerve cells; although anatomically distinct from other autonomic neurones they retain a functional relation to the sympathetic nervous system. It has been suggested on the basis of histochemical evidence that there are at least two cell types, one containing epinephrine and the other norepinephrine. This might signify that the latter cells lack the enzymatic mechanism for methylating norepinephrine.

The catecholamines are concentrated in subcellular particles or granules (26), in close association with adenosine triphosphate, and are released from this storage form into the venous effluent of the medulla by excitation of the splanchnic nerve. The action of this nerve is transmitted through the mediation of acetylcholine, the preganglionic transmitter substance. Acetylcholinesterase in the medullary cell interrupts the action of the humoral agent by hydrolyzing it to choline and acetate. The physiological action of acetylcholine in causing the secretion of the hormone can be mimicked by short intra-arterial injection of methacholine (acetyl-$\beta$-methylcholine chloride, methacholine). In man the intramuscular injection of methacholine has been utilized in a test of autonomic function (Funkenstein's test, *vide infra*). The drug causes an initial fall in blood pressure (peripheral action), with a more or less rapid return to normotensive levels. There has been considerable interest in determining the relative roles of the two chief hemodynamically active catecholamines, epinephrine and norepinephrine, during the latter phase and, therefore, several groups have attempted to measure these compounds in blood and urine after the administration of methacholine. Although a trend to lower norepinephrine in the plasma has been noted at the point of greatest fall in blood pressure there is a great deal of variation among the individual results (27). In urinary studies the epinephrine output has been observed not to change, although there is a slight increase in the excretion of norepinephrine (28, 29), perhaps testament to the role of the latter hormone in the restoration of normal blood pressure.

Apart from the cholinergic drugs and nicotine, factors causing the release of catecholamines from the medulla do so by stimulation of the splanchnic nerve. For example, the marked effect of insulin in causing excretion of epinephrine (28, 30, 31) is not seen in the splanchnectomized animal. The effect of hypoglycemia induced by insulin in the intact animal includes the loss of epinephrine from the adrenal medulla (32). This insulin-induced loss has been demonstrated in man as a highly elevated rate of excretion of epinephrine in the urine during the hypoglycemic period (28, 33). It is accompanied by a steady rise in the epinephrine concentration in the plasma (34, 35). Conversely, the infusion of glucose depresses the secretion of epinephrine and norepinephrine (34). In repeated insulinization, as during the course of somnolent insulin (subcoma) therapy the epinephrinuric response to the administration of insulin falls off after three to four days (31); this is probably due to an actual depletion of the adrenal epinephrine stores. The normal response returns after withdrawal of insulin for a number of days. The relative stability of medullary norepinephrine during this action of insulin points to the existence of separate controls over the secretion of the catecholamines from the gland, a differential effect which also has been confirmed by several experimental techniques. Hence, evidence is at hand (a) for the occurrence of two types of cell in the adrenal medulla, and (b) for the release of epinephrine and norepinephrine from the gland in varying ratios, depending upon the nature of the stimulus applied. The anatomical correlate would then be represented by two types of fiber in the splanchnic innervation of the adrenal medulla (3, 36); but this has not yet been demonstrated. It is interesting that despite the differential secretion of epinephrine and norepinephrine, the amounts of these in the urine of normal persons and those under physical or psychic stress are significantly correlated (cf. 37), with a correlation coefficient of about 0.50. In other words, the sympathoadrenal system tends to act as a unit. Nevertheless, the size of the correlation coefficient shows that there is much room remaining for the operation of additional determinants, and these are the factors which psychiatric research ought to seek, if the qualitative aspect of stress is to be described.

The rate of resynthesis of catecholamines in the adrenal medulla does not seem to be affected either by splanchnic stimulation or by acetylcholine, but it is greater in the intact than in the splanchnectomized animal.

The catecholamines of other tissues are also held in granules, but the proportion bound in this way is not as high as in the adrenal medulla. This has been shown for the splenic nerve, brain, and blood.

The normal binding of amines, including the catecholamines, in granules is impaired in the presence of reserpine, and as a result of its action the concentration of amines in the organs decreases significantly, even to complete disappearance of the amines (38). Moreover, patients under treatment with reserpine have a reduced concentration of norepinephrine in the blood (39). The urinary catecholamines are also diminished in patients receiving reserpine chronically (40).

## Pheochromocytoma

Pheochromocytoma is a tumor of the chromaffin tissue, usually occurring in one or the other adrenal gland, occasionally in both, and sometimes ectopically, as in the case of retained organs of Zuckerkandl. Unlike the normal adrenal medulla whose secretory activity is under nervous control, the pheochromocytoma can release catecholamines spontaneously. The sudden elevation of epinephrine or norepinephrine levels in the blood may provoke a severe episode including the hypertensive experience, blanching of the skin, sweating, palpitations, severe headache, vertigo, and anxiety. Patients with pheochromocytoma occasionally come to the attention of the psychiatrist, and may receive the diagnosis of psychoneurosis before the tumor is discovered. The condition must be differentiated as well from thyrotoxicosis, essential hypertension, and diabetes mellitus (41).

## Relation of Catecholamine Metabolism to Psychiatric States

Adequate physicochemical (fluorometric) methods for the determination of the catecholamines have become available within the period since about 1950. From the point of view of the physiologist these methods now permit the direct measurement of sympathoadrenal function, without dependence upon the more tedious biological assays. In deference to the latter it must be said that they have remained the final arbiter in choice of chemical methods, for they tell whether the material being measured is of physiological importance or not. Fluorometric methods have been coming into use gradually in the psychiatric hospital as a means of assessing the role of the sympathoadrenal system in mental disease and its treatment. It is noteworthy that the ethylenediamine condensation method for estimation of catecholamines was originally devised by Weil-Malherbe and Bone specifically for this purpose. In a sense, the measurement of the catecholamines is one of the closest approaches to the investigation of the functioning of the nervous system in humans, and therefore merits particularly serious attention in consideration of research problems of psychiatry.

The concentrations of epinephrine and norepinephrine in the plasma have been measured in many different mental conditions: psychoses, psychoneuroses, personality disorders, and various mental deficiencies. The epinephrine level is subnormal in the oligophrenias (42), but in all the other states studied the two catecholamines are in the normal range of values (27, 42, 43, 44).

A very extensive study of the urinary excretion of catecholamines has been carried out by Bergsman (45). Eighty-four patients classified under ten categories of mental disease were compared in terms of catecholamine excretion with 27 normal subjects. This work, together with that of Ström-Olsen and Weil-Malherbe on manic-depressive psychosis (46), has revealed abnormal excretory patterns in manic and depressive states. During the manic phase of manic-depressive psychosis the excretion of epinephrine and norepinephrine was higher than during the depressive phase (46). Moreover, manic patients excreted more of these amines than did those suffering from endogenous depression (45, 46). The excretion of epinephrine was normal in chronic schizophrenic patients, but it was elevated in the acute cases (45). Abnormally low rates of excretion of epinephrine were observed in patients with senile dementia and with mongolism. The excretion of norepinephrine tended to be elevated in acute schizophrenia and in neurasthenic cases, but because of the high intragroup variation these differences were not statistically significant (45). Catecholamine excretion in two phenylketonuric subjects was normal.

Friedman and his colleagues have studied biochemical patterns in men exhibiting a behavior pattern characterized by considerable ambition and drive, as well as by a high incidence of coronary artery disease. Their excretion of norepinephrine and epinephrine (especially the former) rises during working hours more than in subjects with a converse pattern (47).

The output of epinephrine and norepinephrine is increased by the consumption of alcohol (48). In delirium tremens and related conditions the excretion of these amines is very high (3 to 4 times normal) and remains high for some time after withdrawal of alcohol, indeed, even after alcohol is no longer detectable in the blood (49).

Some investigators have sought a chemical yardstick of the emotions in the catecholamine levels, taking these as a rough function of the amounts secreted at nerve endings and from adrenal medullary cells. This has proved a difficult undertaking when dealing with the concentration of catecholamines in the plasma, as a study by Regan and Reilly has shown (44). Perhaps for this reason more research has been devoted to the urinary output of epinephrine and norepinephrine. Elmadjian and his colleagues have investigated this aspect of catecholamine metabolism in a number of behavioral groups under emotion-provoking stresses: normal persons in anticipatory states; persons operating controls simulating those of a plane (pursuitmeter test); and contestants in professional and amateur sports. The interpretation of the data by this group of investigators is that "active aggressive emotional displays are related to increased excretion of norepinephrine, whereas tense, anxious, but passive, emotional displays are related to increased excretion of epinephrine in association with normal excretion of norepinephrine" (50). The data provided are, however, open to other explanations; for example, the elevated output of norepinephrine may arise from the intense muscular activity which is known to raise the plasma concentration of norepinephrine (51) as well as the amount of this amine appearing in the urine (52). Silverman et al. have lent their support to Elmadjian's hypothesis (52a). Mendelson et al. (53) studied subjects voluntarily submitting to another type of stress: sensory deprivation. They noted mean increases in the excretion of catecholamines, but the changes from control to experimental periods and from the latter to postexperimental period were not consistent for all subjects. Mason and his colleagues have studied monkeys provoked by noxious stimuli into emotional responses. From the results of multiple-schedule conditioning experiments these investigators concluded that the element of unpredictability may be a critical factor in the release of epinephrine (53A).

The work of Elmadjian and his colleagues has developed out of the experimental aim, attempted so many times in the past, of describing emotional expression in physiological terms, and is theoretically related to the studies of autonomic function conducted by Funkenstein, Green-blatt, and Solomon. According to these investigators individuals, varying as they do in their autonomic patterns of response (detectable by blood pressure changes following the administration of epinephrine or metha-choline (54)), may under certain conditions secrete predominantly either an epinephrine-like substance or a norepinephrine-like substance into the blood (55). States in which elevated blood pressure is mediated by the former are said to be exemplified by certain psychiatric patients and by normotensive students under psychological stress. The reasoning behind this hypothesis is beyond the scope of discussion here, but undoubtedly the establishment of norepinephrine as a normal constituent of the body and the differentiation of its pharmacological properties from those of epinephrine (2) (Table 25-1) have facilitated presentation of the theory. In addition it has received some support from Gellhorn's theory of central sympathetic reactivity (56). In terms of physiological results, Funkenstein and his colleagues have found that these two groups can be differentiated by their vascular response to methacholine. In one group there is a prolonged fall in blood pressure (lasting more than 25 minutes); in the other the hypotension is rapidly compensated, with a return to normal pressures. Funkenstein has suggested that methacholine first demon-strates its peripheral vasodilating activity and then induces, through a central mechanism, the excessive secretion of epinephrine or of nor-epinephrine, depending upon constitutional characteristics of the indi-vidual. From the clinical side the patients with long-lasting depression in blood pressure after methacholine tend to improve with electroshock therapy, in marked contradistinction to the high proportion of failures with this treatment in the second group.

Funkenstein's theory has been extended as a physiological basis not only for the two types (very broadly speaking) of methacholine reactors, but also for two types of emotional expression. According to the argument individuals who express their anger inward, that is, passively, are epinephrine-secretors, whereas those turning their emotion outward in an active way, with aggressive display, are norepinephrine secretors (57). However, the validity of the Funkenstein test and its ability to predict the therapeutic result of electroconvulsive therapy have not been established (58).

Weil-Malherbe has presented a number of lines of evidence be-speaking a relation between the level of epinephrine in the plasma and mental activity (42). This is exemplified by the lower concentration of this hormone in the plasma during states of reduced mental activity, as in natural (42) and in barbiturate-induced (59) sleep. The rate of excretion of epinephrine and norepinephrine in the urine is also lower during sleep, and proportionately more so for the former compound (60). The low concentration of plasma epinephrine in the oligophrenias has already been mentioned. The action of convulsants has also been investigated in several laboratories. The administration of pentylenetetrazol and electroshock induces an elevation in the concentrations of the plasma catecholamines (42, 61). The rise in norepinephrine is not observed if the patient has been premedicated with a barbiturate or a muscle relaxant (59). In studies designed to detect changes in the rate of excretion of catecholamines as a result of electroshock therapy it was observed that the excretion of epinephrine increases as a result of passage of the electric current, but that this effect is abolished by premedication of the patients with atropine and a barbiturate, in addition to a skeletal muscle relaxant (62).

The rate of excretion of catecholamines in the urine is correlated with the patient's ultimate response to a course of electroshock therapy. In a series of patients with various diagnoses (endogenous depression, manic-depressive psychosis, schizophrenia) it was found that subjects having a low rate of excretion of catecholamines in the morning urine tend to fall into the improved group, whereas those with a high rate tend to be in the nonimproved category (63). Although it is an empirical observation of the clinic that patients with a high degree of manifest anxiety do not register as great gains with electroshock therapy as do others, the rates of excretion of catecholamines did not agree in this respect with the clinical picture. Havens et al. (61) followed 25 psychotic patients through their course of electroshock therapy; the increase in plasma epinephrine occasioned by the treatment was greater with successive seizures, up to the ninth. Griswold, however, found no change in the epinephrine response (64).

The specific release of epinephrine during electroconvulsive therapy and insulin shock treatment confirms clinical observation of increased sympathetic activity engendered by these treatments. The enhanced secretion of epinephrine, recognized through the elevated level of the hormone in the plasma, or by its increase in the urine, can be reduced by premedication and, in fact, is not essential to the success of treatment. This has been demonstrated in a case of depression treated successfully by electroconvulsive therapy, even though the patient has been bilaterally adrenalectomized at an earlier date (65). From infusion studies in experimental animals Weil-Malherbe et al. have concluded that epinephrine does not cross the blood-brain barrier except to a small extent in the hypothalamus (66). Nevertheless, central effects of epinephrine and norepinephrine have been observed by many investigators following the administration of the amine intravenously; changes in cerebral electrical activity have been described (67, 68), so that the catecholamines are presumably acting upon hypothalamic receptors or peripheral ones with nervous connections to the brain. It is possible that the permeability of the blood-brain barrier to arterial epinephrine is increased by electroshock treatment (69), but it must also be kept in mind that the activity of the sympatho-adrenal system normally observed peripherally in electroshock may merely reflect an activation of its central counterpart: the adrenergic component of the reticular activating system (67).

# References

1. KRAYER, O. (ed.). *Symposium on Catecholamines,* Baltimore, Williams & Wilkins, 1959; SOURKES, T. L. *In Neurochemistry,* ed. ELLIOTT, K. A. C., I. H. PAGE, and J. H. QUASTEL, 2d ed. Springfield, Ill., Charles C Thomas, 1962.

2. GOLDENBERG, M., K. L. PINES, E. BALDWIN, D. G. GREENE, and C. E. ROG. *Am. J. Med. 5:*792, 1948; HICKAM, J. B., W. H. CARGILL, and A. C. GOLDEN. *J. Clin. Invest. 27:*290, 1948; LANDS, A. M. *Pharmacol. Rev. 1:* 279, 1949; GOLDENBERG, M., V. APGAR, R. DETERLING, and K. L. PINES. *J.A.M.A. 140:*776, 1949; CHEN, G., R. PORTMAN, D. RUSSELL, and C. R. ENSOR. *J. Am. Pharmac. Assoc., Scient. Ed. 11:*273, 1951.

3. VON EULER, U. S. *Noradrenaline,* Springfield, Ill., Charles C Thomas, 1956.

4. DIAZ, C. J., P. DE LA BARREDA, and R. A. NUNEZ. *Rev. Espan. 59:*76, 1955; *Seen in Chem. Abstr. 50:*5878f, 1956.

5. PEART, W. S. *J. Physiol. 108:*491, 1949; MANN, M., and G. B. WEST. *Brit. J. Pharmacol. 5:*173, 1950; *idem. 6:*79, 1951; BURN, J. H., and M. J. RAND. *Nature 184:*163, 1959.

6. SOURKES, T. L., G. F. MURPHY, and A. RABINOVITCH. *Nature 189:*577, 1961.

7. WERLE, E., and J. JÜNGTEN-SELL. *Biochem. Z. 327:*259, 1955; SOURKES, T. L. *Rev. Can. de Biol. 14:*49, 1955.

8. HEACOCK, R. A. *Chem. Revs. 59:*181, 1959.

9. GREEN, D. E., and D. RICHTER. *Biochem. J. 31:*596, 1937.

10. HEACOCK, R. A., C. NERENBERG, and A. N. PAYZA. *Can. J. Chem. 36:*853, 1958.

11. FISCHER, P., and L. LANDTSHEER. *Experientia 6:*305, 1950; FISCHER, P., and J. LECOMTE. *Bull. Soc. Chim. Biol. 33:*569, 1951.

12. SCHAYER, R. W., and R. L. SMILEY. *J. Biol. Chem. 202:*425, 1953.

13. HEIRMAN, P. *Compt. Rend. Soc. Biol. 126:*1264, 1937.

14. BACQ, Z. M. *J. Pharmacol. Exp. Ther. 95:*1, 1949.

15. LEACH, B. E., and R. G. HEATH. *A. M. A. Arch. Neurol. Psychiat. 76:*444, 1956; ANGEL, C., B. E. LEACH, S. MARTENS, M. COHEN, and R. G. HEATH. *A. M. A. Arch. Neurol. Psychiat. 78:*500, 1957.

16. WEIL-MALHERBE, H., and A. D. BONE. *Lancet i:*947, 1953; *idem, Biochem. J. 70:*14, 1958; COHEN, G., B. HOLLAND, and M. GOLDENBERG. *A. M. A. Arch. Neurol. Psychiat. 80:*484, 1958; BERTHIAUME, M., J. LEDUC, and A. D'IORIO. *A. M. A. Arch. Gen. Psychiat. 2:*468, 1960.

17. COHEN, G., B. HOLLAND, and M. GOLDENBERG. *A. M. A. Arch. Gen. Psychiat. 1:*228, 1959; LABROSSE, E. H., J. D. MANN, and S. S. KETY. *J. Psychiat. Res. 1:*68, 1961.

18. APTER, N. *Am. J. Psychiat. 115:*55, 1958.

19. HOFFER, A., and M. KENYON. *A. M. A. Arch. Neurol. Psychiat. 77:*437, 1957.

20. OSMOND, H., and J. SMYTHIES. *J. Ment. Sci. 98:*309, 1952; HOFFER, A., H. OSMOND, and J. SMYTHIES. *ibid. 100:*29, 1954; OSMOND, H., and A. HOFFER. *ibid. 105:*653, 1959.

21. SMYTHIES, J. R. *Lancet i:*1287, 1960.

22. HOFFER, A. *Am. J. Psychiat. 114:*752, 1958.

23. SZARA, S., J. AXELROD, and S. PERLIN. *Am. J. Psychiat. 115:*162, 1958; FELDSTEIN, A. *Am. J. Psychiat. 116:*454, 1959; LAYNE, D. S., and T. L. SOURKES. *J. Nerv. Ment. Dis. 130:*93, 1960; RANDRUP, A., and I. MUNKVAD. *Am. J. Psychiat. 117:*153, 1960.

24. PAYZA, A. N., and M. E. MAHON. *Anal. Chem. 31:*1170, 1959.

25. EVARTS, E. V., L. GILLESPIE, T. C. FLEMING, and A. SJOERDSMA. *Proc. Soc. Exp. Biol. Med. 98:*74, 1958; CHAMPAGNE, J., A. D'IORIO, and A. BEAULNES. *Science 132:*419, 1960; SMYTHIES, J. R., and C. K. LEVY. *J. Ment. Sci. 106:*531, 1960.

26. BLASCHKO, H., and A. D. WELCH. *Arch. Exp. Path. u. Pharmakol. 219:*17, 1953; HILLARP, N. A., S. LAGERSTEDT, and B. NILSON. *Acta Physiol. Scand. 29:*251, 1953; BLASCHKO, H., G. V. BORN, A. D'IORIO, and N. R. EADE. *J. Physiol. 133:*548, 1956; FORTIER, A., J. LEDUC, and A. D'IORIO. *Rev. Can. de Biol. 18:*110, 1959.

27. MANGER, W. M., B. E. SCHWARZ, C. W. BAARS, K. G. WAKIM, J. L. BOLLMAN, M. C. PETERSEN, and J. BERKSON. *A. M. A. Arch. Neurol. Psychiat. 78:*396, 1957.

28. ELMADJIAN, F., E. T. LAMSON, H. FREEMAN, R. NERI, and L. VARJABEDIAN. *J. Clin. Endocrinol. & Metab. 16:*876, 1956.

29. ELMADJIAN, F., J. M. HOPE, and H. FREEMAN. *A. M. A. Arch. Neurol. Psychiat. 77:*399, 1957.

30. LUFT, R., and U. S. VON EULER. *J. Clin. Endocrinol. & Metab. 16:*1017, 1956.

31. SOURKES, T. L., B. D. DRUJAN, and G. C. CURTIS. *A. M. A. Arch. Gen. Psychiat. 1:*275, 1959.

32 HÖKFELT, B. *Acta Physiol. Scand. 25:*Suppl. 92, 1951; OUTSCHOORN, A. S. *Brit. J. Pharmacol. 7:*605, 1952; GOLDFIEN, A., M. S. ZILELI, R. H. DESPOINTES, and J. E. BETHUNE. *Endocrinology 62:*749, 1958.

33. VON EULER, U. S., and R. LUFT. *Metabolism 1:*528, 1952.

34. DUNER, H. *Acta Physiol. Scand.* 28:1, 1953.
35. HOLZBAUER, M., and M. VOGT. *Brit. J. Pharmacol.* 9:249, 1954; MILLAR, R. A. *J. Pharmacol. Exp. Ther.* 118:435, 1956.
36. RAPELA, C. E. *Acta Physiol. Latinoamer.* 6:1, 1956.
37. CURTIS, G. C., R. A. CLEGHORN, and T. L. SOURKES. *J. Psychosom. Res.* 4:176, 1960.
38. HOLZBAUER, M., and M. VOGT. *J. Neurochem.* 1:8, 1956; CARLSSON, A., E. ROSENGREN, A. BERTLER, and J. NILSSON. *In Psychotropic Drugs, ed.* GARATTINI, S., and V. GHETTI, Amsterdam, Elsevier, 1957.
39. BURGER, M. *Arch. Exp. Path. u. Pharmakol.* 230:489, 1957.
40. GADDUM, J. H., W. A. KRIVOY, and G. LAVERTY. *J. Neurochem.* 2:249, 1958; CARLSSON, A., E. B. RASMUSSEN, and P. KRISTJANSEN. *ibid.* 4:318, 1959.
41. DRAKE, F. R., and F. G. EBAUGH. *Am. J. Psychiat.* 113:295, 1956.
42. WEIL-MALHERBE, H. *J. Ment. Sci.* 101:733, 1955.
43. REILLY, J., and P. F. REGAN. *Proc. Soc. Exp. Biol. Med.* 95:377, 1957.
44. REGAN, P. F., and J. REILLY *J. Nerv. Ment. Dis.* 127:12, 1958.
45. BERGSMAN, A. *Acta Psychiat. et Neurol. Scand.* 34:Suppl. 133, 1959.
46. STRÖM-OLSEN, R., and H. WEIL-MALHERBE. *J. Ment. Sci.* 104:696, 1958.
47. FRIEDMAN, M., S. ST. GEORGE, S. O. BYERS, and R. H. ROSENMAN. *J. Clin. Invest.* 39:758, 1960.
48. KLINGMAN, G. I., and M. GOODALL. *J. Pharmacol. Exp. Ther.* 121:313, 1957; PERMAN, E. S. *Acta Physiol. Scand.* 44:241, 1958; ABELIN, I., C. HERREN, and W. BERLI. *Helvet. Med. Acta* 25:591, 1958.
49. GIACOBINI, E., S. IZIKOWITZ, and A. WEGMANN. *Arch. Gen. Psychiat.* 3:289, 1960; WEGMANN, A., and GIACOBINI, E. *Schweitz. Med. Wochschr.* 91:658, 1961.
50. ELMADJIAN, F., J. M. HOPE, and E. T. LAMSON. *J. Clin. Endocrinol. & Metab.* 17:608, 1957; ELMADJIAN, F., J. M. HOPE, and E. T. LAMSON. *Recent Progr. Hormone Res.* 14:513, 1958.
51. GRAY, I., and W. P. BEETHAM, JR. *Proc. Soc. Exp. Biol. Med.* 96:636, 1957; VENDSALU, A. *Acta Physiol. Scand.* 49:Suppl. 173, 1960.
52. KÄRKI, N. T. *Acta Physiol. Scand.* 39:Suppl. 132, 1956.
52A. SILVERMAN, A. J., S. I. COHEN, B. M. SHMAVONIAN, and N. KIRSHNER. *Recent Adv. Biol. Psychiat.* 3:104, 1961.
53. MENDELSON, J., P. KUBZANSKY, P. H. LEIDERMAN, D. WEXLER, C. DuToIT, and P. SOLOMON. *A. M. A. Arch. Gen. Psychiat.* 2:147, 1960.
53A. MASON, J. W., G. MANGAN, JR., J. V. BRADY, D. CONRAD, and D. M. RIOCH. *Psychosom. Med.* 23:344, 1961.
54. FUNKENSTEIN, D. H., M. GREENBLATT, and H. C. SOLOMON. *J. Nerv. Ment. Dis.* 108:409, 1948.
55. DIETHELM, O., M. F. FLEETWOOD, and A. T. MILHORAT. *In Life Stress and Bodily Disease.* Baltimore, Williams & Wilkins, 1950; FLEETWOOD, M. F., and A. HARRINGTON. *Am. J. Physiol.* 166:314, 1951; FUNKENSTEIN, D. H., M. GREENBLATT, and H. C. SOLOMON. *Am. J. Psychiat.* 108:652, 1952; FUNKENSTEIN, D. H., and L. W. MEADE. *J. Nerv. Ment. Dis.* 119:380, 1954.

56. GELLHORN, E. *Physiological Foundations of Neurology and Psychiatry.* Minneapolis, University of Minnesota Press, 1953.

57. FUNKENSTEIN, D. H. *J. Nerv. Ment. Dis. 124*:58, 1956.

58. FEINBERG, I. *A. M. A. Arch. Neurol. Psychiat. 80*:489, 1958.

59. WEIL-MALHERBE, H. *J. Ment. Sci. 101*:156, 1955.

60. ELMADJIAN, F., E. T. LAMSON, and R. NERI. *J. Clin. Endocrinol. & Metab. 16*:222, 1956.

61. HAVENS, L. L., M. S. ZILELI, A. DiMASCIO, L. BOLING, and A. GOLDFIEN. *J. Ment. Sci. 105*:821, 1959.

62. SOURKES, T. L., B. D. DRUJAN, and G. C. CURTIS. *J. Nerv. Ment. Dis. 127*:191, 1958.

63. SOURKES, T. L., R. B. SLOANE, and B. D. DRUJAN. *A. M. A. Arch. Neurol. Psychiat. 78*:204, 1957; *idem, Confinia Neurol. 18*:299, 1958.

64. GRISWOLD, R. L. *J. Appl. Physiol. 12*:117, 1958.

65. GUZE, S. B., G. WINOKUR, and M. E. LEVIN. *J. Nerv. Ment. Dis. 124*:195, 1956.

66. WEIL-MALHERBE, H., J. AXELROD, and R. TOMCHICK. *Science 129*:1226, 1959; WEIL-MALHERBE, H., L. G. WHITBY, and J. AXELROD. *J. Neurochem. 8*:55, 1961.

67. BONVALLET, M., P. DELL, and G. HIEBEL. *EEG Clin. Neurophysiol. 6*:119, 1954; ROTHBALLER, A. B. *EEG Clin. Neurophysiol. 8*:603, 1956.

68. BRADLEY, P. B., and A. MOLLICA. *Arch. Ital. Biol. 96*:168, 1958.

69. ROSENBLATT, S., J. D. CHANLEY, H. SOBOTKA, and M. R. KAUFMAN. *J. Neurochem. 5*:172, 1960.

# 26

# ADRENAL CORTEX

Modern studies on the physiology of the adrenal cortex date back about 30 years to the demonstration that crude cortical extracts can maintain the life of adrenalectomized animals. Thereafter, in a multitude of studies it has been shown that the life-maintaining properties of the adrenal cortex reside in its regulatory actions on multifarious processes of mineral and organic metabolism, actions which are of utmost importance to the organism when forced to adjust to some moderate or severe alteration in the environment. Much of the information in this area has been obtained through studies in experimental pathology but confirmation by biochemical techniques has been sought. However, not until about 1950 did methodological advances finally permit the routine measurement of corticosteroids and their conversion products in blood (Nelson-Samuels technique) and urine (Porter-Silber and Glenn-Nelson procedures) (1), thus extending the scope of studies of adrenal cortical function by another order. The period mentioned witnessed the introduction of deoxycorticosterone, the first cortical hormone available in quantity, and later on the synthesis of cortisone, cortisol, and aldosterone (2). Thus, just at the time when research on the sympathetic nervous system in normal and emergency situations had clarified the function of one part of the adrenal gland, studies on the other portion began which were ultimately to demonstrate for it also a role in the response to stress, albeit a more slowly developing and prolonged response.

## Hormones of the Adrenal Cortex

About 30 steroids have been isolated from the adrenal gland; many of these possess biological activity. The most prominent adrenal cortical steroid in man is cortisol (hydrocortisone; 17-hydroxycorticosterone; 11,17,21-trihydroxy-$\Delta^4$-pregnene-3,20-dione) which appears to be formed in the fasciculate layer of the cortex (3). Corticosterone (11,21-dihydroxy-$\Delta^4$-pregnene-3,20-dione), the major hormone in some species, is not as important a product in man; its concentration in human plasma is less than 10 percent that of cortisol (4). Aldosterone, the salt-retaining factor of the adrenal cortex (electrocortin; 11,21-dihydroxy-18-oxo-$\Delta^4$-pregnene-3,20-dione) is derived from the glomerulosa, and androgenic substances from the reticulate zone.

Steroids which have been demonstrated to be present in the adrenal venous blood of man are cortisol, corticosterone, and 11-$\beta$-hydroxy-$\Delta^4$-androstene-3,17-dione. In a search for other compounds tetrahydrocortisol, tetrahydrocortisone, and $\Delta^4$-androstene-3,17-dione have been tentatively identified, but cortisone, 11-deoxycortisone, deoxycorticosterone, and progesterone have not been found in the adrenal blood (5).

Demonstrated sources in metabolism for this multiplicity of steroids appear thus far to be (a) acetate, which is incorporated into the adrenal compounds as shown by tracer studies and (b) cholesterol, which is degraded and otherwise transformed into the hormones. Other distant precursors may well exist. The cholesterol pathway is influenced positively by corticotropin (ACTH), but the synthesis from acetate is independent of the anterior pituitary gland. Pregnenolone and progesterone lie on one of the defined biosynthetic routes in the adrenal cortex. Their further transformation lead to (a) $\Delta^4$-pregnene-11$\beta$-17$\alpha$-diol-3,20-dione (by hydroxylation at the 11- and 17-positions); (b) corticosterone (by hydroxylation at the 11- and 21-positions); and (c) cortisol (by hydroxylation at all three positions). A second route which is followed by steroid precursors in the adrenal cortex proceeds to dehydroepiandrosterone (the $C_{19}$-steroid route), $\Delta^4$-androstene-3,17-dione and 11$\beta$-hydroxy-$\Delta^4$-androstene-3,17-dione (cf. 6).

The adrenal cortical steroids can be roughly divided on the basis of their physiological actions into those which have a pronounced effect upon the excretion of salt and water and which are also particularly effective in maintaining the blood pressure and in protecting the life of the adrenalectomized animal, and those which favor the deposition of glycogen in the liver and which can antagonize the action of insulin to some extent and reduce the pituitary secretion of ACTH. Selye has classed these steroids as *mineralocorticoids* and *glucocorticoids*, respectively, the terminology referring to their most prominent actions without suggesting that either group is completely devoid of the other's actions. Because of the ability of many steroids, especially in the glucocorticoid category, to prevent experimental granuloma Selye introduced the additional terms *anti-inflammatory* or *antiphlogistic* steroids for describing these.

## Control of Secretion

The effect of ACTH upon the secretion of aldosterone varies from species to species. In man the secretion is independent of the anterior pituitary hormone. The administration of somatotropic hormone may, however, increase the output. Other corticosteroids decrease the output (7). Under normal conditions the secretion of aldosterone is adjusted to changes in electrolyte, primarily sodium, intake. The ability of hypophysectomized animals to retain sodium is attributed to the continuation of the glomerulosa in an intact state, even though the other two layers diminish in size and activity. ACTH, on the other hand, controls the two innermost zones of the gland; administration of corticotropin causes an increase in the output of cortisol and androgens from the gland (3). The several theories which have been put forward to account for the steady-state as well as active secretion of cortisol all focus on the mechanism of control over the prior secretion of ACTH. Three types of mechanism have been proposed. (*a*) *Regulation by the concentration of cortical hormone in the blood reaching the pituitary:* ACTH secretion can be suppressed by the administration of large doses of an appropriate corticosteroid; its secretion is increased, conversely, in the adrenalectomized individual. These facts have suggested that the level of circulating adrenal cortical hormone controls the output of corticotropin through a finely adjusted feedback mechanism. The concentration of cortisol is itself determined by the balance of many factors, such as the level of corticotropin in the circulating blood, the responsiveness of the adrenal cortex to the pituitary hormone, and the rate of utilization and conversion of the steroid in the peripheral tissues. In regard to this last point current methods of determining cortisol are not yet sensitive enough to detect an arteriovenous difference which would permit estimating the rate in this manner (8). (*b*)

*Control of corticotropin release by epinephrine:* According to this view the provoking stimulus initiates at the level of the higher centers the reflex release of epinephrine from the adrenal medulla. This reaches the adenohypophysis through the circulating blood where it causes the release of ACTH; this hormone, in turn, ultimately stimulates the adrenal cortex to secrete cortisol (9). Although experiment demonstrates that this pathway is feasible, it has been shown that the adrenal medulla is not indispensable in the cortical response to stress. Furthermore, the infusion of epinephrine and norepinephrine are without effect in elevating the concentration of cortisol in plasma and urine (10). (*c*) *Nervous regulation of corticotropin secretion:* There is also evidence for regulation of the release of ACTH by some hypothalamic substance, which reaches the pituitary through the hypophysial-portal system of vessels (11). The corticotropin-releasing factor of the posterior pituitary may play the role of mediator (*cf.* Chapter 23). Thus, the neuroendocrine chain begins with the link from the peripheral receptors to the central nervous system, thence to the hypophysis, and finally to the gland in question.

Peterson and Wyngaarden have estimated that the daily turnover of cortisol in adult men is 17 to 29 mg. (12), a figure with which Cope and Black agree (13). Production of the hormone may rise to a maximum of 154 mg. per day when the cortex is stimulated by ACTH. The amount of the hormone present in the body at any given time is normally 1.1 to 2.4 mg. (12).

The normal levels of corticosteroids and their metabolic derivatives in blood and urine are shown in Table 26-1. The plasma level of the hormone shows some diurnal variation; the highest concentration occurs in the morning hours after waking, and then falls to a low level about noon, where it remains until late evening (15). Thus, investigations attempting to relate adrenal cortical activity to some other function, such as exercise or emotional state, must establish control values for the corresponding periods of the day, and ought further to take into account the marked intraindividual variation that may occur from day to day (15).

Slaunwhite and Sandberg have described a plasma protein (transcortin) which binds corticosteroids (22).

# Terminal Metabolism of Corticosteroids

As indicated in Table 26-1, a portion of the hormonal production of the adrenal cortex appears intact in the urine, but much more

TABLE 26-1. ADRENAL CORTICAL HORMONES AND
THEIR METABOLITES IN BLOOD AND URINE

| Steroid | Concentration or Amount | Reference |
|---|---|---|
| Blood | | |
| 17-Hydroxycorticosteroids | 4–10 μg.% | 8 |
| Cortisol | 2.5 μg.% | 14 |
| Aldosterone | 0.05 μg.% | 14 |
| Plasma | | |
| 17-Hydroxycorticosteroids | | |
| Men | 12 μg.% (±6)* | 15 |
| Women | 15 μg.% (±6)* | 15 |
| Cortisol | 14.0 μg.% | 4 |
| Corticosterone | 1.1 μg.% | 4 |
| Dehydroepiandrosterone | 57.5 μg.% (±10.5)* | 16 |
| Dehydroepiandrosterone | 40.5 μg.% (±11.3)* | 17 |
| Androsterone and/or Etio- | | |
| cholanolone | 18.0 μg.% (±6.7)* | 17 |
| Urine | | |
| 17-Hydroxycorticosteroids | 6.42 mg./day (±0.91)† | 18 |
| Copper-reducing lipides (11- | | |
| Oxycorticosteroid-like sub- | | |
| stances) | 0.10–0.44 mg./day | 19 |
| Tetrahydrocortisol | 1.3 mg./day | 18 |
| Tetrahydrocortisone | 3.8 mg./day | 18 |
| Aldosterone | | |
| Men | 0.8–6.8 μg./day | 20 |
| Women | 1.7–5.5 μg./day | 20 |
| 17-Ketosteroids | | |
| Men | 6.7–27.2 mg./day | 21 |
| Women | 3.8–16.9 mg./day | 21 |

* Mean ± Standard Deviation.
† Mean ± Standard Error.

is excreted in the conjugated form, as with glucuronic acid. Ring A
of cortisol and cortisone undergoes reduction to form the corresponding
tetrahydro derivatives. The side chain of these compounds may also
undergo reduction, but its excision, with the formation of neutral
nineteen-carbon 17-ketosteroids, is a better-known process. The measurement of 17-ketosteroid excretion in the urine is widely practiced in
research and laboratory diagnosis in order to detect gross deviation

in function of the gonads, adrenals, and pituitary or to control dosage levels of certain steroids used therapeutically (23, 24). The major fraction of the 17-ketosteroids derives from the adrenal cortex (23): the $C_{21}$-steroids of the corticosteroid series as well as the $C_{19}$ derivatives of the androgens. Compounds of the testosterone series, originating in the testis, also contribute, so that the mean daily excretion of 17-ketosteroids in the urine of normal adult males (15 mg.) is somewhat higher than in normal adult females (10 mg.). The more abundant 17-ketosteroids and their sources are dehydroepiandrosterone (probably entirely produced in the adrenals); 11-keto-androsterone and 11-ketoetiocholanolone (from adrenosterone, cortisol, and cortisone); androsterone and etiocholanolone (from testosterone); and 11$\beta$-hydroxyandrosterone and 11$\beta$-hydroxy-etiocholanolone (from 11$\beta$-hydroxyandrostene-3,17-dione, cortisol, and cortisone).

Metabolic experiments with steroids bearing radioactive carbon in the ring show that virtually no respiratory carbon dioxide appears in the labeled form. This attests to the remarkable stability in the body of the ring structure once it has been formed.

# Clinical Syndromes Caused by Hypo- or Hyperfunction of the Adrenal Cortex

Specific clinical syndromes occur which are related to hypofunction of the adrenal cortex, or to excessive production of aldosterone, hormones of the cortisol series, androgens, or of the last two groups together.

*Addison's disease:* Patients with Addison's disease display weakness and fatiguability, and reduced cardiovascular tone and vascular response. Their skin develops a brownish pigmentation. Metabolically, many of the changes noted following adrenalectomy are seen in this condition, such as a loss of sodium in the urine, reflected in a low blood sodium level; elevated blood potassium; dehydration; a hypoglycemic tendency; increased sensitivity to insulin; reduced rate of gluconeogenesis (from protein); low 17-ketosteroid levels in the urine; and low or normal plasma corticosteroids. The gland is relatively unresponsive to corticotropin as measured by the urinary output of 17-ketosteroids and 17-hydroxycorticosteroids following the administration of ACTH.

Some of the symptoms encountered in Addison's disease—the asthenia, anorexia, and gastrointestinal distress, apathy, anxiety reactions, depression, occasionally psychotic reactions—lend the condition a neuropsychiatric cast which may complicate differential diagnosis (Table 26-2). These mental changes led Klippel (1899) to refer to *l'Encéphalopathie Addisonienne.* Cleghorn (25), Stoll (27), and Drake (28) have reviewed this aspect. Reversal of the metabolic changes by replacement therapy with deoxycorticosterone, cortisone, or both may be accompanied by a return to the premorbid mental state. In cases presenting neuropsychiatric features electroencephalographic changes have been encountered, and these can be abolished by the infusion of extra glucose (29).

*Primary aldosteronism:* This syndrome, formerly known as potassium-losing nephritis, has recently been related to an excessive production of aldosterone (30). As a result of endogenous overdosage with the sodium-retaining hormone patients exhibit "periodic severe muscular weakness, intermittent tetany and paresthesia, polyuria, polydipsia, and hypertension" (30). The metabolic changes embrace high sodium and low potassium content of the blood, alkalosis, and mild proteinuria. Excessive amounts of potassium may be lost in the urine (31). No change is observed in the urinary content of 17-ketosteroids and 17-hydroxycorticosteroids.

*Cushing's syndrome:* This is caused by a hyperfunctioning adrenal cortex, due either to a tumor of the gland or to abnormally high stimulation by corticotropin as a result of basophil adenoma of the adenohypophysis. The symptoms, which are reproducible by chronic overdosage with cortisone or cortisol, include a characteristic type of obesity, plethora, hypertension with edema, skin changes, osteoporosis, asthenia, and mental changes. Hirsutism, cessation of menses, and other virilizing changes may occur in women. There are several types of metabolic occurrence: alkalosis with low blood potassium and chloride; glycosuria with a diabetic glucose tolerance curve; increased level of cortisol in the blood as well as an increased output of 17-hydroxy-corticosteroids and 17-ketosteroids in the urine.

The mental changes in Cushing's syndrome are not of a single pattern (32). Emotional upset is common, particularly depressive states; mania or euphoria is seen in some cases (*cf.* Table 26-2). In some cases the psychiatric picture predominates over the endocrine features (33). Many hypotheses have been proposed to explain the mental disturbances associated with hyperadrenocortical states. After classifying and examining these theories in great detail, Quarton et al. (34) conclude that "a satisfactory explanation . . . is not at present available although the literature in this field in now quite extensive."

Bleuler considers the psychopathological aspects of Cushing's syndrome and of Addison's disease to be basically identical, in spite of their marked endocrine contrasts (35).

*Adrenogenital syndrome:* In this condition there is increased production of androgens by the adrenal cortex resulting from the presence of a functioning tumor. There is some evidence that in the adrenogenital syndrome there is a biochemical lesion in corticosteroidogenesis and that

TABLE 26-2. OCCURRENCE OF PSYCHOLOGICAL CHANGES
IN ADRENAL CORTICAL DYSFUNCTION

| Psychological Change | Percent of Cases |
|---|---|
| Addison's disease* (25) | |
| Psychologic apathy | 84 |
| Negativism | 80 |
| Seclusiveness | 48 |
| Depression | 48 |
| Irritability | 48 |
| Suspiciousness | 16 |
| Agitation | 8 |
| Paranoid delusions | 4 |
| Cushing's syndrome (26) | |
| Severe depression | 25 |
| Frank psychosis | 15 |
| Nervousness and irritability | 15 |
| Mental retardation, dullness | 11 |
| Attempted suicide | 10 |
| Anxiety and insomnia | 10 |

* As seen in 25 cases.

this lesion consists of a deficiency of the enzyme catalyzing oxidation of a precursor at the $C_{21}$ position without any decrease in the formation of the 11,17-oxygenated congener (6). The steroids produced as a result of this pattern of oxidation are androgenic, and they contribute to an elevated output of 17-ketosteroids in the urine.

# Activity of the Adrenal Cortex in Mental Illnesses and Emotional States

The role of the adrenal cortex in metabolic adjustment to injury and other stressful circumstances long ago raised a number of questions: (*a*) Can psychological states act as does a physical stressing agent, to elicit adrenocortical responses? (b) Does mental disease represent the pathophysiological result of continued operation of some stress? (c) Does the adrenal cortex function normally in patients with mental diseases? Increased activity of the adrenal cortex is generally considered to be an invariable accompaniment of stress (36). Specific conditions in which it has been shown that the gland is activated in man are emotional states, surgery, and some types of physical exercise. However, it is not possible to demonstrate this activation, as determined by direct hormone measurements on the body fluids, in every condition falling under the rubric of stress; exercising in the pursuitmeter (37), participating in a stress-provoking interview (38), carrying out a monotonous task (39), or being subjected to perceptual deprivation (40), cold, or oxygen deficit fail in this respect.

Because of the various controls over the activity of the adrenal cortex a decrease in the activity of this organ may result from defects at several points. In the first place, deficient cellular function of the adrenal cortex may occur, resulting in decreased secretion of cortical hormone. Secondly, the adrenal cortex may develop a diminished sensitivity to corticotropin; this is detected by an inadequate increase in urinary excretion or in the plasma level of cortisol following a standard test dose of ACTH. Finally, a change in the responsiveness of the anterior pituitary to ACTH-liberating agents has in the past been determined by the remote effects of such agents. For example, epinephrine has been employed as the test drug used to release ACTH; the liberated corticotropin produces actions at the adrenal level, and the secreted cortical hormones bring about changes in the lymphocyte and eosinophil counts and alteration in the concentration of various blood and urinary constituents which can be quantitated. The mechanism of these changes has been put in question by the finding that neither epinephrine nor norepinephrine causes a change in the level of circulating 17-hydroxycorticosteroids (10). It still remains necessary to measure the changes in blood levels of corticotropin itself, following the administration of epinephrine.

One of the most ambitious programs of study of adrenal cortical function in the psychoses has been conducted for many years by Hoagland, Pincus, and their collaborators. These workers have found that adult schizophrenics excrete less cortical hormone than do normals (41). Their subjects were studied under resting conditions, in the morning. Cortins were estimated for the most part as neutral reducing lipides, but similar results were obtained using the more specific determination of formaldehydogenic steroids. It is interesting, however, that no difference between normal men (air force personnel) and male schizophrenics was found when urinary 17-hydroxycorticosteroids (total Porter-Silber material) were measured over the full 24-hour period (18). The study by Sloane et al. also provided no evidence for abnormally low activity of the adrenal cortex in schizophrenic patients (42). Some investigators have chosen the Talbot-Saltzmann method in the past; this is based upon the reduction of copper by urinary steroids. The urinary excretion measured in this way does not differ as between normals, schizophrenics (acute and chronic), and depressives (including involutional cases) (43).

The output of 17-ketosteroids tends to be elevated in schizophrenic patients as compared with normals (41, 44, 45).

Bliss and his colleagues observed normal levels of plasma cortisol in chronic schizophrenic patients of the hebephrenic type, but significantly elevated values in maniacal patients (39, 46). Persky et al. also found high values of the hormone in plasma in mildly and moderately disturbed patients; significant elevations were found in the neurotics and in those with psychotic depressions. In general, there was some relation between the extent of mental disturbance and the level of the circulating hormone (47).

When schizophrenics are tested under stress, *i.e.*, in one or another condition intended to provoke adrenocortical activity, the results have frequently indicated a deficiency in the adrenocortical response. On the basis of various indirect measures of adrenocortical activity this has been attributed to a relative adrenal insufficiency (41, 48) or to some defect in the connections between the central nervous system and the anterior pituitary gland (49). These conclusions have not been borne out by direct determination of cortisol in the plasma, for both normals and schizophrenics show the same increases in the circulating level of the hormone after receiving a test dose of corticotropin, pyrogen, or insulin (42).

The relation between emotional intensity and adrenal cortical activity has been studied by many different groups (50). Generally, in states associated with strong emotional expression such as competitive sports (51), anticipation of surgery, even apart from the operation itself (52), and emotional disturbances (47, 53) the adrenal cortical hormone level in the plasma rises, and larger amounts of it and its metabolites are excreted in the urine. Increased cortical activity has been found in persons exhibiting anxiety, arising either from life situations (38, 47, 54) or from some experimental situation designed to elicit emotional reactions (39). However, Friedman et al. (55) observed no evidence of increased adrenal cortical activity in subjects exhibiting a pattern of overt behavior associated with high incidence of coronary heart disease. Most of the studies in this area have measured cortisol and its metabolites, but some have measured the ACTH-responsive copper-reducing lipides (54) or aldosterone (56). According to Persky, subjects demonstrating anxiety lose intravenously administered cortisol from the plasma at a much faster rate than do normals, and they excrete less of the exogenous hormone (57). This evidence for a greater rate of utilization of the hormone in anxious subjects, together with higher plasma levels of cortisol, suggests that the cortex is secreting at an inordinately high rate. In spite of the higher concentration of the hormone in the plasma of the anxious persons a given dose of corticotropin raises this level by an even greater amount than in the normal group (58). This indicates either that anxious subjects had increased pituitary activity or that their adrenal cortex had become more sensitive to corticotropin.

As might be expected, electroshock therapy is an adrenal-activating stress, and its employment causes an accelerated output of adrenal cortical steroids in the urine at the beginning of treatment. The plasma 17-hydroxycorticosteroids also rise markedly as a result of the electroshock, even if the grand mal fit is prevented by anticonvulsant premedication (59). There is disagreement about the effect of electroshock therapy on the excretion of 17-ketosteroids (60).

Insulin therapy also causes an elevation of the plasma levels of corticosteroids (59).

## Effects of Adrenal Corticosteroids on Brain Metabolism (61)

The actions of adrenal corticosteroids on physiological and metabolic systems of the brain reveal some interesting correlations. In many cases cortisol and chemically similar compounds, on the one hand, and the 11-deoxycorticosteroids, on the other, have contrasting effects. Further, in a broad way the experimentally observed actions of these steroids appear to go together with the clinical effects: in the one case, with the central nervous system-stimulating responses; in the other, with steroid-anesthetic effects. A brief summary of some of these points will be found in Table 26-3.

TABLE 26-3. EFFECTS OF ADRENAL CORTICAL STEROIDS
ON CEREBRAL FUNCTION AND METABOLISM

| | Effects of Corticosteroids | |
| --- | --- | --- |
| | 11-Deoxy Group (e.g., DOC) | 11-Oxy Group (e.g., Cortisol) |
| Metabolic effects | | |
| Intracellular brain sodium | decreases | increases |
| Serum sodium | increases | — |
| Respiration of brain tissues *in vitro* | inhibited | not inhibited |
| Cerebral metabolic rate | | |
| Normal | decreased | no effect |
| Adrenalectomized animal | little or no effect | increased to normal |
| Glycogen deposition in brain | — | increased |
| Free amino acid content of the brain | Glutamine decreases; others, especially glutamic, aspartic, and γ-aminobutyric acids, increased | Most amino acids increase; glutamine and γ-aminobutyric acid decrease |
| Effects on cerebral blood flow | no effect | variable |
| Electroencephalogram | | |
| Normal | no effect | conflicting reports |
| Slow wave activity following adrenalectomy | no effect | activity restored to normal |
| Electroshock threshold | | |
| Normal | increases | decreases |
| In epilepsy | anticonvulsant | convulsant |

The euphorigenic action of cortisone and of corticotropin has prompted their trial in mental disease. Limited successes have been reported with cortisone [reviewed in (62)]. In a detailed and intensive study of chronic schizophrenics who were bilaterally adrenalectomized for therapy of nonpsychiatric conditions and then maintained on cortisone for many years, no evidence of improvement in mental state was found (63). If a deviant metabolism of the cortex (or medulla) were responsible for maintenance of the schizophrenic state then the removal of the glands followed by substitution therapy ought to have led to some change. Dehydroepiandrosterone, an adrenal 17-ketosteroid, has been tested in some groups of mental patients, especially in cases exhibiting constitutional immaturity (pubertal retardation) (64). Alteration in behavior patterns and mental attitudes has been reported. Elevated dosages cause restlessness, euphoria, and aggressive behavior.

# References

1. BONGIOVANNI, A. M., and W. R. EBERLEIN. *J. Clin. Endocrinol & Metab.* *15*:1524, 1955.
2. GROSS, F. *Ärztl. Fortbildung* 7:153, 1957.
3. LANDING, B. H. *In* Ciba Foundn. *Colloquia on Endocrinol.* 8:52, 1955.
4. PETERSON, R. E. *J. Clin. Endocrinol. & Metab.* *17*:1150, 1957.
5. ROMANOFF, E. B., P. HUDSON, and G. PINCUS. *J. Clin. Endocrinol. & Metab.* *13*:1546, 1953.
6. DORFMAN, R. I. *In* Ciba Foundn. *Colloquia on Endocrinol.* 8:112, 1955.
7. GAUNT, R., A. A. RENZI, and J. J. CHART. *J. Clin. Endocrinol. & Metab.* *15*:621, 1955.
8. NELSON, D. H., L. T. SAMUELS, D. G. WILLARDSON, and F. H. TYLER. *J. Clin. Endocrinol. & Metab.* *11*:1021, 1951.
9. LONG, C. N. H. *In* Ciba Foundn. *Colloquia on Endocrinol.* 4:139, 1952.
10. TYLER, F. H., C. MIGEON, and H. CASTLE. *In* Ciba Foundn. *Colloquia on Endocrinol.* 8:254, 1955.
11. MUNSON, P. L., and F. N. BRIGGS. *Recent Progr. Hormone Res.* *11*:83, 1955.
12. PETERSON, R. E., and J. B. WYNGAARDEN. *J. Clin. Invest.* 35:552, 1956.
13. COPE, C. L., and E. G. BLACK. *Clin. Science* 17:147, 1958.
14. SIMPSON, S. A., and J. F. TAIT. *In* Ciba Foundn. *Colloquia on Endocrinol.* 8:204, 1955.
15. BLISS, E. L., A. A. SANDBERG, D. H. NELSON, and K. EIK-NES. *J. Clin. Invest.* 32:818, 1953.
16. OERTEL, G. W., and K. EIK-NES. *J. Biol. Chem.* 232:543, 1958.
17. MIGEON, C. J. *In* Ciba Foundn. *Colloquia on Endocrinol.* 8:141, 1955.
18. ROMANOFF, L. P., R. M. RODRIGUEZ, J. M. SEELYE, and G. PINCUS. *J. Clin. Endocrinol. & Metab.* *17*:777, 1957.
19. TALBOT, N. B., F. ALBRIGHT, A. H. SALTZMAN, A. ZYGMUNTOWICZ, and R. WIXOM. *J. Clin. Endocrinol.* 7:331, 1947.
20. VENNING, E. H., I. DYRENFURTH, and C. J. P. GIROUD. *J. Clin. Endocrinol. & Metab.* *16*:1326, 1956.
21. FORBES, A. P., E. C. DONALDSON, E. C. REIFENSTEIN, and F. ALBRIGHT. *J. Clin. Endocrinol.* 7:264, 1947.
22. SLAUNWHITE, W. R., JR., and A. A. SANDBERG. *J. Clin. Invest.* 38:384, 1959.

23. ENGEL, L. L. *Methods Biochem. Anal. 1:*479, 1954.

24. MASON, H. L. *J. Clin. Endocrinol. & Metab. 15:*1035, 1955.

25. CLEGHORN, R. A. *Can. Med. Assoc. J. 65:*449, 1951.

26. STARR, A. M. *J. Clin. Endocrinol. & Metab. 12:*502, 1952.

27. STOLL, W. A. *Die Psychiatrie des Morbus Addison* Stuttgart, G. Thieme, 1953.

28. DRAKE, F. R. *Am. J. Med. Sci. 234:*106, 1957.

29. ENGEL, G. L., and S. G. MARGOLIN. *Arch. Int. Med. 70:*236, 1942.

30. CONN, J. W., and L. H. LOUIS. In 5th *Annual Report on Stress,* ed. SELYE, H., and G. HEUSER. New York, MD Publications, 1956.

31. MILNE, M. D., R. C. MUEHRCKE, and I. AIRD. *Quart. J. Med. 26:*317, 1957.

32. TRETHOWAN, W. H., and S. COBB. *A. M. A. Arch. Neurol. Psychiat. 67:*283, 1952.

33. HERTZ, P. E., E. NADAS, and H. WOJTKOWSKI. *Am. J. Psychiat. 112:*144, 1955.

34. QUARTON, G. C., L. D. CLARK, S. COBB, and W. BAUER. *Medicine 34:*13, 1955.

35. BLEULER, M. *Schweitz. Med. Wochschr. 81:*512, 1951; REISS, M. *J. Ment. Sci. 101:*683, 1955.

36. SAYERS, G. *Physiol. Rev. 30:*241, 1950.

37. HOAGLAND, H., J. R. BERGEN, E. BLOCH, F. ELMADJIAN, and N. R. GIBREE. *J. Applied Physiol. 8:*149, 1955.

38. PERSKY, H., R. R. GRINKER, D. A. HAMBURG, M. A. SABSHIN, S. J. KORCHIN, H. BASOWITZ, and J. A. CHEVALIER. *A. M. A. Arch. Neurol. Psychiat. 76:*549, 1956.

39. BLISS, E. L., C. J. MIGEON, C. H. H. BRANCH, and L. T. SAMUELS. *Psychosom. Med. 18:*56, 1956.

40. MURPHY, C. W., E. KURLENTS, R. A. CLEGHORN, and D. O. HEBB. *Can. J. Biochem. Physiol. 33:*1062, 1955.

41. HOAGLAND, H. *Intern. Record Med. 156:*183, 1953.

42. SLOANE, R. B., M. SAFFRAN, and R. A. CLEGHORN. *A. M. A. Arch. Neurol. Psychiat. 79:*549, 1958.

43. SMITH, F. L., A. SIMON, and J. C. LINGOES. *J. Nerv. Ment. Dis. 124:*381, 1956.

44. ALTSCHULE, M. D. *Intern. Record Med. 166:*190, 1953; STEVENSON, J. A. F., J. B. DERRICK, G. E. HOBBS, and E. V. METCALFE. *A. M. A. Arch. Neurol. Psychiat. 78:*312, 1957.

45. BATT, J. C., W. W. KAY, M. REISS, and D. E. SANDS. *J. Ment. Sci. 103:*240, 1957.

46. BLISS, E. L., and C. J. MIGEON. *Am. J. Psychiat. 112:*358, 1955.

47. BOARD, F., H. PERSKY, and D. A. HAMBURG. *Psychosom. Med. 18:*324, 1956.

48. PINCUS, G., H. HOAGLAND, H. FREEMAN, F. ELMADJIAN, and L. P. ROMANOFF. *Psychosom. Med. 11:*74, 1949; FAURBYE, A., P. VESTERGAARD, S. KOPPERNAGEL, and A. NIELSEN. *Acta Endocrinol. 8:*215, 1951.

49. PARSONS, E. H., E. F. GILDEA, E. RONZONI, and S. Z. HULBERT. *Am. J. Psychiat. 105:*573, 1949.

50. ANONYMOUS. *Brit. Med. J. ii:*496, 1958.

51. HILL, S. R., F. C. GOETZ, H. M. FOX, B. J. MURASKI, L. J. KRAKAUER, R. W. REIFENSTEIN, S. J. GRAY, W. J. REDDY, S. E. HEDBERG, J. R. ST. MARC, and G. W. THORN. *A. M. A. Arch. Int. Med.* 97:269, 1956.

52. FRANKSSON, C., C. A. GEMZELL, and U. S. VON EULER. *J. Clin. Endocrinol. & Metab.* 14:608, 1954; BIRKE, G., C. FRANKSSON, and L. O. PLANTIN. *Acta Endocrinol.* 18:201, 1955; FRANKSSON, C., and C. A. GEMZELL. *J. Clin. Endocrinol. & Metab.* 15:1069, 1955; PRICE, D. B., M. THALER, and J. W. MASON. *A. M. A. Arch. Neurol. Psychiat.* 77:646, 1957.

53. HETZEL, B. S., W. W. SCHOTTSTAEDT, W. J. GRACE, and H. G. WOLFF. *J. Clin. Endocrinol. & Metab.* 15:1057, 1955.

54. MERIVALE, W. H. H., and R. A. HUNTER. *J. Ment. Sci.* 101:890, 1955.

55. FRIEDMAN, M., S. ST. GEORGE, S. O. BYERS, and R. H. ROSENMAN. *J. Clin. Invest.* 39:758, 1960.

56. LAMSON, E. T., F. ELMADJIAN, J. M. HOPE, G. PINCUS, and D. JORJORIAN. *J. Clin. Endocrinol. & Metab.* 16:954, 1956; VENNING, E. H., I. DYRENFURTH, and J. C. BECK. *ibid.* 17:1005, 1957.

57. PERSKY, H. *J. Clin. Endocrinol. & Metab.* 17:760, 1957.

58. PERSKY, H. *A. M. A. Arch. Neurol. Psychiat.* 78:95, 1957.

59. BLISS, E. L., C. J. MIGEON, D. H. NELSON, L. T. SAMUELS, and C. H. H. BRANCH. *A. M. A. Arch. Neurol. Psychiat.* 72:352, 1954.

60. ASHBY, W. R. *J. Ment. Sci.* 95:275, 1949; KAY, W. W. *In Psychoendocrinology*, ed. REISS, M. New York, Grune and Stratton, 1958.

61. GORDAN, G. S., R. C. BENTINCK, and E. EISENBERG. *Ann. N.Y. Acad. Sci.* 54:575, 1951; HOAGLAND, H. *Recent Progr. Hormone Res.* 10:29, 1954.

62. CLEGHORN, R. A. *In Hormones, Brain Function and Behavior*, ed. HOAGLAND, H. New York, Academic Press, 1957.

63. APTER, N. S. *Am. J. Psychiat.* 115:55, 1958.

64. STRAUSS, E. B., D. E. SANDS, A. M. ROBINSON, W. J. TINDALL, and W. A. H. STEVENSON. *Brit. Med. J.* ii:64, 1952; STRAUSS, E. B., and W. A. H. STEVENSON. *J. Neurol. Neurosurg. Psychiat.* 18:137, 1955; STRAUSS, E. B., and W. A. H. STEVENSON. *In Psychoendocrinology*, ed. REISS, M. New York, Grune and Stratton, 1958; BENAIM, S. *Brit. Med. J.* ii:801, 1959.

# 27

## INSULIN AND GLUCAGON

Insulin is a protein hormone secreted by the $\beta$-cells of the islets of Langerhans in the pancreas. Its structure is now known: the fundamental unit consists of two peptide chains of 21 and 30 amino acids, respectively, and these are joined to one another through cysteinyl residues common to both chains, *i.e.*, through disulfide bridges. This unit has a molecular weight of 6000, but the actual insulin molecule consists of many such units. There are serious difficulties in the way of measuring insulin in the plasma, for it is present in small amounts and has no characteristic functional groups on its molecule to distinguish it from the many other proteins present in plasma. As knowledge of its actions has advanced, some biological assays have been developed. Thus, its stimulatory effect upon glucose uptake by isolated skeletal muscle or by adipose tissue can be employed to measure the activity of insulin in small samples of circulating blood.

The adult human is said to secrete the equivalent of 30 to 50 international units of insulin per day. This is a very small fraction of the amount of hormone in the pancreas. It has been claimed that chemoceptors in the lower brain stem can initiate impulses along the right vague nerve, which has branches to the pancreas. This nervous connection has led some authors to write of a vago-insulin system as counterposed in autonomic regulations to the sympathoadrenal system.

Such a mechanism must play a minor role in the secretion of insulin, for the blood sugar remains normal even in the animal whose pancreas has been denervated.

In normal animals the concentration of the blood sugar plays an important role in the rate of secretion of insulin, a role which may be highly specific. Glucose may have a direct action upon the $\beta$-cells of the islets, causing them to release the hormone. The insulin secreted therefrom passes into the blood stream directly to the liver.

Among the factors regulating the output of insulin are other hormones, such as the somatotropic hormone, which is necessary for the growth of islet cells. Thyroid, adrenal cortical hormones, female sex hormones, and ACTH also stimulate the secretory activity of islet tissue and foster its growth. Nonhormonal measures accomplishing this are infusion of glucose and the administration of high carbohydrate diets. Conversely, the restriction of total calories (or of carbohydrate calories, specifically) leads to a reduction in islet activity. Hypophysectomy or the injection of a sufficient amount of insulin will decrease insulin secretion, and it has been reported that electrically induced convulsions will also do this temporarily.

## Action of Insulin (1, 2)

Insulin favors the utilization of glucose in metabolism, a process reflected in the deposition of glycogen in the liver, muscle, adipose tissue and other tissues. It stimulates the synthesis of fatty acids and the laying down of fat. Furthermore, it promotes the synthesis of protein. As part of the complex of reactions which it influences insulin inhibits gluconeogenesis and ketogenesis. A deficiency of insulin results in the reverse of many of these processes.

The injection of insulin is followed by metabolic changes indicating that the above reactions are occurring. A most notable effect is the fall in the blood sugar accompanied by the facilitated entry of glucose through cell membranes. The decrease in the amount of sugar available from the blood causes the cerebral metabolic rate to fall by as much as 50 to 75 percent. The consequences of this are that when hypoglycemia occurs the symptoms are pre-eminently mental and neurological (3). Himwich (4) has described the symptoms of insulin hypoglycemia according to the terms of Hughlings Jackson. He considers the changes to take place in a progressive and reproducible order, beginning with cortical depression, characterized by somnolence, clouding of consciousness, and muscular relaxation. In this stage there is sweating and salivation. Electroencephalographic changes occur simultaneously with the depression of cortical centers. When the blood sugar declines to about 30 mg. percent or less, the patient loses contact with the environment (diencephalic stage); there are small muscular movements (grasping, twitching) and the release of epinephrine becomes evident through increased sympathetic phenomena (sweating, tachycardia, mydriasis). As lower centers are affected by the deficient sugar supply convulsions occur; later the muscles become flaccid, and reflex activity and autonomic functions are depressed. Hypoglycemic symptoms of this intensity indicate a dangerous depth of coma, in which the vegetative centers begin to undergo irreversible or at least difficultly reversible changes. However, cerebral damage can occur in higher centers also, as a result of hypoglycemia; this has been shown experimentally by Grayzel (5). Gibbs and Murray have described a patient (6) with a functioning tumor of the islet cells which caused hypoglycemia with occasional lapses of memory, and then convulsions and coma. Even though the blood sugar returned to normal following the removal of a portion of the pancreas, the electroencephalographic tracings indicated irreversible and unilateral damage to one region of the cortex.

The activation of the adrenal medulla in hypoglycemia is detectable clinically as well as by an outpouring of epinephrine in the urine. The release of epinephrine from the medulla is of such an order that, with repeated insulinizations as practiced in shock therapy, depletion occurs, with a progressive decrease in the epinephrinuric response to the hormone injection (see p. 314). Important as the adrenal medulla is in the body's general responses, it is not necessary for the restoration of the blood sugar to its normal concentration; this has been demonstrated in bilaterally adrenalectomized humans, whose blood sugar level returned to normal after insulin administration just as rapidly as before operation (7). Glucagon (see below) release may be instrumental in restoring the euglucemic state.

Like the blood sugar, the level of amino acids also declines under the influence of insulin. These compounds become available for protein formation and less of them undergo conversion to glucose (gluconeogenesis).

The effect of insulin on glucose utilization is particularly marked in skeletal muscle, but the hormone also stimulates the uptake of glucose by the liver, allows glycogen to accumulate, and ultimately results in a reduction in the amount of glucose-6-phosphatase, an enzyme which increases in diabetic states. Because glucose-6-phosphate is involved not only in the formation of glycogen and in the glycolytic pathway of glucose breakdown, but also serves as the starting point of the pentose phosphate cycle (*cf.* Chapter 11), one of the functions of which is the maintenance of a steady supply of reduced triphosphopyridine nucleotide (TPNH), any reduction in its concentration in the tissues through an excess of glucose-6-phosphatase will be reflected in a variety of metabolic imbalances. Thus, in the conversion of glucose to fat, acetyl-coenzyme A units derived from carbohydrate by way of the oxidation of pyruvic acid must be condensed and reduced appropriately to form the fatty acid chains; the enzymatic reductions are effected with TPNH as cofactor. If insufficient insulin is present in the tissues where lipogenesis occurs, the acetyl-coenzyme A units are not utilized in this way, but then become substrate in enzymatic processes yielding acetoacetic acid and other ketone bodies. The abolition of ketosis by insulin signifies that pyruvate is being metabolized normally. In line with these effects of insulin there is experimental evidence that insulin increases the proportion of glucose-6-phosphate funneling into the pentose phosphate shunt as compared to the glycolytic pathway. The provision of extra TPNH in this way would be consonant with the stimulation by insulin of synthetic processes and of growth.

In spite of the diverse actions of insulin which have been observed in the intact animal as well as in isolated tissue, many investigators have expressed the view that ultimately these actions will be explained by some specific unitary action of the hormone. Of the theories which have been offered thus far to explain the mechanism of action of insulin none has satisfied this criterion (8). Experimental work has narrowed down the possibilities considerably, however. For example, in the absence of insulin the utilization of glucose is defective, but not so for fructose. Fructose enters metabolism through a phosphorylation reaction catalyzed by fructokinase; the fructose-1-phosphate which is formed is converted to fructose-6-phosphate, and this latter compound can then undergo glycolysis or alternatively can be converted into glycogen by way of glucose-6-phosphate. Glucose and fructose thus have identical pathways of metabolism except for the initial step, and this fundamental fact must be taken into account by the theories of insulin action.

The most favored theory at the present time states that insulin's primary action in carbohydrate metabolism is to increase the permeability of the tissues toward glucose by an active process altering the physico-chemical character of the cell membrane (9). Krahl (10, 11) describes the net effect as follows:

$$\text{Glucose} \xrightarrow[\text{+ATP}]{\text{Insulin}} \text{Glucose-6-phosphate (G-6-P)}$$
$$\text{(extracellular)} \qquad\qquad \text{(intracellular)}$$

Conversely, the primary metabolic lesion in diabetes mellitus may be considered to be the reduced permeability of the peripheral cells to glucose (12). Insulin binds rapidly to some tissues, particularly muscle the lactating mammary gland, adipose tissue, and others, and the union thus formed with an unknown constituent at the cell surface may be the first step in altering the membrane structure. The action of insulin on some isolated tissues is an immediate one and in that respect resembles the rapid effects on metabolism ensuing from the injection of insulin. However, the hormone does not effect as rapid changes in liver slices of diabetic animals as in the diaphragm; in order to observe the effect of insulin on diabetic liver tissue *in vitro* it is necessary to inject the hormone into the animal some hours beforehand.

The differences between glucose and fructose assimilation in the diabetic animal have thus concentrated attention on two processes, the penetration of the cell by glucose and the phosphorylation of the sugar, as being the likely processes in which insulin acts. An alternative to the permeability theory was at one time proposed on the basis of experimental evidence that an anterior pituitary factor inhibits glucokinase and that insulin relieves this inhibition. On this view the normal animal would have a satisfactory balance of the two hormones. However, the lack of consistent confirmatory data following the original finding places this theory in an even more tentative position than the first.

In spite of the evidence implicating glucokinase and the formation of glucose-6-phosphatase as the metabolic locale for the action of insulin, some facts are not explicable as a consequence of increased phosphorylation or permeability of glucose (13). In this category are the increased utilization of pyruvate and the increased formation of protein brought about by insulin in excised tissues under certain conditions. Equally at variance with the hypothesis proposed is the observation that by increasing the concentration of glucose in the medium bathing separated tissues the intracellular concentration of this sugar can be increased with metabolic consequences which prove to be different from those of insulin. It is therefore necessary to consider the possibility that glucose is introduced into cellular metabolism, to be synthesized into glycogen, by some enzyme not presently recognized.

Another change noted in pancreatic diabetes is a defect in oxidative phosphorylation. The liver mitochondria of depancreatized rats consume oxygen and form high-energy phosphate bonds at subnormal rates. After treating the animals with insulin the deficiency is repaired.

## Effect of Insulin on Brain Chemistry

The study of the effects of insulin upon the metabolism of isolated tissues taken from normal, diabetic, and other endocrine-deprived animals now occupies the attention of many researchers and plays an important role in pin-pointing the sites and mechanism of action in metabolism. Thus far, the hormone has not been found to exert any action on separated cerebral tissue. Nevertheless, in the animal given insulin biochemical changes in the brain are soon evident. The cerebral metabolic rate suffers a pronounced fall which is due, not to any change in the blood supply to the brain, but to the hypoglycemia, *i.e.*, the failure of the blood to supply the brain with its principal foodstuff. The carbohydrate components of the brain all decrease, the glycogen as well as the free glucose, lactic, and pyruvic acids, and the sugar phosphate intermediaries decline. The drop in glycogen has been reported to occur first in those parts of the brain that have the highest metabolic rate. Additional changes caused by insulin are a decrease in the intracellular potassium and an increase in the sodium.

The reduced supply of glucose to the brain has consequences also for the balance of free amino acids. Glucose is a precursor of cerebral glutamic acid; in the insulin-treated animal brain glutamic acid decreases as does γ-aminobutyric acid and a fall in glutamine has been observed by some. It is possible that the decrease in glutamic acid represents not only a deficiency in its precursor but also oxidation of the amino acid itself as a substitute cerebral fuel. In spite of the fact that a number of other amino acids also decrease, the total concentration of free amino acids and that of ammonia in the brain remain at normal levels. This can be explained by the shift through transamination toward other amino acids, most notably aspartic acid, which increases in brain under the influence of insulin.

Among other cerebral constituents which decrease in concentration during insulin treatment are the important humoral agents, norepinephrine (14) and acetylcholine (15). Serotonin may increase in some regions but not in others. With repeated insulinization some changes in the cerebral lipides occur: the phospholipides and the triglycerides decrease.

## Insulin Tolerance and Insulin Antagonism

The terms insulin sensitivity and resistance have been used with various connotations in the past in discussing the responses of diabetics to the hormone (1). Their proper definition requires a statement of the duality of the clinical disorder: whether it is juvenile or post-maturity-onset diabetes, the stability of the blood sugar response to insulin administration, presence of associated conditions (*e.g.*, infections), and other modifying circumstances. Thus, *sensitivity* may mean unduly great lowering of the blood sugar following a given dose of insulin, or it may signify lability of the blood sugar and glycosuria after these have come under the control of the hormone. Investigators, attracted by the possibility of some defect of carbohydrate metabolism in the psychoses (*cf.* Chapter 11), have attempted to assess the sensitivity (using the first meaning above) of their patients toward insulin. Freeman (16) tested a large series of psychiatric cases by injecting 0.1 international unit of insulin per kilogram body weight; the mean blood sugar at 30 minutes was 41 mg. percent, whereas a control group of normal subjects had a mean of 30 mg. percent. Insulin sensitivity—or the inverse condition, resistance to the hormone—bore no relationship to diagnosis in this study. Others have also found that many mental patients respond to intravenous insulin with less change in the blood sugar level than do normals, again without correlating with the diagnosis (17). This appears to be an adaptive change, for when abnormal reactors received increased carbohydrate supplements in their diet they eventually gave the normal hypoglycemic response to the insulin (18). It has long been known, of course, that glucose tolerance and the hypoglycemic response to insulin are both reduced on low-carbohydrate diets (1).

The phenomenon of insulin resistance has found a basis in the existence of numerous anti-insulin factors, whose number promises to increase (11): proteolytic enzymes, certain serum proteins, antagonistic hormones, and antibodies. Berson and Yalow, summarizing the literature on this topic, declare that "the multiplicity of technics employed in the detection of such insulin 'antagonists' has led to some confusion regarding the kinship of these various factors and the nature of their opposition to insulin" (19). Anti-insulin antibodies appear in the serum within a few weeks of the commencement of insulin therapy. The titer is in most cases low and has been revealed only by the newer electrophoretic and related methods for separating plasma proteins. In some diabetics—the resistant types—antibodies are present in many times the usual concentration and then they reduce appreciably the effectiveness of a given dose of insulin.

An important mechanism limiting the action of insulin is its enzymatic hydrolysis, preceded by reduction of the molecule's disulfide bridges. Mirsky has designated the proteolytic activity associated with the inactivation of insulin by the term insulinase (20). Whether insulinase is a specific enzyme or one of the tissue cathepsins (proteases) has not yet been determined. Insulinase activity is high in muscle, pancreas, liver, kidney, and testis; it occurs among the soluble cytoplasmic constituents of the cell. A number of aromatic acids and amino acids, among them tryptophan, 5-hydroxytryptophan, serotonin, anthranilic acid, and nicotinic acid, inhibit it (20).

# Glucagon

Many hormones have a diabetogenic or hyperglycemic action. Included among these are certain anterior pituitary hormones, adrenal cortical hormones, epinephrine, and glucagon. Glucagon is a polypeptide consisting of 29 amino acid residues, with a molecular weight of almost 3500. It is generally believed to be synthesized in the α-cells of the islets of Langerhans and in certain analogous cells of the upper part of the small intestine. Its peptide chain is quite unrelated to those of insulin. A common name for it, hyperglycemic-glycogenolytic factor, reveals its actions on carbohydrate metabolism. Indeed, its actions are essentially restricted to this sphere. Specifically, it increases the concentration of cyclic adenosine monophosphate (cf. Chapter 10) in the liver cytoplasm, probably by shifting the nucleotide from some intracellular particle. Cyclic AMP, together with adenosine triphosphate and magnesium ions, then converts phosphorylase in the cells into its active (phosphorylated) form. This ensures that glycogen will be broken down (to glucose-1-phosphate) and ultimately supply glucose to the peripheral tissues. The action of glucagon on phosphorylase is shared with epinephrine. Because of its hyperglycemic action glucagon has been classed by some investigators as an anti-insulin. Indeed, with chronic administration it causes not only hyperglycemia but also glycosuria, ketosis, and a negative nitrogen balance; these changes do not persist when glucagon administration ceases. However, glucagon secretion is enhanced during insulin hypoglycemia, and this has led to another interpretation of its function, that of supplementing the action of insulin by making more sugar available from the liver stores and also by facilitating the conversion of glucose absorbed from the intestine into hepatic glycogen. Glucagon brings about a fall in plasma amino acid concentration and favors gluconeogenesis. It has been used with success to terminate the hypoglycemic coma of insulin therapy in psychiatry (21).

Several authors have reported insulin antagonists in the serum of animals made diabetic experimentally. Anti-insulins have also been found in the serum in clinical diabetes (11, 19). Often these have been identified simply by their action on the uptake of glucose or synthesis of glycogen by the isolated rat diaphragm muscle, activities which are enhanced by insulin and by normal human blood sera, presumably because of their insulin content. In this way it has been found that many substances are able to diminish the effects of insulin; even 6 percent serum albumin reduces utilization of glucose by the rat diaphragm. Using the *in vitro* assays for insulin activity it has been found that the serum of human diabetics contains an insulin-antagonizing protein (22). A lipoprotein with similar actions has also been identified in serum taken from alloxan-diabetic as well as normal rats (23); this fraction inhibits hexokinase in cell-free muscle extracts. Another anti-insulin, globulin in nature, has been detected in depancreatized cats; its production is under the control of the anterior pituitary gland and of the adrenal cortex, the two organs apparently acting in concord (24). This protein resembles the insulin antagonist in plasma noted in clinical diabetes. The presence of anti-insulin substances in the blood serum of some psychotic patients has been reported by Walaas and Lingjaerde (25). They consider that in addition a dialyzable factor, necessary for the normal effect on rat diaphragm, is absent from those sera which contain the insulin antagonist.

Hyperglycemic factors have also been found in the urine (26). Where psychotic patients and normal subjects have been compared, the urine of the former contained more hyperglycemic activity. Like their counterparts in the serum these factors require characterization chemically and biologically in order to determine their physiological role.

## Irreversible Coma (27)

In a small group of subjects the administration of insulin leads to the phenomenon of protracted or irreversible coma. This state does not change in the usual way when glucose is administered. That is to say, even with an elevated blood sugar level guaranteed by infusion the patient is not aroused, and may remain in the coma for hours or days. Most cases occur in the early stage of insulin shock therapy regime. The mechanism is unknown. It appears as though changes brought about in the brain through the hypoglycemic action of the insulin are only slowly reversed even when glucose is finally supplied, and that these changes interfere with the utilization of glucose itself. Setchell (28) has carried out an important study on the biochemical changes in the brain of sheep brought into protracted insulin coma. This species resembles man (and cat) in the susceptibility to dangers arising from prolonged hypoglycemia. In contrast to the increased respiratory rate of excised slices of normal sheep brain when stimulated electrically, the brains of the treated animals showed little or no increase. Many biochemical parameters were normal, but mitochondrial changes were evidenced by a low rate of respiration with little or no energy storage resulting from it. As the metabolism of this organelle is highly dependent upon structure, and the organized structure itself is maintained with the expenditure of energy, it appears that at some point in hypoglycemia the mitochondrion undergoes changes which render it considerably less efficient in the economy of the cell.

In addition to glucose, substances which have been tested as arousal agents for ordinary as well as protracted insulin coma include various vitamins, adrenal cortical hormones, pituitrin, epinephrine, and calcium and potassium salts. Vitamins have been given as catalysts of intracellular oxidations; but there is no evidence at all that any vitamin becomes deficient through the action of insulin or that injection of an excess of a vitamin will reverse the action of the hormone. Epinephrine carries the danger of increasing the incidence of convulsions. Carbon dioxide has been proposed as a reactivator of the tricarboxylic acid cycle acting through combination with pyruvic acid (*cf.* p. 142, Reaction 11-12) to form oxaloacetic acid (29).

Spencer (27) has summarized the theories of the etiology of protracted shock. The condition is variously ascribed to anoxia, formation of a toxic metabolite during the hypoglycemia, deprivation of the cerebral cells of their glucose supply, and autonomic imbalance, respectively. The last theory proposes an effect of insulin hypoglycemia first of all on the hypothalamus. Interference with the function of centers there causes a radiation of effects to other systems.

In irreversible coma treated by the infusion of glucose it is quite possible that the elevated blood sugar causes the pancreas to secrete more insulin, which aggravates the situation. Information is required about the level of insulin in the blood during protracted coma; the values may be low if, for example, insulin is bound in the liver and elsewhere, and does not circulate. In this respect one or other of the anti-insulins may eventually prove of value; for example, a preparation of antibodies species-specific for the insulin that was administered.

## Oral Insulins

This term refers to certain sulfonylureas and biguanides which, on oral administration, cause a lowering of the blood sugar. Sulfonylureas are effective only if the pancreas is intact as is the case in patients with diabetes of the postmaturity-onset type. The biguanides differ in exerting some activity in the juvenile form of the disease also, where there is an absolute deficiency of insulin in the pancreas. From the theoretical aspect there is no reason why compounds of this type could not be used in the induction of hypoglycemic coma for therapeutic purposes in psychiatry, and indeed, two sulfonylureas have been tested as insulin-sparing agents in insulin shock therapy (30).

## References

1. PETERS, J. P., and D. D. VAN SLYKE. *Quantitative Clinical Chemistry*, Vol. I, 2d ed. Baltimore, Williams & Wilkins, 1946.
2. OAKLEY, W. *Brit. Med. J.* i:1291, 1959.
3. KEPLER, E. J., and F. P. MOERSCHE. *Am. J. Psychiat.* 94:89, 1937.
4. HIMWICH, H. E. *Brain Metabolism and Cerebral Disorders.* Baltimore, Williams & Wilkins, 1951.
5. GRAYZEL, D. M. *Arch. Int. Med.* 54:694, 1934.
6. GIBBS, F. A., and E. L. MURRAY. *EEG Clin. Neurophysiol.* 6:674, 1954.
7. GINSBURG, J., and A. PATON. *Lancet* ii:491, 1956.
8. STADIE, W. C. *Physiol. Revs.* 34:52, 1954.
9. LEVINE, R., and M. S. GOLDSTEIN. *Recent Progr. Hormone Res.* 11:343, 1955.
10. KRAHL, M. E. *Recent Progr. Hormone Res.* 12:199, 1956.
11. KRAHL, M. E. *Perspectives Biol. Med.* 1:69, 1957.
12. ROSS, E. J. *Medicine* 35:355, 1956.
13. CHAIN, E. B. *Brit. Med. J.* ii:709, 1959.
14. VOGT, M. *In Metabolism of the Nervous System*, ed. RICHTER, D. London, Pergamon Press, 1957.
15. CROSSLAND, J., K. A. C. ELLIOTT, and H. M. PAPPIUS. *Am. J. Physiol.* 183:32, 1955.
16. FREEMAN, H. *Arch. Neurol. Psychiat.* 56:74, 1946.

17. BRACELAND, F. J., L. J. MEDUNA, and J. A. VAICHULIS. *Am. J. Psychiat.* *102*:108, 1945; LANGFELDT, G. *Acta Psychiat. Neurol. Scand. Suppl. 80*:189, 1953; LINGJAERDE, P., and O. E. SKAUG. *Ibid. Suppl. 136, 34*:370, 1959.

18. LINGJAERDE, O. *Acta Psychiat. Neurol. Scand., Suppl. 80*:202, 1953; *Suppl. 106*:302, 1956.

19. BERSON, S. A., and R. S. YALOW. *Am. J. Med. 25*:155, 1958.

20. MIRSKY, I. A. *Recent Progr. Hormone Res. 13*:429, 1957.

21. SCHULMAN, J. L., and S. E. GREBEN. *J. Clin. Invest. 34*:74, 1957; ESQUIBEL, A. J., A. A. KURLAND, and D. MENDELSOHN. *Dis. Nervous System 19*:485, 1958.

22. MARSH, J. B., and N. HAUGAARD. *J. Clin. Invest. 31*:107, 1952; VALLANCE-OWEN, J., B. HURLOCK, and N. W. PLEASE. *Lancet ii*:583, 1955.

23. BORNSTEIN, J. *J. Biol. Chem. 205*:513, 1953; KRAHL, M. E., and J. BORN-STEIN. *Nature 173*:949, 1954; KRAHL, M. E., M. E. TIDBALL, and E. GREG-MAN. *Proc. Soc. Exp. Biol. Med. 101*:1, 1959.

24. VALLANCE-OWEN, J., and F. D. W. LUKENS. *Endocrinol. 60*:625, 1957.

25. WALAAS, O., O. LINGJAERDE, F. LÖKEN, and E. HUNDEVADT. *Scand. J. Clin. Lab. Invest. 6*:245, 1954; HAAVALDSEN, R., O. LINGJAERDE, and O. WALAAS. *Confin. Neurol. 18*:270, 1958.

26. MEDUNA, L. J., and J. A. VAICHULIS. *Dis. Nerv. System 9*:248, 1948; SHIRAISHI, J. *Igaku to Seibutsugaku 36*:238, 1955; *ibid. 38*:168, 1956, *seen in Chem. Abstr. 52*:2240g, 6580a, 1958; MOYA, F., J. DEWAR, M. MAC-INTOSH, S. HIRSCH, and R. TOWNSEND. *Can. J. Biochem. Physiol. 36*:505, 1958.

27. SPENCER, A. M. *J. Ment. Sci. 54*:513, 1948.

28. SETCHELL, B. P. *Biochem. J. 72*:275, 1959.

29. LITTERAL, E. B., W. E. WILKINSON, H. S. KOLMER, and W. D. BENHAM. *Dis. Nerv. System 17*:123, 1956; FELD, M., P. FREEMAN, and F. V. HOFF-MAN. *Ibid. 18*:138, 1957.

30. BAYREUTHER, H., and N. SPECHT. *Arch. Psychiat. Nervenkrankh. 195*:132, 1956; BAYREUTHER, H. *Ibid. 195*:435, 1957; FROST, I. *Brit. Med. J. ii*:381, 1958.

# 28

# BIOCHEMICAL PHARMACOLOGY

*Canst thou not minister to a mind diseased,*
*Pluck from the memory a rooted sorrow,*
*Raze out the written trouble of the brain,*
*And with some sweet oblivious antidote*
*Cleanse the stuff'd bosom of that perilous stuff*
*Which weighs upon the heart?*
*Shakespeare, Macbeth, Act V, Scene III*

Elsewhere in this book we have considered primarily the biochemical changes which accompany mental and emotional illnesses. In this chapter some of the changes brought about in cerebral metabolic processes by chemical agents and by electroconvulsive procedures will be reviewed. The current expansion of the psychiatrist's armamentarium of drugs represents an outstanding advance in an area whose needs were formulated by Kraepelin at the turn of the century and which were included in the term pharmacopsychiatry (1). But, what could not be done sixty years ago has now been made possible by advances in neurochemistry and in the electrophysiology of the brain. After 1930, the main direction of pharmacological interest and emphasis turned away from the galenicals and, except for occasional excursions back to them as in the case of the Ephedra alkaloids and Rauwolfia root, pharmacology has followed the path laid out by the synthetic organic pharmaceuticals industry. It was in the thirties also that biochemical pharmacology crystallized as a subdiscipline. With Woods's discovery of the antivitamin action of the sulfonamides, the earlier fundamental studies of Quastel and Wooldridge on competitive inhibition of enzymes through displacement of substrate from the enzyme surface moved up to the status of a major biochemical theory. The principle of metabolite antagonism received extensive practical and theoretical development in Woolley's laboratory (2), and grew into an important working hypothesis in the search for new drugs. Concurrent advances in our knowledge of the intermediary metabolism of carbohydrates, lipides, amino acids, nucleic acids, and vitamins suggested places where one might look, on the basis of the antimetabolite hypothesis, for the biochemical site of action of the useful drugs already at hand as well as of the new agents being synthesized by the chemist. On the same basis the chemist could request specifications as to the structure of desirable and potentially useful compounds which the biochemist anticipated might antagonize this or that metabolite *in vivo*. One further stage had to be reached for the successful scientific investigation of the action of drugs used in psychiatry, and that was the development of techniques to examine the action of drugs on specific functional sites in the brain itself; the classical pharmacodynamic techniques, useful as they would be in the general assessment of the action of the drug, were inapplicable here, but the methods of electrophysiology have proved eminently suitable for this purpose.

Of major concern in this chapter are (*a*) the methods employed by the biochemist to study the action of drugs upon the central nervous system and (*b*) some of the results he has obtained. As yet only a few of these drugs have had their action explained in terms of enzyme inhibition or by their alteration of the concentration of important metabolites. It is not the function of this chapter to serve as a drug formulary, but rather to seek out some of the essential relationships between biochemistry and pharmacology; this will be done in part by specific examples.

Because of a certain unpreparedness of pharmacology and of physiology for the developments in the use of drugs in psychiatry there has been some difficulty in the choice of terminology to be applied. If administration of a drug such as reserpine leads to a reduction in activity through a central action, but without exhibiting the other attributes of hypnotic action, is it to be classed as a central nervous system depressant, or is this too general a term to suit this case?

Furthermore, if it evokes actions upon the extrapyramidal system, to which of the conventional categories is it to be assigned? A similar argument can be adduced for imipramine, for example. How is one to classify a drug which brings about an elevation of mood? Obviously one must first learn which parts of the brain it affects. Because of the difficulties in locating the site of action of many drugs, classification has more frequently than not resorted to subjective terms of a most limited character: tranquilizer, psychic energizer, ataractic, thymoleptic, psychostimulant, psychosedative, to mention but a few. From the standpoint of the fundamental sciences the word *psychopharmacology* focuses attention upon the action of drugs on the "mind," instead of upon the cerebral substance of "mind." It is to be expected that this is a temporary situation which will be resolved by further research in neurophysiology aimed at detecting the anatomic sites and physiological modes of action of neuropharmacological agents. Meanwhile, the superficial and the spurious should not be mistaken for the fundamental: coining a new term* does not explain how a drug acts.

# Methods of Investigation

TECHNIQUES USED *in vivo*

The investigation of the biochemical actions of a drug serves practical and heuristic ends. In conjunction with the tests of the pharmacologist and the toxicologist it is important to know how seriously the drug upsets homeostasis, and in what direction. The biochemist learns this by measuring the blood constituents and by urinary analysis. Such studies can be made as elaborate as the preliminary investigation requires, and can be extended to include nitrogen balance studies, tests of liver and kidney function and of endocrine activity, analysis of the cerebrospinal fluid, and others. Moreover, chronic trials can be instituted, along the lines of Gjessing's longitudinal studies in periodic catatonia (Chapter 24).

Acute tests may be exemplified by studies on the effects of lysergic acid diethylamide (LSD) in man. This substance is active in amounts of 0.5 to 1.0 $\mu$g./kg., causing hallucinations and certain autonomic effects. LSD is thus one of the most potent substances known, ranking with vitamin $B_{12}$, aconitine, and Botulinus toxin in possessing high

---

* Thomas Hobbes pointed out that "words are wise men's counters, they do but reckon by them: but they are the mony of fooles. . . . "

specific biological activity. Can a significant biochemical action be detected? Because of the dominant role of carbohydrate metabolism in the brain it has been natural to look there for a biochemical mechanism to explain the action of LSD. Mayer-Gross et al. considered that LSD must act as an antienzyme to be able to exert such potent effects (3). They found that the administration of LSD is followed by a rise in the sugar phosphates of the blood, whereas a placebo treatment caused a fall. The disturbance of carbohydrate metabolism was further indicated by a slight rise in the fasting blood sugar, beginning about one hour after ingestion of the drug. These investigators concluded that LSD causes a metabolic block in the catabolism of sugar (4). It is interesting that the observed changes imply also a change in the metabolism of organic phosphates and, by extension, of the body's pool of inorganic phosphate. Hoagland, Rinkel, and Hyde (5) studied the effects of LSD upon phosphate excretion and found that the drug reduces the output of phosphate by normal men. Following the administration of ACTH, volunteers who received LSD gave exaggerated responses in respect to urinary excretion of phosphate as compared with those not given the ergot derivative. These responses were similar to those of schizophrenics given ACTH (but not LSD), and were interpreted as indicating some relationship between mental changes and phosphate metabolism, or between these and some third factor.

Sometimes a biochemical test is run as an aid in the detection of liver damage resulting from a drug. Lately, measurement of enzymes in the serum has proved useful because of the great sensitivity of such methods. Transaminase and alkaline phosphate are known to increase in the serum when hepatic cells are damaged. Phenothiazine drugs may induce such changes, and these are reversed upon withdrawal of the drug. Serum glutamic acid-oxaloacetic acid transaminase (SGOT) increases in chlorpromazine-induced hepatitis to a moderate degree, and falls quickly upon withdrawal of the drug. In this respect it precedes the decrease of bilirubin and alkaline phosphatase to the normal range (6). Hippius (7) has reported that treatment with chlorpromazine or imipramine causes a small rise in the alkaline phosphatase of serum which returns to normal as therapy is continued. Measurements of the $\alpha_2$-and $\beta$-globulins of the serum showed that these proteins are slightly elevated in the schizophrenic patients selected for chlorpromazine therapy and are restored toward normal limits during the course of pharmacotherapy. Imipramine, given to depressive subjects, raised the globulin fraction during the initial period of therapy but its concentration returned to normal as drug administration continued (7). Although the mechanism of these changes is not clear, such measurements often permit the recognition by biochemical means of incipient changes having a toxic significance and against which the necessary countermeasures may be taken at an early stage.

Animal tests offer a greater scope for investigation than do the clinical trials; not only can the blood and urine be examined, but also specific tissues. In acute experiments, analyses can be made on the body fluids or organs at various stages in the development of pharmacological actions of the drug under study. The following example illustrates the biochemical investigation of the action of a convulsant drug.

Killam and Bain (8) found that thiosemicarbazide-induced convulsions are associated with a reduction in the concentration of γ-aminobutyric acid (GABA) in the brain. Because of the inhibitory action of GABA in the nervous system (Chapter 4) this experiment suggested that a certain level of cerebral GABA is required to prevent the development of spontaneous convulsive activity. Several lines of evidence point to an associated role of vitamin $B_6$ here: thiosemicarbazide and semicarbazide, both carbonyl reagents (and therefore potential binding agents of the vitamin $B_6$ coenzyme, pyridoxal phosphate, *in vivo*), are convulsants; pyridoxal phosphate is the coenzyme of glutamic decarboxylase, an enzyme found almost exclusively in the brain and responsible for the formation of GABA; and a deficiency of pyridoxine in the diet, leading to a reduction in the cerebral coenzyme, lowers the electroshock threshold in rats, and may result in spontaneous seizures in humans (*cf.* Chapter 19). However, not all carbonyl reagents act like thiosemicarbazide. Hydroxylamine actually causes an elevation of the cerebral level of GABA, the effect of a single injection lasting up to 5 hours (9). How this contradictory action may arise can be seen from the metabolic path pursued by GABA. This amino acid is metabolized through transamination to succinic semialdehyde and oxidation of this compound to succinic acid. The transamination step also requires the participation of pyridoxal phosphate, so that hydroxylamine seemingly exhibits specificity to this particular pyridoxal phosphate-linked enzyme, as against the glutamic decarboxylase. However, this mechanism has not been proved, nor does it explain a recent finding of Baxter and Roberts (9) that through the use of both hydroxylamine and thiosemicarbazide convulsions can be elicited in rats without a reduction in the concentration of cerebral GABA.

Two important drugs used in psychiatry, iproniazid and reserpine, cause alterations in the cerebral levels of certain biogenic amines. One of the pharmacological actions of iproniazid, central stimulation, seems to stem from its ability to increase cerebral amines. The correlation of increased activity of the central nervous system with the monoamine oxidase-inhibiting activity of iproniazid has led over the last few years to a search for additional compounds to inhibit this enzyme, on the supposition that a portion of them, at least, would stimulate the brain under experimental conditions, and that of these some might prove useful in human disease. A similar situation has arisen through the finding that the administration of reserpine causes the release of various amines such as serotonin (5HT) and norepinephrine from cellular storage sites, and ultimately leads to a depletion of the amines of the adrenals, brain, and other organs. Brodie and Shore (10) correlated the 5HT concentration in the brain with overt behavior in rabbits given iproniazid (100 mg./kg.), reserpine (5 mg./kg.), or both drugs administered two hours apart. The animals were sacrificed one hour after the second drug was given. The results of this experiment showed that reserpine causes a drop in the level of 5HT, and that this is not affected by the later injection of iproniazid; reserpine, given alone or followed by iproniazid causes sedation. The injection of iproniazid alone resulted in some small increase in 5HT without an alteration in behavior. On the other hand, when reserpine was injected after the iproniazid, there were signs of central stimulation; moreover, reserpine did not now cause the pronounced fall in brain 5HT, presumably because the monoamine oxidase was inhibited and because the intact amine does not readily leave the brain through the cellular or intracellular membranes.

On the basis of these and related findings attempts have been made to find other agents with similar or other advantageous pharmacological properties which are contemporaneous in appearance with a decrease or increase in cerebral amines. For this purpose the screening tests have usually been based upon measurement of the 5HT content of the brain; the methods for this amine are simple and more convenient than those for norepinephrine, dopamine, and related compounds. Sheppard and Zimmerman (11) have suggested looking for other mechanisms of action than the release of amines by reserpine because in guinea pigs injected subcutaneously with 0.1 mg. of reserpine/kg. they found no correlation between pharmacological response and the amine content of the brain.

Other means of increasing the cerebral amines have been tried, among them the parenteral administration of the amine itself. This has proved to be rather ineffective in most cases tried, except that of tryptamine. Given in sufficient quantity tryptamine causes convulsions in laboratory animals. This is in contrast to 5HT, which does not have any central effects, but only the peripheral ones; however, its precursor, 5-hydroxytryptophan, passes into many tissues, including the brain, and undergoes decarboxylation there. Udenfriend et al. have shown (12) that it is the increase in cerebral serotonin caused by the injection of 5-hydroxytryptophan with which the central excitatory phenomena are associated (Table 28-1). This amino acid may be

TABLE 28-1. BRAIN CONTENT OF 5-HYDROXYTRYPTOPHAN (5-HTP) AND SEROTONIN (5-HT)*

| Compound injected | ($\mu g./gm.$) | | |
| --- | --- | --- | --- |
| | 5-HTP | 5-HT | Change in 5-HT |
| None | 0.0 | 0.6 | — |
| Iproniazid | 0.0 | 1.1 | 0.5 |
| 5-HTP | 11.8 | 1.3 | 0.7 |
| Both | 15.7 | 4.1 | 3.5 |

* Adapted from reference (12).

found after its injection in various tissues, including the liver and brain. The data shown in Table 28-1 were obtained 3 hours after administration of the compound. By pretreating the rats with iproniazid (75 mg./kg.), given one hour before the 5-hydroxytryptophan, the cerebral concentration of serotonin can be raised to high levels, although the concentration of the administered amino acid in the brain increases only by about one third. The excitatory action can be seen in the animals getting 5-hydroxytryptophan, but the amino acid is much more effective if given together with the monoamine oxidase inhibitor, which protects the amine from destruction. This animal experiment is the basis for the trial of 5-hydroxytryptophan in mental patients for its possible modifying action upon the schizophrenic process (p. 88).

The discovery that it is possible to obtain significant pharmacological effects having therapeutic applications by the use of drugs which affect the metabolism of cerebral amines suggests the possibility that substances interfering with other pathways of metabolism of amines found in the brain may also prove useful. The formation of an amine is preceded in biosynthesis by one or more amino acid precursors, the last one of which undergoes decarboxylation. The amine itself may give rise to other similar compounds, as in the catecholamine sequence of dopamine, norepinephrine, and epinephrine. Serotonin is the precursor of melatonin (5-methoxy-N-acetyltryptamine). The amines eventually serve as substrates in the cell for detoxifying enzymes, such as methyl transferases, amine oxidases, acylases, and conjugases, and are thus withdrawn from pharmacological action to a greater or lesser degree. A working hypothesis might then indicate that agents interfering with the decarboxylation process or favoring the detoxication would result in a lowering of the concentration of brain amines, whereas substances which inhibit the detoxifying enzymes and thus interfere with the degradation of the amines would increase their concentration. Antidecarboxylases have been known for some time from experimental work with dopa decarboxylase, and have had experimental trials *in vivo* (13). One antidecarboxylase, alpha-methyldopa, has proved in clinical trials to have an antihypertensive effect. Its action upon the catecholamine content of rat brain and upon the excretion of amines in man are shown in Table 28-2. Its amine-releasing action is matched by the related compound alpha-methyl-*meta*-tyrosine (AMMT), which causes a rapid depletion of both cerebral dopamine and norepinephrine. In contrast to dopamine, the norepinephrine returns to normal levels only after a delay of some days (18). Alpha-methyldopa has been reported to have some sedative action in man (17), and this may be associated with its ability to liberate endogenous brain amines. In spite of this reserpinelike action, it has not proved effective as a tranquilizing agent in psychotic patients (19).

Inhibitors of catechol O-methyltransferase are known, such as pyrogallol and catechol itself. These compounds are capable of potentiating the action of injected epinephrine, presumably by serving as substrates for the inactivating enzyme, in place of the catecholamine. As yet, such inhibitors have not been found to affect directly the cerebral norepinephrine or dopamine, possibly because in the brain this enzyme plays a less important role in terminating the action of these compounds than does monoamine oxidase.

## TECHNIQUES USED *in vitro*

It has become an important part of biochemical research in pharmacology to look for enzymatic processes that are affected by drugs *in vitro*. Pharmacological agents are better characterized as to their mode of action when it is known how they affect the sensitively poised, steady-state processes of metabolism. Knowledge of which process or which specific reactions are affected by the drug allows one to compare it with chemically similar or pharmacologically related compounds. It may

TABLE 28-2. EFFECT OF ANTIDECARBOXYLASES UPON
AMINES OF BRAIN AND URINE

| Treatment and Amine Measured | Controls | Treated with Antidecar- boxylase* | Refer- ence |
|---|---|---|---|
| Amine content of the brain | | | |
| Norepinephrine (rat), μg. | 0.62 | 0.46 | 14 |
| Dopamine (rat), μg. | 0.84 | 0.70 | 14 |
| Serotonin (guinea pig), μg./gm. | 0.30, 0.28 | 0.03, 0.02 | 15 |
| Serotonin (mouse), μg./gm. | 1.02, 0.96 | 0.48, 0.38 | 15 |
| Urinary excretion in rat of | | | |
| Dopamine (following intraperitoneal injection of 10 mg. L-dopa/kg.), | | | |
| Experiment 1, mg. | 0.56 | 0.24 | 16 |
| Experiment 2, mg. | 0.46 | 0.14 | 16 |
| Urinary excretion in man of | | | |
| Tryptamine (following ingestion of 50 mg. L-tryptophan/kg.), μg. | 246 | 110 | 17 |
| Tyramine (following ingestion of 125 mg. L-tyrosine/kg.), μg. | 808 | 155 | 17 |
| Serotonin (following infusion of 30 mg. of 5-hydroxy-DL-tryptophan), mg. | 2.97 | 1.10 | 17 |

* Alpha-methyldopa was used in the experiments on brain and on urinary excretion in man. Alpha-methyl-*m*-tyrosine was used in Expt. 1 on urinary excretion of dopamine in the rat, and alpha-methyl-5-hydroxytryptophan in Expt. 2.

even lead to design of a simpler or more effective drug. But it is obvious that the mere finding of stimulation or inhibition of an enzymatic reaction by a drug *in vitro* cannot by itself constitute proof that this is the metabolic site of action of the drug, or even that the drug acts at all in this way when it is administered to the intact animal or human. Numerous drugs inhibit cholinesterase, but their diverse pharmacodynamic actions indicate that they can not all be acting *in vivo* through inhibition of this enzyme. The attempt to associate the effects of a drug in the animal organism with some well-defined or pronounced action observed *in vitro* cannot be successful until further experimental evidence of a critical nature has been amassed. Writing on this question, Welch and Bueding (20) have stipulated several important criteria for studies in biochemical pharmacology: (*a*) The concentration of the drug producing the effect on the isolated system and that determined at the anatomical site of action should be of the same order. (*b*) If the action of the drug *in vivo* is primarily on one tissue, then the effect of the drug *in vitro* on other tissues must be smaller in magnitude, or the inhibited system must be shown to have greater functional significance in the one than in the other tissues. (*c*) Within a given chemical series, compounds active *in vivo* must also be active *in vitro,* and those inactive *in vivo* must also be inactive *in vitro*. The last condition may not be met in specific cases for reason of poor absorption, permeability barriers, or too rapid termination of drug action *in vivo* by excretion or detoxication.

There are various levels at which the action of a drug can be studied by the biochemist; use of intact animals as described above represents the most complex. Probably the commonest technique used *in vitro* in the study of tisue metabolism, including that of the brain, is the measurement of gaseous exchange, making use of the Barcroft-Warburg apparatus. The tissue is prepared in the form of a thin slice containing mainly intact cells, or as a broken-cell preparation (the homogenate) in which the nucleus, mitochondria, and microsomes are suspended in a suitable medium, usually isotonic potassium chloride solution, or one containing sucrose. Inasmuch as the subcellular particles have different complements of enzymes, it is often useful to separate these particles according to their varying density by differential centrifugation. The effect of drugs may then be studied on the separated particles. Ultimately, drug effects are sought on organ extracts containing the enzyme, and finally, on the purified enzymes. Recently, specialized techniques, such as perfusion of the brain or of isolated nerve and ganglia, have become available for metabolism studies (*cf.* Reference 21 for description of methods). The results obtained by these various methods may not all agree, and then this raises the question of the permissive role of organ and cellular structure in the action of the drug.

The following examples have been drawn from the literature of neurochemistry in order to illustrate the application of these techniques in research on neurotropic agents.

*Biochemical Effects of Chlorpromazine.* The actions of chlorpromazine upon the respiration and phospholipide metabolism of brain tissue have been studied by Magee et al. (22). As shown in Table 28-3 high concentrations of the drug ($10^{-3}$ M) strongly inhibit the respiration of cortical slices of guinea pig brain and also interfere with the incorporation of inorganic phosphate into the phospholipides (lipide phosphorus). A lower concentration of the drug, on the other hand, inhibits respiration only to a small extent, but now it increases the rate of incorporation of inorganic phosphorus. A similar effect can be obtained

TABLE 28-3. EFFECT OF CHLORPROMAZINE ON BRAIN METABOLISM (22)

| Concentration of Chlorpromazine | Guinea Pig Brain Slices | | Rat Brain Mitochondria |
| | Oxygen Uptake ($\mu l./100$ gm./hr.) | Lipide Phosphorus* | Lipide Phosphorus* |
| --- | --- | --- | --- |
| Control | 112 | 39 | 151 |
| 0.1 mMolar | 96 | 69 | 190 |
| 1.0 mMolar | 16 | 3 | 28 |

* The preparations were incubated with inorganic phosphate-$P^{32}$, present in the medium, and under an atmosphere of oxygen. Figures shown are specific activity of the lipide phosphorus fraction.

with the mitochrondrial fraction of rat brain cells, so that some localization of this particular action of chlorpromazine in the cell has been achieved.

Another and more specific type of action has been attributed to chlorpromazine and related phenothiazines; this is their antagonism to the action of some flavoproteins, such as cerebral D-amino acid oxidase and a mitochondrial enzyme which functions in oxidative phosphorylation (23).

Gey and Pletscher have observed an indirect effect of chlorpromazine (as well as chlorprothixene) on the metabolism of cerebral amines (24). Although the drug did not affect the concentration of these substances directly, it did diminish the magnitude of the changes usually observed when reserpine or iproniazid is injected. As chlorpromazine is not known to be an inhibitor of enzymes concerned with the formation or metabolism of amines, it was concluded that this drug may act by reducing the permeability of the intracellular granules for certain of their stored amines.

*Electrical Stimulation of Brain Slices.* The tissue slice excised from an organ for studies *in vitro* can no longer perform metabolic exchanges as it does *in situ*. However, these processes are mimicked by incubating the slice in a medium containing suitable nutrients and into which metabolic products can diffuse. In the case of brain slices there is the additional problem that the tissue is divorced from the normal electrical environment. Methods for stimulating cerebral slices with electrical pulses during metabolic incubations have now been developed, largely in the laboratory of McIlwain, and experiments using these methods show that electrically stimulated tissue has a remarkably higher rate of metabolism than silent tissue. Indeed, McIlwain has shown (25) that electrical pulses make the respiratory rates observed *in vitro* with brain slices reasonably concordant with estimates of the cerebral respiratory rate *in vivo*. Another important finding made with cerebral tissue receiving applied electrical pulses is the very high sensitivity of the stimulated respiration to the action of drugs, compared to the sensitivity of the resting or unstimulated respiration. In their study of the biochemical effects of anticonvulsant drugs, Greengard and McIlwain (26) found many processes which are quite unaffected by diphenylhydantoin ($10^{-4}$ M). Among these were respiration of brain slices (*i.e.,* oxygen utilization) in the presence of glucose or glutamic acid as substrate, and chemically stimulated respiration or glycolysis (see below), among others. Trimethadione at $10^{-4}$ to $10^{-3}$ M concentration likewise had no effect on these processes or on glutamic acid metabolism. On the other hand, when these drugs were incubated with the slices during the passage of electrical pulses (a.c. 2000 cycles/second, 3.5 volts), inhibition of the excess respiration was observed (Table 28-4). The formation of lactic acid was not affected by the applied current nor by the drugs.

*Chemical Stimulation of Cortical Slices.* Metabolic processes in the brain can also be accelerated by certain chemicals. Some of the effective substances are 2,4-dinitrophenol and a high concentration of potassium ion. The results obtained in these ways are somewhat different from those with applied pulses. One drawback to the chemical stimulants is that they can be applied only once in the experiment, and then irreversibly, whereas electrical stimulation can be varied momentarily. How these substances exert their effects upon metabolism is not clear although it is believed that potassium ions work partly through the terminal oxidative pathway (tricarboxylic acid cycle) of the cerebral cells. High potassium concentrations also affect the formation of glutamic acid, glutamine, and $\gamma$-aminobutyric acid; the importance of the disturbance of ionic equilibrium for these processes has not yet been fully

TABLE 28-4. EFFECT OF ANTICONVULSANTS ON RESPIRATION OF SLICES OF CEREBRAL CORTEX (GUINEA PIG) (26)

| Anticonvulsant | Concentration (mols/l.) | Electrical Stimulation | Respiration ($\mu$mols $O_2$/gm./hr.) | |
|---|---|---|---|---|
| | | | No Drug | Drug Added |
| Diphenylhydantoin | $10^{-4}$ | − | 55 | 56 |
| Same | " | + | 90 | 60 |
| Trimethadione | $10^{-3}$ | − | 63 | 63 |
| Same | " | + | 95 | 80 |

TABLE 28-5. EFFECT OF ETHANOL AND ACETALDEHYDE ON RESPIRATION OF SLICES OF RAT CEREBRAL CORTEX (27)

| Addition | Concentration (mols/l.) | Respiratory Rates (as % of control resting rate) | |
|---|---|---|---|
| | | Resting Rate | Potassium-stimulated Rate |
| Ethanol | — | 100 | 161 |
| | 0.4 | 128 | 114 |
| | 0.6 | 111 | 138 |
| Acetaldehyde | — | 100 | 175 |
| | 0.002 | 92 | 134 |
| | 0.004 | 87 | 97 |

assessed. The effect of potassium ions upon the oxidation of alcohol has been studied by Beer and Quastel, as summarized in Table 28-5 (27). The respiration of brain slices in this experiment was stimulated (61 percent above the resting rate) by 0.1 M potassium ions, but the addition of ethanol reduced the effect significantly (only 20 percent above the unstimulated rate). The concentrations of ethanol needed to show these effects are much higher than the blood values at which pharmacological changes occur (0.01 to 0.10 M), so that it is possible that some product of the metabolism of alcohol is actually responsible for the inhibition of the chemically stimulated respiration. An investigation of acetaldehyde, the immediate oxidation product of ethanol, showed that it exerts a much more powerful inhibitory effect (Table 28-5). If acetaldehyde were responsible for the specific inhibitory action of ethanol upon cerebral respiration, this would imply the presence of an alcohol dehydrogenase. The enzyme has, in fact, been reported in brain by Dewan (28), but Beer and Quastel (27) were unable to confirm this and concluded that the action of ethanol (and other aliphatic alcohols which were studied) takes place at the membrane of the brain cell. Even if inhibition by aldehyde cannot then explain the metabolic action of ethanol, it is conceivable that other aldehydes, which are known to be formed in cerebral tissue through the action of monoamine oxidase, may under certain conditions exert drug effects upon metabolic processes within the brain cell.

**Cholinesterase Inhibitors.** An outstanding example of the detailed research necessary to fulfill the criteria of Welch and Bueding comes from the field of anticholinesterases. This group of inhibitors includes the classical example of eserine, but also the more recent nerve gases and some economic poisons used in agriculture. The inhibition by eserine is readily reversible, but that by the nerve gases is relatively irreversible. DFP (di-isopropylfluorophosphate), for example, combines with the enzyme rapidly to form a new compound, and the linkage is hydrolyzed only very slowly. The same is true for many other inhibitors such as tetraethylpyrophosphate, sarin (isopropylmethylfluorophosphate) and schradan (octamethylpyrophosphoramide). The relative efficacy of eserine and DFP as inhibitors of the true and pseudocholinesterases is shown in Table 28-6. These data illustrate the high potency of the anticholinesterase drugs and correlate well with the intense cholinergic activity that accompanies their administration to animals and man. Nachmansohn and Feld (31) injected rabbits with a median lethal dose of DFP under prescribed conditions. Assuming more or less rapid equilibration of the drug through the body, the dose of 0.3 mg./kg. would give concentrations in the organs of the same order as are required to inhibit cholinesterases. The investigators found, in fact, that the brains of animals which died as a result of the drug contained very little true cholinesterase activity, whereas the brains of the survivors were still substantially active, although far below normal values. Other metabolic measurements (respiration, glycolysis, adenosinetriphosphatase) were made on the brains of the animals which died as a result of the DFP, and these proved to be in the control range. Nachmansohn and his colleagues have also found that conduction of the nerve impulse ceases when the acetylcholinesterase activity of the nerve is inhibited by DFP to the extent of 80 to 90 percent (*cf.* pp. 40–41).

TABLE 28-6. CHOLINESTERASE INHIBITION

| Cholinesterase | | Concentration Required to Inhibit 50% | |
|---|---|---|---|
| Type | Source | DFP | Eserine |
| **True** | | | |
| | Human erythrocytes | $1.5 \times 10^{-7}$ | |
| | Human brain | $1.3 \times 10^{-7}$ | |
| | Dog brain | — | $10^{-6}$ |
| | Mouse brain | — | $10^{-6}$ |
| | Pigeon brain | $5.7 \times 10^{-7}$ | |
| **Pseudo** | | | |
| | Human plasma | $0.029 \times 10^{-7}$ | |
| | Horse serum | — | between $10^{-8}$ and $10^{-7}$ |
| | Dog pancreas | — | ca. $10^{-8}$ |
| Reference | | 29 | 30 |

Inhibition of cholinesterases has been one of the most intensively studied topics in biochemical pharmacology; numerous drugs have been tested on these enzymes in attempting to associate their autonomic effects with enzymatic inhibition. LSD has also been examined for its action on cholinesterases and, indeed, has been found to inhibit the pseudocholinesterases of serum and brain of humans (50 per cent inhibition at $10^{-6}$ M), but has very little inhibitory action upon the true cholinesterase of erythrocytes and brain. Other ergot alkaloids inhibit pseudocholinesterase less than LSD does (32). It is of interest that this inhibitory action displays a species difference. Whereas the pseudocholinesterases of human plasma and of mouse plasma and brain are sensitive to LSD and to 2-bromo-LSD (BOL), much less effect is seen using the enzyme obtained from rat, guinea pig, and certain other species. This difference in sensitivity to the ergot alkaloids is probably related to the structure of the enzyme at its active site inasmuch as only the enzymes from human and mouse, among the species tested, hydrolyse the imidazolyl ester of choline, dihydromurexine (33).

*Mescaline.* The experiments with DFP give reasonable assurance that the concentrations of this drug which are effective on a particular system *in vitro* are of the same order as those encountered when the drug is administered *in vivo*. It often happens, however, that even after considerable experimentation no metabolic process can be found

TABLE 28-7. BIOCHEMICAL EFFECTS OF MESCALINE (34)

| System Examined | Concentration of Mescaline (mols/l.) | Percent Inhibition |
|---|---|---|
| Brain slices: oxidation of glucose, production of lactate | $10^{-2}$ | 0 |
| Same, but with electrical stimulation of slices | $10^{-3}$ | 50 |
| Brain mince: oxidation of carbohydrates and of glutamate | $4 \times 10^{-3}$ | 65 |
| Brain homogenate: oxidation of pyruvate | $10^{-2}$ | 42 |
| Succinic dehydrogenase: cytochrome oxidase | $10^{-2}$ | 0 |
| Brain mitochondria: oxidative phosphorylation | $10^{-3}$ | 0 |
| Hallucinogenic action in man | $10^{-5}$ | — |

which is affected by concentrations of the drug that are effective *in vivo*. This is the present status of research on mescaline. Of course, a low concentration of the drug in the plasma or cerebrospinal fluid does not necessarily mean that the concentration in the tissue is similarly low, for drugs may be concentrated at membranal surfaces through their properties of lipoidal solubility. Within the cell, local concentration of a drug may occur also at some organelle. Bain (34) has summarized the results of many research papers on the metabolic actions of mescaline, and Table 28-7 has been adapted from his summary. It can be seen that mescaline has been tested upon intact cells treated in various ways, upon homogenates, mitochondria, and specific enzymes. At relatively high concentrations it exerts some biochemical affects, but these levels are very much above the estimated concentration achieved in humans who experience the mescaline hallucinations. For this reason it is not yet possible to correlate the neuropharmacological action of mescaline with a biochemical one. Further testing of mescaline on other enzyme systems important in the metabolic economy of cerebral tissue may yet reveal one or more that are particularly sensitive, as in the case of inhibition of cholinesterases by DFP.

TABLE 28-8. EFFECTS OF PROTOVERATRINE ON RESPIRATION AND GLYCOLYSIS OF GUINEA PIG CEREBRAL CORTEX (35)

| Treatment | Respiration | Aerobic Glycolysis | Anerobic Glycolysis |
|---|---|---|---|
| *In vivo* | | | |
| None (Control No. 1) | 10.7 | 1.1 | 18.2 |
| None (Control No. 2) | 10.8 | 0.7 | 18.3 |
| 0.187 μmol protoveratrine/kg. injected intraperitoneally (Experimental No. 1) | 17.0 | 9.6 | 11.6 |
| Same (Experimental No. 2) | 17.3 | 9.7 | 10.8 |
| *In vitro* | | | |
| None (Control) | 10.8 | 0.3 | 21.6 |
| $9.4 \times 10^{-7}$ M protoveratrine added to incubation medium | 14.1 | 21.4 | 6.5 |

The rates in the table are for the period beginning 50 to 60 minutes after the start of incubation, when the effects of the alkaloid were well established. Rates are expressed as Q values = μl. of substance utilized (oxygen) or produced (lactic acid, expressed as a gas at N.T.P.) per hour per milligram of dry tissue used.

**Protoveratrine.** Wollenberger (35) has shown that a correlation of effects *in vivo* and *in vitro* exists for protoveratrine (a mixture of two Veratrum alkaloids). The drug acts as a chemical stimulant of cerebral metabolism. Using guinea pigs poisoned with protoveratrine (0.15 mg./kg.) he found that slices of their cerebral cortices respire at an accelerated rate. Aerobic glycolysis (lactic acid production in the presence of oxygen) was also strongly stimulated, but the anerobic process was inhibited (Table 28-8). In order to exclude the possibility that these effects result from local vascular or extracerebral changes causing metabolic disturbances, the drug was tested also by adding it to the medium in which the cerebral slices were bathed. Again the same metabolic effects were observed with very low concentrations of the same order as those required to produce toxic and biochemical effects in the intact animal (Table 28-8).

## Some General Biochemical Actions of Drugs Acting Upon Nerve and Brain

The actions of drugs upon the nervous system have been studied from several aspects which can be resolved into two primary coordinates, metabolic and functional. Each of these in turn has been examined at several levels. The functional approach has analyzed the behavioral and pharmacodynamic effects of drugs, as well as their action upon cellular permeability, conduction, synaptic transmission, and other physiological activities of the nervous system. As for the metabolic coordinate, the gross changes have been detected by blood analysis, arteriovenous differences, and measurement of the cerebral metabolic rate, whereas the cellular and subcellular actions of drugs have required the specialized techniques for the study of intermediary metabolism that have been described earlier in this chapter. Integrating these two approaches is the structural or organizational coordinate; this comprises the functional anatomy of the brain, and the structure of the nerve fiber and cell body. Rosenberg (36) has emphasized the multiform aspects of drug action and the difficulties which arise in interpretation of experimental results when the metabolic coordinate is considered apart from the structure-function grid of nervous tissue.

The aims of biochemical research in the sphere of drug action are to find specific chemical or metabolic effects attributable to drugs. If any such effects are found, it is then important to know whether these chemical changes can explain the physiological changes; whether congeners of the drug do the same chemically and physiologically and whether other drugs with the same pharmacological actions act at the same point in intermediary metabolism. Many attempts have been made to get answers to these questions in regard to depressants of central nervous system activity, particularly the anesthetic agents, but even for these there are many gaps in our knowledge, as well as contradictions awaiting resolution. Corresponding to this experimental situation is the meager theoretical development of the subject. Some generalizations have been adduced but none has withstood all the experimental criteria. The Meyer-Overton theory, which at one time proposed to relate narcotic action to achievement of a suitable partition of the drug between aqueous (blood, tissue fluid) and lipoidal (myelin) phases, has been surpassed by thermodynamic treatments of the subject. From these have come the principle of Ferguson, that substances which are present at the same proportional saturation in a given medium have the same degree of biological action (37). This principle has received some experimental verification in the work of Brink and Posternak (38).

Another physical theory has arisen from studies on the effects of high pressure upon enzymes. Certain enzymes have been found to undergo an expansion in protein molecular volume during drug inhibition; placing the incubated system under high pressures overcomes this inhibition, by opposing the reversible denaturation of the catalytic protein. The theory of narcotic action through inhibition of respiratory enzymes has been examined by many investigators and is well documented (39). It has been put forward particularly by Quastel (40), who showed many years ago that some central nervous system depressants inhibit respiration of brain tissue when the substrate is pyruvate, lactate, or glucose, but not when succinate is used. This fact provides an important clue to the site of action of the narcotic drugs used, for the pathway of electron transfer from succinate is different from that of the other compounds mentioned. By expanding the list of substrates tested and by comparing inhibition with biochemical pathways, Quastel, and later Greig, came to the conclusion that the narcotics act on a flavoprotein which functions as a cytochrome reductase. The proof has not been conclusive and has been arrived at primarily by excluding other possibilities. The theory of enzyme inhibition has been criticized for the fact that synaptic transmission can be depressed by pentobarbital without causing any change in the oxygen consumption; this evidence based upon a peripheral system requires substantiation for central synapses. The relatively high concentrations of the narcotics necessary to produce the metabolic inhibitions have also been held against the theory, but the possibility of increased permeability barriers occurring in vitro must be kept in mind. With the demonstration of the unusual sensitivity toward narcotics of respiring cerebral slices stimulated by potassium ions or electrical pulses, this argument has been somewhat reduced. An important consequence of inhibited oxidation is that lesser amounts of energy will be conserved in the form of adenosine triphosphate, creatine phosphate, and related compounds, whose continuing formation in the tissues is necessary for synthetic reactions and for maintenance of intact structure in the cell. Thus, the formation of adenosine triphosphate can be demonstrated directly or indirectly during the course of respiration, as well as the parallel disappearance of inorganic phosphate. But a reduction in respiratory rate leads to a fall in the associated phosphorylation processes. Moreover, a drug which inhibits respiration and, consequently, phosphorylation may in addition bring about a dissociation of these two processes. The effect of uncoupling is the continuation of oxygen consumption, or even its stimulation, with a concomitantly lower rate of phosphorylation. Uncoupling of oxidation and phosphorylation by barbiturates has now been demonstrated using brain and liver mitochondria. It is noteworthy that succinate oxidation, unaffected by the presence of the barbiturates, is not accompanied by phosphorylation when these drugs are added in low concentrations. These findings with mitochondria are, however, not easy to reconcile with the fact that in the brains of anesthetized animals the stores of adenosine triposphate and of phosphocreatine are usually high, whereas the inorganic phosphate is low. Furthermore, the uncoupling effect is not common to all anesthetic agents that have been tested (41).

The changes in cerebral phosphate balance as a result of barbiturate anesthesia are also accompanied by a fall in the lactic acid content of the brain. These changes are just the opposite that occur in hypoxia resulting from low oxygen tension or cyanide poisoning, and distinguish the lowered cerebral metabolic rate as a result of these causes from the decreased metabolism during reversible anesthesia (25).

Drugs which increase the activity of the central nervous system have also received some attention in the biochemical laboratory, and some useful information has accrued on the chemical accompaniments of convulsive activity, for example. CNS stimulants exhibit little specific action on the metabolism of separated cerebral tissue, whether stimulated electrically or not. However, pentylenetetrazol lowers the threshold at which the respiration of brain slices responds to electrical pulses. Convulsions bring about many chemical changes in the blood and brain (cf. Table 28-9), and these changes are reasonably similar whether the fit is induced pharmacologically or electrically. The permeability of the cerebral cells is increased during the convulsions; this affects particularly the phosphate and potassium, among the inorganic ions. Acetylcholine leaks into the cerebrospinal fluid. In contrast to the reduced oxygen consumption during anesthesia, oxygen utilization now increases, as does the utilization of glucose by the brain. (Following the convulsive state there is a period of lowered cerebral respiratory rate.) Glycolysis also increases, as shown by the elevated lacticacidemia; this persists as long as the convulsions do. The concentration of adenosine triphosphate in the brain is little affected by the convulsion *per se*, but presumably is subject to an increased turnover. The concentration of cerebral ammonia also rises sharply, but the

TABLE 28-9. BIOCHEMICAL CHANGES DURING CONVULSIONS

| *Measurement* | *Change Detected* |
|---|---|
| Blood-brain barrier | Permeability of the cerebral cell is increased. Inorganic phosphate and potassium ions leak into cerebral venous blood. Venous blood sodium falls slightly. Cerebrospinal fluid acetylcholine, inorganic phosphate, and albumin increase. |
| Oxygen consumption | Increases with each convulsion. |
| Brain carbohydrate | Glycogen stores decrease; glucose may or may not decrease. |
| Blood sugar and lactic acid | Increase in peripheral venous blood, but not in blood flowing from the brain. Lactic acid rises with first convulsion, remains high until end of convulsive activity. |
| Blood phosphocreatine | Decreases. |
| Brain ATP | More or less constant; decreases if blood pressure falls. |
| Brain ammonia | Greatly increased. |
| Blood urea | Increases, remaining elevated for many hours. |
| Blood calcium | Increases at first, then falls during a few hours; slowly returns to normal. |
| Plasma epinephrine | Increases rapidly; falls rapidly after convulsion. |
| Blood protein | Rises; returns to normal in 2 to 4 hours. |
| Blood glutamic acid | Increases in the peripheral venous blood, but not in jugular blood. |

source of this substance has not yet been discovered; this question represents one of the important problems in neurochemistry. The release of epinephrine from the adrenal medulla causes the peripheral hyperglycemia which is observed. A rise in norepinephrine also occurs in the plasma during convulsions but, unlike the rise in epinephrine, it is overcome by premedication with a skeletal muscle relaxant.

# Drug Metabolism

## PATHWAYS OF DETOXICATION (42, 43)

The action of drugs in the body is terminated or antagonized by several mechanisms: elimination in the urine or through the lungs, by enzymatic conversion to other compounds with less or no pharmacological activity (but sometimes with greater pharmacological or toxic action), or by the development of tolerance to the drug.

The metabolism of drugs, known as detoxication, is a most important means of ending their action and consists, in general, of converting them to more polar derivatives. Because of their reduced lipide-solubility these derivatives are more readily excreted by the kidney (42). Some detoxication mechanisms have already been described in this book. The following presentation sets out the main reactions, classified as to biochemical process.

*Oxidations Carried Out by Microsomal Enzymes* (44). The microsomal particles of the liver contain enzymes which oxidize diverse functional groups. These catalysts are characterized by their requirement for oxygen and reduced triphosphopyridine nucleotide (TPNH); the mechanism of these unusual oxidations has not yet been worked out. Amphetamine (1-phenyl-2-aminopropane), which is not affected by monoamine oxidase (and which, in fact, inhibits this enzyme *in vitro*) is oxidized by the microsomal system to phenylacetone and ammonia. In another type of reaction catalyzed by these enzymes codeine and meperidine lose their N-methyl group. The oxidation of the aliphatic side chain of certain barbiturates to yield an alcoholic group also falls into this category of oxidations. A substance that has proved useful in the laboratory study of the microsomal oxidations is β-diethylaminoethyl diphenylpropylacetate; it has no drug action itself, but it inhibits many of the microsomal enzymes carrying out these reactions. It is often given as SKF 525A in the literature.

*Other Oxidative Reactions.* These are catalyzed by enzymes which have been known for a longer time and whose properties are better characterized than the above. Among them are the dehydrogenation reactions which alcohols and aldehydes undergo. Dehydrogenases in this group require diphosphopyridine nucleotide (DPN) as coenzyme; one of them is responsible for the metabolism of ethanol to acetic acid, through acetaldehyde as intermediary. Similarly chloral hydrate is metabolized to trichloroacetic acid. Amines are also detoxified by oxidative deaminations performed by monoamine oxidase (iproniazid-sensitive) and diamine oxidase (inhibited by cyanide and other carbonyl reagents). The physiological substrates for monoamine oxidase include tyramine, tryptamine, metanephrine, normetanephrine, and methylhistamine, among others. The product of enzymatic action is the corresponding aldehyde. Diamine oxidase acts upon histamine and mescaline, again forming aldehydes.

*Reduction Reactions.* Metanephrine and normetanephrine are oxidized by monoamine oxidase to 3-methoxy-4-hydroxyphenylglycolaldehyde. Most of this product is further oxidized (aldehyde dehydrogenase) to the corresponding acid, vanilmandelic acid, but a small portion is reduced to the alcohol, thus forming a catecholamine-derived glycol. Another type of reduction is exemplified by the metabolism of the prontosils, the first sulfonamides used chemotherapeutically; these compounds are azo derivatives (Ar—N=N—Ar) of sulfanilamide. They are reduced *in vivo* to yield sulfanilamide itself. Chloral hydrate is reduced to trichloroethanol, the specific narcotically active molecule derived from it in the body.

*O-Methylation of Catecholamines.* This has been described on pp. 102 and 310.

*Hydrolysis of Esters.* The hydrolysis of acetylcholine by cholinesterases has been discussed in Chapter 3. Tropinesterase is another esterase responsible for the detoxication of atropine and of cocaine, two drugs with similar structures. Atropine is hydrolyzed by this enzyme to yield the tropine ring, bearing a secondary alcoholic group, and the acid, 2-phenyl-3-hydroxypropionic acid. Cocaine, after hydrolysis of a methyl ester group, is further split by tropinesterase to ecgonine (tropine carboxylic acid) and benzoic acid.

*Hydrolysis of Amides.* The best-known example of this is the hydrolysis of procaine to $p$-aminobenzoic acid and diethylaminoethanol.

*Conjugation.* This type of detoxication is a synthetic process in which a functional group on the drug is conjugated with glucuronic acid, sulfuric acid, acetic acid, cysteine, glutamine, or other constituent. The conjugand must first be activated in one or more reactions utilizing a high-energy phosphate compound to form the immediate donor. The formation of uridine diphosphate glucuronic acid has already been described in Chapter 11. The activation of sulfate occurs in two steps (45), with the ultimate formation of 3'-phosphoadenylylsulfate, the specific donor of the sulfate group. The thioester, acetylcoenzyme A, is involved in acetylation reactions (p. 169ff.).

## METABOLISM OF SOME SPECIFIC DRUGS

The detoxication reactions which have been schematized above can be illustrated more fully by examining the metabolism of some drugs which are used in psychiatric practice.

*Succinylcholine.* This drug has a short duration of action in most subjects, because of its ready hydrolysis by the pseudocholinesterase of plasma. However, in some patients the apnea lasts longer; the plasma is

TABLE 28-10. EFFECT OF PSEUDOCHOLINESTERASE LEVEL
ON THE ACTION OF SUCCINYLCHOLINE IN MAN (46)

| Case | Enzyme Units in Plasma | | Duration of Apnea Following Succinylcholine (sec.) | |
|---|---|---|---|---|
| | Before Injection* | After Injection* | Before Injection | After Injection |
| 1 | 90 | 183 | 130 | 66 |
| 3 | 34 | 73 | 375 | 135 |

\* Of the human plasma pseudocholinesterase.

then found to contain a low level of enzyme. Evans et al. (46) have demonstrated the inverse correlation between pseudocholinesterase level in the plasma and duration of apnea, using an injectable preparation of the enzyme concentrated from human plasma. Two of their cases are shown in Table 28-10. Succinylcholine is a double ester; it is first hydrolyzed to choline and succinylmonocholine; the latter is then split to succinic acid and another molecule of choline.

*Lysergic Acid Diethylamide (LSD).* Most of our knowledge of the metabolism of this ergot derivative comes from the laboratories of Rothlin (47) and of Axelrod (48). There is considerable species difference in its breakdown as indicated by the biological half-life (based upon its concentration in the blood) in the mouse and rat of 7 minutes, and in the monkey and cat of 1.5 to 2 hours. The drug is very rapidly bound by the plasma proteins but nevertheless is released to the various organs,

Excretion occurs in the bile, but substantial reabsorption from the intestine takes place. LSD is converted in the liver (but not in brain and other organs) to 2-hydroxy-LSD, a biologically inactive compound (48). This oxidation is accomplished by the microsomal enzyme system and is inhibited strongly by chlorpromazine and SKF 525A at $10^{-4}$ M concentration; 5HT and reserpine also inhibit, but to a smaller extent.

*Mescaline.* Three types of detoxication reaction are known for this drug. (*a*) Oxidative deamination, followed by dehydrogenation, results in the formation of a carboxyl group on the side-chain. (*b*) Demethylation also occurs. Finally, (*c*) the mescaline-derived carboxylic acid is conjugated with glutamine. The study of mescaline metabolism in man has shown that about 35 percent of the administered drug is excreted in the urine in the first 24 hours and only a trace can be found after that (49). A very small amount of product (1 to 2 percent) has been identified in the urine as 3,4-dihydroxy-5-methoxyphenylacetylglutamine. Harley-Mason has suggested that mescaline must be converted to some other derivative for biological activity (49). This view is based upon the large doses required and the delay in onset of hallucinations. Evidence put forward by Goldstein et al. suggests that this derivative is 3,4,5-trimethoxy-phenylacetaldehyde (49A).

*Barbiturates.* Members of this group of drugs are classified according to their duration of action. Some have a prolonged duration of action because of their slow metabolism and slow excretion; thus, substantial proportions of phenobarbital are excreted unchanged. The short-acting and ultrashort-acting barbiturates undergo extensive conversion.

Detoxication reactions catalyzed by microsomal enzymes include N-demethylation and oxidation of the aliphatic side chain. The thiobarbiturates lose their sulfur atom, with the formation of the corresponding oxygen analogue; only small amounts of the latter have been detected, presumably because of other detoxifying reactions. Thus, thiopental is oxidized to pentobarbital and some of its sulfur, at least, is oxidized to sulfate. Although knowledge of these reactions comes mainly from animal experimentation it can be inferred that they occur in much the same way in man.

*Amphetamines* (50, 51). The amphetamines are characterized by an isopropylamine side chain. They are not attacked by monoamine oxidase, but instead inhibit the enzyme. The inhibition occurs *in vitro*, but cannot be demonstrated in the intact animal; hence the mechanism of action of the amphetamines must be sought elsewhere than in inhibition of monoamine oxidase. Degradation of the molecule takes place in several ways. After oral administration of amphetamine a large proportion of the compound is excreted unchanged, and after withdrawal the drug can be found in the urine for as long as 4 to 7 days. Connell (51) found that with an oral intake of about 0.1 to 1.0 gm. the urine contains 6 to 112 $\mu$g./ml. The drug is also found in the urine after an inhaler containing it is used. Methamphetamine is N-demethylated to amphetamine by the microsomal enzymes of liver. Enzymes also catalyze the oxidation of the amphetamine ring to form $p$-hydroxyamphetamine. Beyer has ascribed a role to ascorbic acid in the oxidative deamination of amphetamine, based upon studies *in vitro*. He has found, moreover, that the administration of large amounts of ascorbic acid to the dog reduces the proportion of a given dose of amphetamine which is excreted (52).

*Morphine.* Morphine is excreted in the bile but is reabsorbed from the intestine and is finally excreted by way of the kidneys. In the dog, most of an injected dose of morphine can be accompanied for as urinary products (53). Twenty percent is excreted as the unchanged alkaloid; much of the remainder is in the form of conjugates. A conjugated product has been demonstrated in the urine of morphine addicts (54); it also occurs in the urine of nontolerant individuals. By use of morphine labeled isotopically in the N-methyl group it has been shown (55) that this carbon is removed very early in metabolism, for labeled carbon dioxide can be found among the respiratory gases. Only a small percentage of the total dose is metabolized in this way because 30 to 75 percent of the labeled material is excreted in the urine within 6 hours. Heroin and codeine follow similar routes of metabolism, but these compounds are first degraded to morphine. For heroin this involves hydrolysis of two acetic acid ester linkages; codeine undergoes O-demethylation.

*Chlorpromazine* (56, 57). This phenothiazine drug yields many urinary metabolites in man, through 3 types of detoxication reaction: (*a*) N-demethylation; (*b*) partial oxidation of the sulfur atom to form the sulfoxide of chlorpromazine (but not the sulfone); (*c*) glucuronide formation. Humans under treatment with chlorpromazine excrete only a small proportion of the unchanged drug. The major pathway is the formation of the sulfoxide, and most of this product undergoes additional reactions. Thus, the main metabolites of chlorpromazine in man are the mono- and di-N-demethylated sulfoxides. Three of the urinary metabolites are excreted as glucuronides.

*Imipramine* (57, 58). Imipramine is an iminodibenzyl derivative differing from promazine only in the substitution of a dimethylene bridge

$$(-CH_2 \cdot CH_2-)$$

for the sulfur atom. Its metabolic degradation is similar to that of chlorpromazine. Among its many urinary products are 2-hydroxyimipramine, 2-hydroxynorimipramine, norimipramine, and imipramine itself.

## TOLERANCE TO DRUGS (59, 60)

Tolerance or resistance to the usual actions of a drug assumes two forms, each representing a complex type of physiological adjustment whose mechanism is not understood at present. The more rapidly developing type of tolerance, *tachyphylaxis,* can be detected in the intact organism as well as with isolated smooth muscle systems; by repeated administration of small amounts of a drug such as sympathomimetic amine the vasoconstrictor response gradually diminishes, and then disappears altogether. The tachyphylactic effect is lost quickly after withdrawal of the drug, and there are no persistent effects as a result of this deprivation. By contrast, the state of *drug dependence* develops slowly and is demonstrable only in the intact organism. It is best known in the form of addiction to narcotics. The resistance that develops is never complete, and is exhibited only with respect to the depressant, but not the stimulant, actions of morphine and the other narcotic analgesics. Along with tolerance there is imposed upon the organism another set of physiological adjustments which result in a dependence of normal function upon the presence of the drug in the tissues. According to Seevers (60) the abstinence syndrome represents the unmasking of a latent state of hyperexcitability, and can be provoked by cessation of the drug or by adequate dosage with the antagonistic drug, nalorphine.

The dependent state and the adaptive changes which it entails present a challenge to the physiologist and biochemist. Some enzymological studies have been made using the tissues of animals given large doses of narcotics or made tolerant to the drug; one of these studies shows that the chronic administration of morphine to the rat causes a decreased activity of the N-demethylating enzyme in the liver (61). But the nature of the cellular adaptations in states of drug tolerance remains unsolved. Seevers has given some reasons why studies of enzymic adaptation in the dependent state have not been fruitful (59). In the first place too much attention has been focused on the wrong organs—liver and muscle—instead of nerve. Furthermore, the dependent state has often not been adequately developed in the experimental animals; the smaller species require frequent dosing with morphine during the whole 24-hour period, and this regime must be maintained daily for long periods of time.

## Relation of Chemical Structure to Biological Activity

Studies of the relation of chemical structure to biological activity are bound up with the development of modern chemotherapy, from Ehrlich's time on. The variations in biological activity encountered when, beginning with some effective organic molecule, one changes this or that functional group, adds or subtracts carbon atoms from the aliphatic chains, moves functional groups to alternate positions in the molecule, or reverses the configuration of an asymmetric carbon atom, are of great scientific interest. They may reveal which part of the molecule is essential for useful pharmacological activities and in this way assist in the design of chemically simpler drugs. Choice of substituents for compounds patterned after a known biologically active molecule may determine their potency, penetration into the tissues, and egress into channels of detoxication and excretion. Qualitative changes also result from alteration of molecular structure, for organs are affected to differing extents even by closely related molecules, and these differences may ultimately find their expression as undesirable side effects, as loss of activity, or even as a different type of activity. Pertinent here are the studies of drug metabolism, for it is important to know which of the metabolites derived from the administered drug retain pharmacological action.

Knowledge of structure-activity relationships is largely empirical. In a chemical series such as the catecholamines, one can recognize the similarities and differences in pharmacological activities in comparing norepinephrine, epinephrine, and isoproterenol, but one cannot yet explain the differences in terms of chemical structures (see Table 25-1). Stated in another way this means that, given a set of new, chemically related compounds and the pharmacologist's test results, one may be able to deduce from them the general structure of a biologically active molecule, but one could not predict what type of activity this would be without resorting ultimately to experiments with the synthesized compounds. The mechanistic aim of being able to predict biological activity from the chemical and physical properties of a drug has not yet been achieved, but it occupies a dominant position in the field of medicinal chemistry, and is one of the motive forces there. From these empirical approaches has come one of the major developments in biochemical theory, the *antimetabolite hypothesis.* This hypothesis stems from the fusion of knowledge of intermediary metabolic processes and of chemotherapy. In essence, it states that a change in structure of some essential metabolite, such as a vitamin or an amino acid, results in a new compound which may not only be incapable of functioning as the metabolite, but may also serve as a metabolic antagonist to the normal partner and, indeed, may even bring about the syndrome associated with a deficiency of this metabolite (2). This hypothesis has acted as a spur to the synthesis of hundreds of new compounds to be tried as potential therapeutic agents, and has had some successes in this direction.

The difficulties of predicting pharmacological activity from chemical structure are illustrated by a series of alkaloids derived from Rauwolfia (62). Although some have a sedative action others do not, in spite of their close chemical relationship to the active member of the series. Nevertheless, those compounds with sedative activity release cerebral amines, whereas those without this action have little or no amine-liberating effect. This illustrates one of the principles enunciated by Welch and Bueding for relating biochemical and drug actions.

Since the discovery of the inhibitory action of iproniazid on monoamine oxidase other derivatives of hydrazine have been found to possess this property. Zbinden et al. (63) have compared many compounds in terms of their monoamine oxidase inhibitory action, their ability to increase the cerebral serotonin, and their potentiation of the central stimulatory action of dopa. Enzyme inhibition was tested by measuring the activity of monoamine oxidase in organ extracts to which the compound had been added, as well as by measuring the enzymatic activity in organs removed from animals which had been treated with the inhibitors. It can be seen in Table 28-11 that the hydrazide inhibitors of the enzyme vary considerably in their relative effects upon the organs. Iproniazid and $\beta$-phenylisopropylhydrazine (PIH) are equally effective in inhibiting the liver enzyme *in vivo,* but PIH exerts a much more potent effect after parenteral administration upon the brain enzyme. Data of this type are important in determining the tissue selectivity of a particular drug. Table 28-11 also illustrates the clear-cut difference between the activity of iproniazid and isoniazid. Amphetamine has long been known as an inhibitor of monoamine oxidase and, indeed, at one time it was thought that it may exert its pharmacological actions in this way, by protecting sympathin as it is released at sympathetic nerve endings. Because amphetamine has no action upon monoamine oxidase *in vivo,* this hypothesis has had to be abandoned. Tranylcypromine (phenylcyclopropylamine) is a very potent inhibitor of monoamine oxidase, *in vivo*, especially in brain and heart. It is much more effective than iproniazid in potentiating dopa or effecting an increase in the serotonin concentration of the brain. Amphetamine, long used for its central action, also potentiates the action of dopa very effectively. Harmaline is a very active inhibitor of monoamine oxidase *in vivo* and, unlike the hydrazides, is readily reversible in its action; however, it has only weak inhibitory action *in vitro*.

TABLE 28-11. ACTIVITY OF MONOAMINE OXIDASE INHIBITORS*

| | | *Inhibition of MAO* | | | | |
| | | | *In vivo* | | *Potenti-* | *Increase* |
| *Compound* | *In vitro* | *Brain* | *Heart* | *Liver* | *ation of Dopa* | *of Brain 5HT* |
|---|---|---|---|---|---|---|
| Hydrazine derivatives | | | | | | |
| Iproniazid | 1 | 1 | 1 | 1 | 1 | 1 |
| Isocarboxazid | 7 | 33 | 8 | 1.8 | 17 | 5.9 |
| β-Phenylisopropyl-hydrazine | 8 | 43 | 40 | 1 | 67 | 13 |
| Nialamide | 2 | 0.5 | 2.4 | 0.1 | 25 | 3.5 |
| Isoniazid | 0 | 0 | 0 | 0 | 0 | 0 |
| Phenylethylamine derivatives | | | | | | |
| DL-Amphetamine | 0.005 | 0 | 0 | 0 | 50 | 0 |
| Tranylcypromine | 0.6 | 100 | 53 | 3 | 50 | 28 |
| Harmaline | 0.01 | | | | 33 | |

* Adapted from reference (63).

Viaud has described the structure-activity relationships in the phenothiazine series in great detail (64). A few of these are sketched in Table 28-12. Antihistaminic activity, which was initially the objective of the phenothiazine studies, is restricted to but two of the compounds shown. These are characterized by having only two methylene groups between the nitrogen of the phenothiazine ring itself and the dimethylamine group of the side-chain. Substitution of three methylene groups in the straight portion of the aliphatic chain or of a diethylamino group renders the compound inactive in the antihistamine tests. Similarly, small differences in the structure of the side chain affect the ability of the compound to protect animals against experimental (tumbling) shock or emetic agents. Rees has compared the pharmacological actions of the phenothiazines from the clinical aspect (65).

Compounds containing the indole nucleus provide interesting examples of differences in pharmacological activity between structurally related molecules. Inasmuch as numerous alkaloids contain the indole

TABLE 28-12. STRUCTURE AND PHARMACOLOGICAL ACTIVITY IN THE PHENOTHIAZINE SERIES (64)

| | | Pharmacological Action | | | | | |
|---|---|---|---|---|---|---|---|
| Generic Name | R | A* | B | C | D | E | F |
| Chlorpromazine† | —CH$_2$CH$_2$CH$_2$·N(CH$_3$)$_2$ | + | ++ | 0 | +++ | ++ | +++ |
| Phenethazine | —CH$_2$CH$_2$·N(CH$_3$)$_2$ | | | + | | | |
| Promethazine | —CH$_2$CH·N(CH$_3$)$_2$ <br> \| <br> CH$_3$ | ++ | | + | ++ | + | + |
| Diethazine | —CH$_2$CH$_2$·N(C$_2$H$_5$)$_2$ | + | + | 0 | + | | |
| Prophenamine | —CH$_2$CH·N(C$_2$H$_5$)$_2$ <br> \| <br> CH$_3$ | + | ++ | 0 | | | |
| Promazine | —CH$_2$CH$_2$CH$_2$·N(CH$_3$)$_2$ | | | 0 | +++ | ++ | |

* Activities are: $A$, parasympatholytic; $B$, central nicotinolytic; $C$, antihistaminic; $D$, psychoplegic; $E$, antemetic; $F$, antishock.

† All compounds have a hydrogen atom at position 2, except chlorpromazine, which possesses a chlorine atom.

nucleus chemically integrated into one or more other structures, the mere presence of the indole ring in two molecules does not in any way ensure that they will have similar biological actions. These are all modeled upon tryptamine ($\beta$-indolylethylamine), an amine which is normally formed in the body from tryptophan and appears in the urine in small amounts; in humans and in experimental animals treated with inhibitors of monoamine oxidase the excretion of this compound increases, presumably through its protection from deaminative oxidation. The pure compound causes convulsions upon injection into laboratory animals, and central depressants can be compared on the basis of the protection they afford against a convulsive dose of the amine. Serotonin has been discussed extensively already (Chapter 6), and its lack of central effects has been noted. Its N-dimethyl derivative, bufotenine, occurs in *cohoba*, a snuff used at one time for its hallucinatory actions. Bufotenine itself causes hallucinations when injected intravenously. This fact, together with its reported occurrence in the urine, supports the suggestion that it may be an endogenously formed hallucinogen playing a role in mental illnesses. Of interest in this connection is the discovery of a mammalian enzyme (in lung) which catalyzes the methylation of serotonin and tryptamine, among other amines, to hallucinogenic substances (66).

Another derivative of serotonin, melatonin, has been isolated from the pineal gland; it causes contraction of melanophores. Chemically it is N-acetyl-5-methoxytryptamine.

The 4-hydroxy analog of bufotenine has been described, and is known as *psilocin*. In its O-phosphorylated form it occurs in certain species of mushroom indigenous to the southern highlands of Mexico. 6-Hydroxy-N-diethyltryptamine is known as a urinary metabolite of the synthetic indole, diethyltryptamine (T-9). Psilocybin, which is 4-O-phosphorylpsilocin, and diethyltryptamine are both hallucinogenic in man. It is believed that the latter is active only after it has been oxidized in the 6-position. The harmala alkaloids, once used in therapeutics against the tremor of Parkinson's syndrome and now recognized as potent inhibitors of monoamine oxidase, also possess a 6-hydroxyindole type of structure.

The ergot alkaloids have also been classified among the indoles, although their structure is far more complex than this. The diethylamide of lysergic acid (LSD) has a number of characteristic pharmacological actions, some of which are reproduced by closely related chemical species. 1-Methyl-LSD, 1-acetyl-LSD, and 2-bromo-LSD (BOL), for example, have a more marked antiserotonin activity upon smooth muscle than LSD itself. In respect to the psychic effects of LSD, however, only lysergic acid monoethylamide and 1-acetyl-LSD reproduce the psychic effects of LSD itself. Indeed, of 4 known diastereoisomers of LSD, only one (*d*-LSD, LSD-25) has great activity (67).

Smythies and Levy (68) have reviewed the subject of methoxy-substituted phenylethylamines, *i.e.*, compounds similar in structure to mescaline in regard to their behavioral effects in experimental animals. The pharmacodynamic actions of others in this series, the *meta*-O-methylated catecholamines, have been described by Champagne et al. (69).

The development of chemical methods for the synthesis of peptides has made available large numbers of analogues of the hormones of the posterior pituitary gland. Boissonas and his colleagues have attempted to assess the structure-activity relationships in this series by detailed pharmacological testing (70).

# References

1. MAYER-GROSS, W. *Nervenarzt 3*:97, 1957.
2. WOOLLEY, D. W. *A Study of Antimetabolites.* New York, Wiley, 1952.
3. MAYER-GROSS, W., W. McADAM, and J. W. WALKER. *Nature 168*:827, 1951.
4. MAYER-GROSS, W., W. McADAM, and J. W. WALKER. *J. Ment. Sc. 99*:804, 1953.
5. HOAGLAND, H., M. RINKEL, and R. W. HYDE. *Arch. Neurol. Psychiat. 73*: 100, 1955.
6. KESSLER, G., P. HALPERN, and H. BRODY. *J. Lab. Clin. Med. 50*:250, 1957.
7. HIPPIUS, H. *Can. Psychiat. Assoc. J. 4*:S182, 1959.
8. KILLAM, K. F., and J. A. BAIN. *J. Pharmacol. Exp. Ther. 119*:255, 1957.
9. BAXTER, C. F., and E. ROBERTS. *Proc. Soc. Exp. Biol. Med. 104*:426, 1960.
10. BRODIE, B. B., and P. A. SHORE. *Ann. N.Y. Acad. Sci. 66*:631, 1957.
11. SHEPPARD, H., and J. H. ZIMMERMAN. *Nature 185*:40, 1960.
12. UDENFRIEND, S., H. WEISSBACH, and D. F. BOGDANSKI. *Ann. N.Y. Acad. Sci. 66*:602, 1957.
13. SOURKES, T. L., and A. D'IORIO. *In Metabolic Inhibitors,* ed. HOCHSTER, R., and J. H. QUASTEL. New York, Academic Press, Inc. In press.
14. MURPHY, G. F., and T. L. SOURKES. *Rev. canad. Biol. 18*:379, 1959.
15. SMITH, S. E. *Brit. J. Pharmacol. 15*:319, 1960.
16. MURPHY, G. F., and T. L. SOURKES. *Arch. Biochem. Biophys. 93*:338, 1961.
17. OATES, J. A., L. GILLESPIE, S. UDENFRIEND, and A. SJOERDSMA. *Science 131*:1890, 1960.
18. SOURKES, T. L., G. F. MURPHY, B. CHAVEZ, and M. ZIELINSKA. *J. Neurochem. 8*:109, 1961.
19. SOURKES, T. L., G. F. MURPHY, and B. CHAVEZ-LARA. *J. Med. Pharm. Chem. 5*:204, 1962.
20. WELCH, A. D., and E. BUEDING. *In Currents in Biochemical Research,* ed. GREEN, D. E. New York, Interscience, 1946.
21. QUASTEL, J. H., (ed.). *Methods in Medical Research,* Vol. 9. Chicago, Year Book Publishers, 1961.
22. MAGEE, W. L., J. F. BERRY, and R. J. ROSSITER. *Biochim. et Biophys. Acta 21*:408, 1956.
23. YAGI, R., T. NAGATSU, and T. OZAWA. *Nature 177*:891, 1956; LÖW, H. *Biochim. et Biophys. Acta 32*:11, 1959.
24. GEY, K. F., and A. PLETSCHER. *J. Pharmacol. Exp. Ther. 133*:18, 1961.

25. McIlwain, H. *Biochemistry and the Central Nervous System.* London, E. and S. Churchill, 1955.

26. Greengard, O., and H. McIlwain. *Biochem. . 61:*61, 1955.

27. Beer, C. T., and J. H. Quastel. *Can. J. Biochem. Physiol. 36:*531, 543, 1958.

28. Dewan, J. G. *Quart. J. Studies Alc. 4:*357, 1943.

29. Adams, D. H., and R. H. S. Thompson. *Biochem. J. 42:*170, 1948.

30. Mendel, B., and H. Rudney. *Biochem. J. 37:*59, 1943.

31. Nachmansohn, D., and E. A. Feld. *J. Biol. Chem. 171:*715, 1947.

32. Thompson, R. H. S., A. Tickner, and G. R. Webster. *Brit. J. Pharmacol. 10:*61, 1955.

33. Tabachnik, I. I. A., and M. E. Grelis. *Nature 182:*935, 1958.

34. Bain, J. A. *Ann. N.Y. Acad. Sci. 66:*459, 1957.

35. Wollenberger, A. *Biochem. J. 61:*68, 1955.

36. Rosenberg, A. J. *In Proceedings 3rd Intern. Cong. Biochem., Brussels, 1955, ed.* Liébecq, C. New York, Academic Press, 1956.

37. Albert, A. *Selective Toxicity,* New York, Wiley, 1951. *Cf.* also Mullins, L. J. *Chem. Rev. 54:*289, 1954.

38. Brink, J., and J. M. Posternak. *J. Cell. Comp. Physiol. 32:*211, 1948.

39. McElroy, W. D. *Quart. Rev. Biol. 22:*25, 1947; Wikler, A. *The Relation of Psychiatry to Pharmacology,* Baltimore, Williams & Wilkins, 1957; and Butler, T. C. *J. Pharmacol. Exp. Ther., Part II, 98:*121, 1950.

40. Quastel, J. H. *Physiol. Rev. 19:*135, 1939.

41. Brody, T. M. *Pharmacol. Rev. 7:*335, 1955.

42. Brodie, B. B., R. P. Maickel, and W. R. Jondorf. *Federation Proc. 17:* 1163, 1958.

43. Williams, R. T. *Detoxication Mechanisms: the Metabolism of Drugs, Toxic Substances and Other Organic Compounds.* 2d ed. New York, Wiley, 1960.

44. Brodie, B. B., J. Axelrod, J. R. Cooper, L. Gaudette, B. N. LaDu, C. Mitoma, and S. Udenfriend. *Science 121:*603, 1955.

45. Lipmann, F. *Science 128:*575, 1958.

46. Evans, F. T., P. W. S. Gray, H. Lehmann, and E. Silk. *Brit. Med. J. i:*136, 1953.

47. Rothlin, E. *Nature 178:*1400, 1956.

48. Axelrod, J., R. O. Brady, B. Witkop, and E. V. Evarts. *Ann. N.Y. Acad. Sci. 66:*435, 1957.

49. Harley-Mason, J., A. H. Laird, and J. R. Smythies. *Confin. neurol. 18:*152, 1958.

49A. Goldstein, M., A. J. Friedhoff, S. Pomerantz, C. Simmons, and J. F. Contrera. *J. Neurochem. 6:*253, 1961.

50. Leake, C. D. *The Amphetamines.* Springfield, Ill., Charles C Thomas, 1958.

51. Connell, P. H. *Amphetamine Psychosis.* London, Chapman and Hall, 1958.

52. Beyer, K. H. *Physiol. Rev. 26:*169, 1946.

53. Thompson, V., and E. G. Gross. *J. Pharmacol. Exp. Ther. 72:*138, 1941.

54. Oberst, F. W. *J. Pharmacol. Exp. Ther. 69:*240, 1940.

55. Elliott, H. W., B. M. Tolbert, T. K. Adler, and H. H. Anderson. *Proc. Soc. Exp. Biol. Med. 85:*77, 1954.

56. Fishman, V., and H. Goldenberg. *Proc. Soc. Exp. Biol. Med. 104*:99, 1960.
57. Goldenberg, H. and V. Fishman. *Clin. Chem. 6*:398, 1960.
58. Herrmann, B., W. Schindler, and R. Pulver. *Medicina Experimentalis 1*:381, 1959; Schindler, W. *Helv. Chim. Acta 43*:35, 1960.
59. Seevers, M. H. *Federation Proc. 17*:1175, 1958.
60. Seevers, M. H. *Federation Proc. 13*:672, 1954.
61. Axelrod, J. *Science 124*:263, 1956.
62. Shore, P. A., A. Pletscher, E. G. Tomich, A. Carlsson, R. Kuntzman, and B. B. Brodie. *Ann. N.Y. Acad. Sci. 66*:609, 1957.
63. Zbinden, G., L. O. Randall, and R. A. Moe. *Dis. Nerv. System 21*:Section 2, 89, 1960.
64. Viaud, P. *J. Pharm. Pharmacol. 6*:361, 1954.
65. Rees, L. *Brit. Med. J. ii*:522, 1960.
66. Axelrod, J. *Science 134*:343, 1961.
67. Rothlin, E. In *Psychotropic Drugs,* ed. Garattini, S., and V. Ghetti, Amsterdam, Elsevier, 1957.
68. Smythies, J. R., and C. K. Levy. *J. Ment. Sci. 106*:531, 1960.
69. Champagne, J., A. D'Iorio, and A. Beaulnes. *Science 132*:419, 1960.
70. Boissonas, R. A., S. Guttmann, B. Berde, and H. Konzett. *Experientia 17*:377, 1961.

# INDEX